Implementing World Class Manufacturing

Includes Lean Enterprise

BUSINESS MANUAL

Larry Rubrich and Mattie Watson

WCM Associates

Fort Wayne, Indiana

Implementing World Class Manufacturing

Second Edition

By
Larry Rubrich and Madelyn Watson

WCM Associates
P.O. Box 8035
Fort Wayne, IN 46898-8035
260-637-8064
Fax: 260-637-2284
www.wcmfg.com

Disclaimer

Demonstrations and illustrations contained herein provide only a description of general improvement techniques and methods. Illustrations and directions may not provide all necessary or relevant information and the authors suggest that you refer to appropriate equipment manuals specific to the particular task or contact a qualified craftsman or professional. By purchasing this book and not immediately returning it after reviewing this disclaimer, you agree that the authors may not be held responsible for any omissions or inaccuracies in any information provided herein.

References to manufactured products in this book is neither an endorsement of that product nor application approval for use of that product. Contact the companies that manufacture products directly for questions or assistance regarding their products.

ISBN: 0-9662906-1-5

Front and rear cover design by:
    Pearl & Associates
    Boca Raton, FL (561) 338-0380

Book and text design by WCM Associates
Illustrations by Larry Rubrich
Printed and bound by:
    Thompson-Shore, Inc.
    Dexter, MI (734) 426-3939

Layout was completed using Adobe® Pagemaker 6.0. Text typeface is Bookman, 11 point.
Charts and graphs were completed on Visio® 4.0
Photographs were scanned using a Umax S6E scanner with Adobe® Photoshop Le.

Library of Congress Catalog Card Number: 2004100948

Acknowledgments

To my wife Shirley, and my daughter and son, Kelly and Todd, who allowed me to turn a dream into reality by supporting and putting up with my (years?) sitting at the computer weeknights, weekends, and even during vacation.

My wife Shirley was also responsible for the book's excellent design and easy to read layout. As my partner in this project, she helped keep the writing directed toward a nontechnical style. She also put up with my crankiness as hours of writing become hundreds and even thousands. I owe her.

Mattie Stephens Watson, good friend and associate, helped in writing the book, and provided special insight during the review of many of the chapters from her training and consulting background.

Paul Lemond, good friend and probably the best trainer in world class manufacturing techniques that I know, helped me develop the concept for the book. When Paul and I worked together implementing these advanced manufacturing techniques in the early 1990s for United Technologies Automotive, we sometimes found ourselves wishing we had some additional guidance on implementing these techniques on the shop floor. Since a book or manual did not exist, we decided we should write one. However, Paul went back to work for Dana Corporation, and both of us spent some time at different ends of the country. The concept and need for such a book continued for me.

My good friends and fishing buddies, Dave Devaughn and Jim Jones encouraged me and helped review the chapters. Dave's keen insight into manufacturing (and fishing) were inspirational! As an outstanding plant manager with excellent people skills, Jim helped make sure the information as presented in the book met our criteria of writing which would be understood by both managers and machine operators.

Bob Rosinski, an extremely competent manufacturing consultant, provided valuable feedback on the chapters and direction that we were taking the book in.

Several of my daughter Kelly's friends, Christine Marx, Ripley Worman, and Jenny McAfee, helped us decide what type face to use (Bookman).

Contents

Introduction

World class manufacturing techniques can be used to return American manufacturing to the leadership position it formerly held. Clearly, if we continue to lose our wealth-generating manufacturing base to foreign competition, future generations will live with a degenerating standard of living. While we may all find employment in the growing economic sector referred to as Service America, these service jobs pay one-third less than manufacturing jobs and generally do not create wealth but only trade the same used dollars. The good news is, however, that we still have the most innovative and productive workforce in the world and, with trust and communication, this workforce can use world class manufacturing techniques to return America to this leadership position.

Recent studies indicate that only 15 percent of all U.S. manufacturing companies are upgrading the competitive capability of their facilities by using a World Class Manufacturing (WCM) or Total Quality Management (TQM) related activity. Two-thirds of these programs fail and are terminated after only two years. Some authors indicate that these failures result from uncommitted management trying to quick-fix their organization by transplanting a successful company's quality program to their own company. These authors also state that cloning a program does not ensure a successful implementation. Having learned this cloning lesson the hard way, we heartily agree with this assessment! While there are many books about the lessons and best practices of American companies that have made major improvements in their global competitiveness, these books, unfortunately, are more about actual practices and results produced than about providing insight into how WCM or TQM is implemented. However, reviewing these lessons and practices can provide an excellent source of ideas for continuous improvement once a WCM or TQM initiative is in place. These books are also excellent resources for determining the current benchmarks in various improvement categories and industries.

We wrote *Implementing World Class Manufacturing* because cloning does not work! While implementing change, we had many questions: What preparations are necessary? How do we implement? In what order do we implement? We wished someone could help us bridge the gap from traditional manufacturing to the advanced methods of world class manufacturing. After several implementations, we began to recognize the difference between problems that resulted from the normal resistance to change and those that resulted from an implementation that was built out of sequence. The knowledge and experience passed on in *Implementing World Class Manufacturing* is the result of learning from both successful and unsuccessful implementations. *Implementing World Class Manufacturing* is written, using our front-line experience, as a guide to building the bridge that will take you from traditional manufacturing to WCM.

The system suggested in *Implementing World Class Manufacturing*, if understood and followed by committed management, will start to change the personality, or culture, of your organization. This cultural shift, which stresses the elimination of all waste and the development of customer satisfaction through the use of teamwork, applies to all manufacturing businesses. It is this basic strategy that has helped vault the Japanese to their economic superpower status. Although all the advanced manufacturing techniques as presented in *Implementing World Class Manufacturing* will not fit every organization, they are the epitome of simplicity and the basics of manufacturing. They are easily understood and adaptable to your organization.

The bridge between traditional manufacturing and WCM is built in a series of firm foundations and supports. While each module in *Implementing World Class Manufacturing* will provide improvement to your facility in a stand-alone mode, some elements need to be in place before others are implemented. The real power is unleashed when all the modules, built in sequence, work together. Implementing the elements in proper sequence is important.

> Vince Lombardi, when asked the secret of his team's great success, said that they concentrated on the basics, and on doing them better than anyone else!

The following foundations, presented in Chapters 1 through 5, must be in place before the bridge to world class manufacturing can be built.

♦ Proof of the need to change (Chapter 1)

♦ Top management vision, leadership, trust, communication, and commitment (Chapter 2)

♦ Employee empowerment (Chapter 2)

♦ Planning the implementation in your facility (Chapter 3)

♦ 5S workplace organization and housekeeping (Chapter 4)

♦ Development of facility-wide teamwork (Chapter 5)

When these foundations are in place, the supports (modules) explained in Chapters 6 through 10 are then constructed in the following order:

♦ Total Productive Maintenance (Chapter 6)

♦ Manufacturing Cells (Chapter 7)

♦ Setup Reduction (Chapter 8)

♦ Inventory *Kanbans* (Chapter 9)

♦ *Kaizen* (Chapter 10)

When the final construction element, *Kaizen* (continuous improvement) becomes a permanent part of your culture, you will insure your manufacturing future against significant competitive gaps.

Does implementing WCM ultimately guarantee the future of your organization? Unfortunately, no! Even the most quality-conscious and cost-competitive organization cannot stay in business without customers. As Dr. W. Edwards Deming noted, "Employees do not close plants and force companies out of business, customers not buying products do." Staying close to the customer is therefore an essential element of a successful manufacturing organization.

Implementing World Class Manufacturing also focuses on customer satisfaction through the development of teamwork and the elimination of waste. But how do you know what satisfies your customer? That is the easy part. You ask them! While this task can be accomplished by surveys and market studies, we believe the most effective way is an across-the-table, face-to-face interview with the customer. If your product has a customer beyond the company you ship to, seek that company's input also. Motorola executives have been known to ride around in cabs in the Chicago area to find out what cabbies like or do not like about the radios they use.

In addition to asking your current customers about satisfaction, researching why former customers no longer do business with you can be a powerful tool in setting your customer satisfaction requirements. Programs like Quality Function Deployment (QFD) are also extremely powerful tools for getting the voice of the customer into your current or future product designs.

Because customers' perceptions evolve and their needs change, world class companies are now seeking to understand the latent needs of their customers. A latent need reflects a customer's need or requirement for which they would never think to ask. The sales success of the Mazda Miata two-seat sport car, developed despite market survey indications that there was no market demand for such a product, is a classic fulfillment of a latent customer need. Once your WCM program implementation is mature and a continuous improvement process is in place, you must add latent need to the definition of customer satisfaction.

Implementing World Class Manufacturing contains considerable discussion about how the Japanese do business and the history of their success story in general. During the 1950s, the Japanese never considered trying to be as good as American manufacturers; their goal was always to be better. They knew that they had to be better if they were to take market share away from American manufacturers. They observed our systems and borrowed those that fit. Over the years, by applying continuous improvement techniques (*kaizen*), they improved on our ideas. Since the late 1970s, the global marketplace has said that, in many cases, Japanese products are preferred. We admire those who are the best at what they do, and the Japanese fit this bill in many areas of manufacturing.

All this copying and admiration of the Japanese seems to bother some Americans. They would rather have us call *poka-yoke* "error proofing" and *kanbans* the "card system." We can honor these requests, but regrettably, changing the names of these systems will not bring back the dozen or so major industries which have been lost to the Japanese in the last twenty years. If we are to regain these lost industries, we must endeavor to become better than the Japanese. Blindly ignoring their numerous success stories will only lower our aim and slow our improvement.

How This Book is Organized

Implementing World Class Manufacturing was developed for use by everyone in a facility, but in particular, it was designed, laid out, and written to be used on the shop floor.

> "Some companies resist TPM (Total Productive Maintenance) due to their automatic dislike for anything Japanese. Having taken their share of bumps and bruises from these tough competitors, they want nothing to do with this 'Japanese improvement process.' Unfortunately, such companies are likely to continue their losing ways."
>
> CHARLES J. ROBINSON AND ANDREW P. GINDER
> IMPLEMENTING TPM
> THE NORTH AMERICAN EXPERIENCE

The advanced manufacturing methods in this book are presented in a modular form that we believe to be the optimum building order of a WCM implementation. It is the natural linking of all these techniques that provide a performance improvement that is greater than the sum of its parts.

The modular approach to training breaks the total WCM implementation into small units. This affords a facility the opportunity to adapt to both the cost of training (versus time) and the speed at which it is able to absorb the new techniques.

Chapters 1 through 4 should be required reading for the entire team, especially, for all managers and supervisors.

Chapters 4 through 10 are designed to be used for actual training courses. These chapters were developed from the notes we used to teach the individual courses. They are designed with space for note-taking.

Illustrations and charts are separate from the text so they easily can be made into overhead transparencies.

Notes to the Second Edition

The application of the waste elimination techniques of Lean and World Class Manufacturing have been expanded to include all parts of manufacturing businesses (the office also) and to all types of business in general. Hospitals, construction, credit card, and insurance companies are just a few examples of where Lean Enterprise is being successfully used outside of its initial focus of manufacturing. The bottom line is that any business process, which is a series of steps or operations that the customer is willing to pay for, can be improved.

Hence, the expansion and revision of the first edition of this book to include the enterprise.

World Class Manufacturing Terms

5S

The 5S's are the keys to workplace organization and housekeeping.

Advanced Manufacturing Techniques

The basic elements of world class manufacturing which are described in Chapter 5 through Chapter 10.

Baseline

Developing an understanding of a facility's knowledge, understanding, and capability regarding any training or improvement activity.

Benchmarking

The process of developing ideas and goals for improvements in your plant by comparing it to facilities that are currently performing at world class levels.

Champion

A person who has, or who can develop, an occupational hobby.

Continuous Improvement

The relentless challenge of the status quo with regard to the elimination of waste and customer satisfaction. Also known as the Kaizen process.

Culture

A plant's personality.

Employee Involvement and Participation

The management art and style of being able to collectively pool all of the human resources in a facility in order to obtain a specific goal or objective.

Empowerment

The individual plant culture and environment which allows everyone in a facility to grow and develop into the managers of their own work area, and their individual careers.

Kaizen

Kaizen is a Japanese word that means to "change for the good."

Kanban (pronounced kohn-bohn)

A Japanese word that means signboard or signal.

Islands of Excellence

Islands are areas of a plant developed as improvement models for the rest of the facility to use as a guide.

JIT Manufacturing

The manufacturing philosophy of producing only what a customer needs and only when they need it.

Manufacturing Cell

The grouping and arrangement in one area, of all tools, fixtures and machines which are used to completely process a family of similar parts.

Manufacturing Waste

Any part of the manufacturing process that the customer would be unwilling to pay for. Any operation that does not add value to the product.

Module

The concept used in writing this book that allows each chapter to be implemented separately.

Quality Function Deployment (QFD)

A process for determining and converting the actual needs and desires of a customer into the technical specifications of a product.

Quality

Meeting a customer's expectations.

Quality @ Source

Means that every individual in a facility (both office and factory) is always responsible for the quality of the product which leaves his or her area and goes to the customer, whether the customer is internal to the plant or external.

Poka Yoke (pronounced pokay yohkay)

A human error-proofing device. These devices are designed to prevent defects from occurring during people controlled processes.

Preventative Maintenance

This is the periodic or scheduled maintenance involving oiling, greasing, adjusting, repair or replacement of machine components in order to prevent premature wear and major problems.

Red Tag System

A method of identifying all the items in a work area or department.

Setup Reduction

Techniques which reduce the elapsed time required to changeover a machine from manufacturing part "A" to part "B."

Smoothing Factor

A factor used to compensate for fluctuating demand in calculating a kanban quantity.

Statistical Process Control (SPC)

The use of statistical techniques to analyze and adjust a process to achieve and maintain a state of statistical control.

Supporting Management Base

The level of management/supervision responsible for plant operations.

Traditional Manufacturing

A traditional manufacturing system is basically one that measures direct labor efficiency. Attributes of this system are: keep all machines running, produce parts without regard to customers' orders, inventory, or waste. Scrap and rework are considered a cost of doing business. Producing direct labor hours via parts production is the manufacturing managers prime directive. Low factory wages are imperative to the survival of the business. The management style is autocratic. There is no leadership. Only top management is asked to think in the performance of their jobs. There is no empowerment.

Throughtime

The ratio of the amount of value added time which a part or product contains to the total length of time a part or product was in the facility.

Unplanned Downtime

The inability of any resource in a plant to perform when it is needed.

Visible Arrangement Storage

A method of clearly identifying items and their storage location.

World Class Manufacturing (WCM)

An advanced set of manufacturing techniques that can be adapted and used to elevate a facility's manufacturing performance to world class levels.

Chapter 1

Why Implement World Class Manufacturing?

Proof of the Need to Change

- - - - - - - - - - - -

Profits are the Reward of Satisfied Customers!

In business, *customer satisfaction* is defined as meeting a customer's expectation for the quality, delivery, price, performance, and service of its products. While many people call this *Total Quality* (TQ) or *Total Quality Management* (TQM), we believe that the word quality, in American manufacturing, has referred only to making the part "to print." Making the part to print, however, understates the company's requirement to meet customers' expectations. The requirements of customer satisfaction are much greater!

Customer satisfaction requires execution by the entire company team on the customer's requirements. From the time the order is received until the customer has successfully received the product, everyone must be focused on the customer.

The Cost of Customer Satisfaction

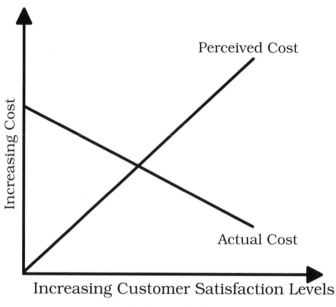

Figure 1.0

The goal of any company must be customer satisfaction. While these words are an axiom as old as business itself and may seem like "a blinding flash of the obvious," until recently they have been nothing more than a salesman's rhetoric. Unfortunately, customer satisfaction and higher product quality have always been considered synonymous with higher costs. Providing customer satisfaction was something most American companies never willingly attempted because of the distorted view that it raised costs and reduced profits. See Figure 1.0.

Profits are the reward of satisfied customers and, ultimately, the source of jobs. Unfortunately, U.S. manufacturers have been so misled that both management and labor feel no connection between their job performance and the company's profitability via customer satisfaction. Due to poor communication, 99.9% of what top management knows is never communicated to their employees,

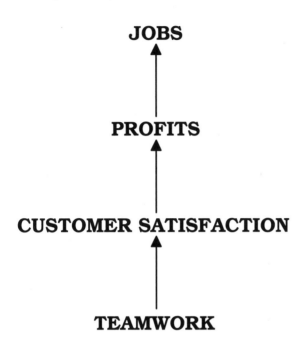

JOBS

↑

PROFITS

↑

CUSTOMER SATISFACTION

↑

TEAMWORK

who remain uninformed, unempowered, and therefore, unable to influence the results. Companies then find themselves with 30–40% more employees than they would need if they had a focused group of people. Companies temporarily see this excess during economic downturns, but never search for the root cause of the problem. The hiring and firing repeat just like economic cycles.

Both management and labor share the blame for the decline of our wealth-generating manufacturing base in the U.S. Although management and labor have traditionally had a rocky relationship, both approach the pursuit of their goals (profits/jobs) with the same short sighted vision.

Management's short-term approach is epitomized by the attitude commonly found around most corporations: *do what is best for your career and not necessarily what is in the best interest of the company.* This leads to a management style which emphasizes results that can be accomplished in six months to two years. This on-going mindset encourages managers to manipulate processes and customers to achieve monthly sales and profit. The financial results are pumped-up in the short-term at the expense of the company's future competitiveness. The long-term result of this management manipulation is an America with reduced manufacturing competitiveness and an over-all weakened manufacturing base.

Success in corporate politics—promotions, salaries, and bonuses—has become the principle management objective. Somewhere in our manufacturing history we seem to have dismantled the "American Way," a system that rewarded people because they worked hard and did a good job.

Labor also suffers from similar mismanagement and lack of long-term vision. Unfortunately, labor's traditional position is to negotiate job security contractually with the employer. Job security and guarantees occur by successfully competing in the global marketplace. Companies that compete, in the long run, always experience growth because customers reward them with sales and profits. Long-term job security comes only from competing and not from labor contract guarantees. Companies with excess management or labor will suffer profit and job losses as a result of this lack of competitiveness. While unions are busy fighting for job guarantees, manufacturing productivity continues to slip, and companies remain stuck with old work rules that no longer make sense.

While management and labor squabble, foreign companies are devouring our businesses. The enemy is not management or labor. The enemy is the competition. While American manufacturing drowns in a flood of foreign competition, all that management and labor do is point fingers at each other. Cooperation, participation, and teamwork are the keys to regaining our manufacturing losses.

Customer satisfaction alone has the power to guarantee profits and jobs! Customers guarantee the jobs of employees and companies. Customers will not pay the wages of anyone, hourly or management, who does not add value to the future product.

"It's not the employer who pays the wages. Employers only handle the money. It's the customer who pays the wages."

HENRY FORD

The Decline of the United States Automobile Industry

U.S., Japan, and World Wide Passenger Car Production with % of Market Share

Year	U.S. Production Units (% of World Wide)	Japanese Production Units (% of World Wide)	World Wide Units Total
1950	8,006,000 (76%)	32,000 (0.3%)	10,578,000
1955	9,204,000 (67%)	69,000 (0.5%)	13,743,000
1960	7,905,000 (48%)	482,000 (2.9%)	16,377,000
1965	11,138,000 (45%)	1,876,000 (7.6%)	24,542,000
1970	8,284,000 (28%)	5,289,000 (18%)	29,666,000
1975	8,987,000 (27%)	6,942,000 (21%)	33,263,000
1980	8,010,000 (21%)	11,043,000 (29%)	38,643,000
1985	11,653,000 (26%)	12,271,000 (27%)	44,811,000
1990	9,783,000 (20%)	13,487,000 (28%)	48,345,000
1995	11,985,000 (24%)	10,196,000 (20%)	49,863,000
2000	12,832,000 (22%)	10,145,000 (17%)	59,704,000

Figure 1.1

In 2000, the remainder of the world wide production total was produced in Europe (30%), Canada (5%), and other (26%).

1977 Hertz Corporation Study on Automotive Product Quality

Car Model	Average Number of Repairs Required Per Vehicle
Ford	3.26
Ford - Pinto	3.06
Chevrolet	4.25
Toyota	0.55

Figure 1.2

It is interesting to note that Hertz no longer tracks this data. We were told by a Hertz Public Relations Spokesperson that the person who accumulated the data retired and Hertz decided it was no longer worthwhile to collect it. We were also told that the data collected was not available. Since product quality seems relevant to rental car customer satisfaction, one can only wonder whether it was Hertz or Hertz's parent at that time, Ford, who decided to quit collecting the data.

America's Success in the 1950s and 1960s Sows the Seeds of Our Decline

Lack of concern for the customer has left our countryside littered with the signs of lost industries—closed manufacturing plants. In 1950, the U.S. enjoyed 76% of the world's market share of automotive production (Figure 1.1). While automotive customers were busy telling Detroit there were problems with cost and quality (Figure 1.2), unfortunately for Detroit and the U.S., no one was listening. By 1990, nearly ten years after America's first dose of global competition, our share had dropped to 20% (Figure 1.1).

As the marketplace began to shift to a global arena in the early 1970s, economic power shifted from the producers to the buyers. As a result of our concern with only producing products, we essentially have lost to foreign competitors the following industries:

Cameras	**Shoes**	**Steel**
Machine Tools	**Televisions**	**Pianos**
Radios	**Textiles**	**VCRs**
Ships	**Watches**	**Stereos**
Autos	**Guitars**	**Motorcycles**

and many others.

Many experts would say industries were lost because of lower foreign labor costs. The truth lies closer to our inability to develop facilities where all the people work together as a team to confront the competition. Today, no one person can hope to single-handedly develop customer satisfaction—but a group of people working together as a team can!

WARNING! WARNING!

Your industry may be next!

The Japanese manufacturing success story is not about lower wages, a homogenous population, work ethic, culture, or new equipment and factories. It's about managing and developing a team of people using advanced manufacturing methods, to eliminate all waste and provide customer satisfaction. The bottom line reason for Japanese success in U.S. markets is that they currently out manage us. The sooner American managers swallow their pride and come to grips with this reality, the sooner we can regain our leadership position in manufacturing. The marketplace has the final say!

The advanced manufacturing methods that the Japanese use are not equipment-based, but people-based. These advanced methods are based primarily on ideas the Japanese picked up during their visits to American facilities in the 1950s and from American quality experts they recruited to help them: W. Edwards Deming and Joe Juran. Japanese methods such as *Quality @ Source, Statistical Process Control* (SPC), *Kanbans* - an automated inventory replenishment system, and *Poka Yoke* - human error proofing, are all based on ideas that originated in America. Other Japanese advanced manufacturing methods such as *Setup Reduction, Employee Involvement* and *Participation*, and *Preventative Maintenance* owe their origins more to post World War II politics than to great management. The Japanese borrowed our ideas and, through years of implementation, substantially improved on them. As noted in the Introduction, the Japanese plan was not to be as good as American manufacturers to take away market share, but to be better.

America let its success lull itself to sleep—fat, dumb, and happy?—and we made no improvements to our original ideas.

WASTE

Waste is anything other than the MINIMUM amount of people, time, equipment, material, parts, and space required to ADD VALUE to the product.

ADDING VALUE

Any operation or process the customer is willing to pay for. Adding value generally means changing the shape or form of the product.

The 8 General Types of Waste

Scrap/Rework/Remake

Transportation

Motion

Waiting Time

Inventory

Overproduction

Overprocessing

**Underutilized
Human Resources**

Improved Profitability

**Improved Customer
Satisfaction**

Waste Elimination

It should be noted that while the Japanese were listening intently and implementing the Deming quality message, Deming could not find an audience in the U.S. In Japan, however, the highest award any Japanese company can receive for industrial excellence is the Deming Prize.

Customer satisfaction cannot be accomplished without an investment. The majority of the investment required is not in building, property, or equipment, but in changing mindsets and bad habits through reeducation. The engine that drives customer satisfaction is people, not manufacturing equipment or products. People are the most underutilized, but most flexible asset in our facilities. There has always been a great concern about measuring utilization of equipment and assets, yet people were never part of this equation.

General Motors is one of the best examples of how spending dollars on equipment and technology alone will not improve customer satisfaction. During the 1980s, GM spent $40 billion upgrading and modernizing its facilities. GM purchased new computers, lasers, robots, wire-guided vehicles, and all the latest in leading-edge technology. But by 1991, this extensive investment in plant, property, and equipment could not stop an additional ten point loss in the U.S. automobile market share. With the average American paying $15,000 for a car in 1992, ten points of market share are roughly equivalent to a loss of $15 billion annual sales for GM.

Furthermore, of the $40 billion originally invested in new equipment, an estimated $8 billion has been pulled out of the plants and scrapped. This equipment was scrapped because it failed to perform as well as the human it replaced. The GM improvement plan did not include its people as the foundation of the plan; therefore, it was doomed to failure.

GM had a unique opportunity to learn advanced manufacturing techniques from one of the best—Toyota. In 1983, GM formed a joint venture with Toyota to produce cars in a closed down GM facility in Fremont, California. The joint venture company, New United Motors Manufacturing, Inc. (NUMMI) would produce cars in the same facility and with the same workers that GM laid off because of quality and labor problems. The Fremont facility had the reputation of being the worst performing assembly plant in the GM system. Toyota supplied the operating capital and the top management.

The NUMMI plant was almost an immediate success and the lessons that GM could have learned from NUMMI were numerous:

♦ Assembly costs of about $750.00 less per car than a traditional GM plant

♦ Four job classifications instead of as many as 183

♦ A no lay off contract

♦ Cars consistently rated in the top three of all GM models for product quality

♦ Workers assembled cars in teams

Unfortunately for General Motors, the NUMMI experience was never transplanted to any of its other facilities, probably because it was unprepared for the NUMMI success. (GM required Toyota to rehire the laid-off Fremont workers who GM felt were unmanageable.)

The lesson: Technology alone does not insure success. Teamwork, using and supporting technology to focus on the customer's requirements, does insure success.

IMPROVEMENT = CHANGE

If you always do what you have always done, you will always get what you have always got!

JAPANESE SUCCESS FACTORS

1. **Teamwork.**
2. **A company-wide war on waste.**
3. **Dedication to perfect quality.**

Other companies did learn the lesson of trust, respect, and teamwork. In 1977, Motorola sold its Quasar television manufacturing plant in Illinois to the Japanese company, Matsushita. Matsushita produces consumer electronics under Panasonic, Technics, and National brand names. Two years later the performance of the plant had dramatically improved as shown in Figure 1.3. Motorola used this and other experiences to transform itself into a company that is recognized globally as world class. Motorola, in 1988, was awarded the U.S. Department of Commerce Malcolm Baldrige National Quality Award. This award is the highest level industrial award given out by the U.S. Government.

Quasar Plant Performance

	Under Motorola	Under Matsushita (two years later)
Direct Labor Employees	1000	1000 (same people)
Indirect Labor	600	300
TVs Produced Per Day	1000	2000
Assembly Repairs	130%	6%
Annual Warranty Expense	$16,000,000	$2,000,000

Figure 1.3

How is the American Automobile Industry doing in 2003 vs. 1997?

In 1998, it was reported: "If you listen to the news out of Detroit, you often hear 'we are as good as' statements. While we want to believe, for the good of U.S. manufacturing, that these statements are not just sales talk, there is evidence to the contrary.

In the "1997 model year J.D. Power and Associates Car and Truck Initial Quality Studies," which is based on consumer satisfaction studies, nine of the eleven first place initial quality categories were won outright by Japanese cars. Toyota tied Saturn for the tenth category, and Ford F-Series won the full-size pickup category outright.

The "1997 model year J.D. Power and Associates Vehicle Dependability Study," which reports on consumer's satisfaction with their cars and trucks at five years of ownership, showed the Toyota Lexus as the only winner.

For 1997 *Consumer Reports* magazine also had some bad news to report about American automobiles (based on consumer feedback). The magazine's list of thirty used cars that it recommends for purchase contains no American cars. On the list of used cars that *Consumer Reports* recommends staying away from—all but four are American."

2003 results:

For the "2003 model year J.D. Power and Associates Car and Truck Initial Quality Studies," the number of categories has been expanded from the eleven used in 1997 to sixteen. Seven of these sixteen first place categories were won by American manufacturers. The remaining nine categories were won by Japanese (8) and German (1) manufacturers.

For the "2003 model year J.D. Power and Associates Vehicle Dependability Study," which reports on consumer's satisfaction with their cars and trucks has also been changed. In 1997 it reported results at five years of ownership. Now it uses three years of ownership with seventeen vehicle categories. Five of the seventeen first place categories were won by American manufacturers. The remaining twelve categories were won by Japanese (11) and German (1) manufacturers.

For 2003 *Consumer Reports* magazine continued to report disappointing news about American automobiles. The magazine's list of thirty eight used cars that it calls "CR Good Bets" for purchase contains two American cars. On the list of used cars that *Consumer Reports* calls "Reliability Risks"—all but four are still American."

CUSTOMER SATISFACTION

Customer Satisfaction is meeting a customer's expectations for the quality, delivery, price, performance, and service of our products.

Improved Profitability

Improved Customer Satisfaction

Waste Elimination

Customer Satisfaction = Lower Costs

The reality of satisfying the customer is that it does not raise costs. Customer satisfaction always costs less!

The reason for the lower cost is simple. In every manufacturing plant, there are inherent roadblocks which prevent it from performing in a manner that meets the customer's expectations.

Customer Satisfaction Roadblocks (Waste in Business is Often Disguised as One of These Activities)

Scrap/Rework

♦ Limits competitiveness in establishing selling prices because these costs are ultimately borne by the buyer.

♦ Prevents on-time deliveries which cause additional costs in overtime, premium freight, warranty, and/or administrative costs.

♦ Represents quality problems which may reach the customer even if 100% inspection methods are in place. It is a statistical fact that 100% inspection is only 85% effective.

Machine Setups/Machine Unplanned Downtime

♦ Reduces manufacturing capacity.

♦ Prevents on-time deliveries.

♦ Promotes building inventory by running as many pieces as possible once a difficult setup is finished.

♦ Supports the requirement for indirect labor and higher costs.

Supplier Lead Times

♦ Prevents the reduction of product lead times.

♦ Prevents us from becoming a world class company, since world class companies require world class suppliers.

Inventories

♦ Adds carrying cost of inventories—approximately 25–30% per year is waste.

♦ Hides unsolved manufacturing problems: scrap, re-work, etc.

Lost Time Accidents

♦ Causes physical and mental hardships on our team members and their families.

♦ May limit the full participation and involvement of the team member.

♦ Prevents a member from being available to serve the customer.

♦ Injury claims add cost to our products.

These roadblocks have one thing in common—they are all examples of manufacturing waste. Operations that do not add value to the part are waste and customers will not pay for waste.

Other Types of "Disguised" Waste

Material Handling

Inspection

Inventory Storage

WASTE

Waste is anything other than the MINIMUM amount of people, time, equipment, material, parts, and space required to ADD VALUE to the product.

Product Test

♦ When used as an audit of manufacturing or assembly processes, this is not a value-added operation.

Counting Inventory

To remove roadblocks to customer satisfaction, we must eliminate the business waste in our facilities. This elimination of waste reduces our business costs and improves

---

The 8 General Types of Business Waste

Scrap/Rework/Reconciliations/Remake

Transportation - Part or product material handling, or information transportation

Motion - Non-value-added time such as looking for, searching, obtaining items such as prints, tools, fixtures, materials, files, reports, memos, or office supplies

Waiting Time - Non-value-added time such as waiting for materials, instructions, the supervisor, the fax machine, or the copier

Inventory - Raw, work-in-process, finished goods including office and janitorial supplies

Overproduction - Producing more than the customer ordered

Overprocessing - Doing more than what the customer is willing to pay for

Underutilized Human Resources - The lack of involvement and participation of all the members of the workforce

---

profitability. Developing customer satisfaction drives down business costs. Lower costs can mean lower prices, greater profit margins, or both.

Eliminating Office Waste—Becoming a World Class Enterprise

Almost always overlooked in the journey to eliminate business waste is office waste. Like waste in our manufacturing areas, office waste has become part of the process. Office waste occurs because, as part of the process, it is thought to be necessary. It is not recognized because its in the background, part of the woodwork.

Identifying office waste begins with the customer and the definition of value-added. While offices normally do not produce physical products, they do produce "knowledge or information products."

The office waste journey begins by understanding that office processes (like manufacturing) contain up to 75% waste and that the goal, as shown in Figure 1.4, is to work "smarter" in the office, not harder. Eliminating wasteful activities and substituting activities the customer will pay for is the goal.

A classic example of office waste is supplier invoices. Suppliers are required to setup an Accounts Receivable department and send invoices to customers even though the customer's receiving department received and signed for the material. If the customer has issued a blanket purchase order for the material, the price of the item is known. Why force the supplier to supply invoices with information that is already known by the customer? Ultimately, the cost of maintaining an Accounts Receivable department at the supplier is borne by the customer—all waste!

Value Stream Mapping, explained in Chapter 5, is an excellent tool for identifying office waste.

PROFITS ARE THE REWARD OF SATISFIED CUSTOMERS!

OFFICE VALUE ADDED PROCESSES

A process is a series of steps, operations, or procedures that the customer is willing to pay for. Adding value generally means changing the shape or form of the "knowledge or information product." If we listed all the steps, operations, or procedures on our invoice, the customer would be willing to pay for each of them.

How Does Implementing World Class Enterprise Improve Office Productivity?

By working smarter! Converting the team's time spent on waste:

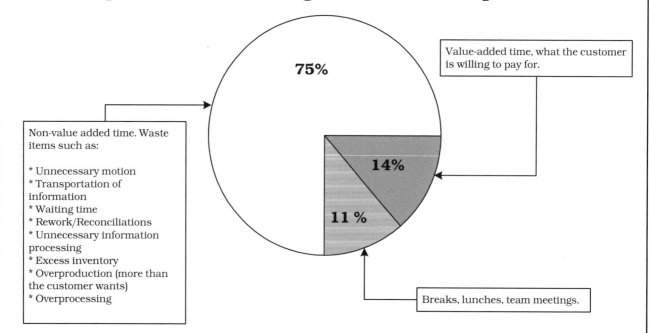

75%

Value-added time, what the customer is willing to pay for.

Non-value added time. Waste items such as:

* Unnecessary motion
* Transportation of information
* Waiting time
* Rework/Reconciliations
* Unnecessary information processing
* Excess inventory
* Overproduction (more than the customer wants)
* Overprocessing

14%

11 %

Breaks, lunches, team meetings.

To value-added time:

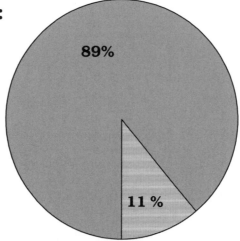

89%

11 %

Figure 1.4

This figure illustrates the large improvements in productivity that can occur when wasteful activities are identified and replaced with value-added activities. Again, it is never about working harder.

Waste in Office Areas is Usually Disguised as:

Conflicting Department Goals - Not everyone on the same page or not pulling in the same direction

Traditional Accounting Methods - Rewarding people for creating waste, for example: excess inventory

Poor Product Designs - Designs which do not include the needs of both the internal (manufacturing) and external customers

Order Processing Time - In World Class companies, orders go from the customer to the line, cell, or area that will produce the part, product, or service

Hunting, Looking, Searching - For files, orders, invoices, reports, memos, supplies, etc.

Waiting Time - Waiting for batched paperwork, a signature, instructions, the fax machine, the copier, a meeting to start or end on time, or the supervisor

Purchasing Reorders, Transactions, Supplier Invoices

Authorizations - Usually an indicator of poor communication or a lack of empowerment

Other Office Activities Disguised as Work

Summary

World Class Manufacturing and World Class Enterprise (WCE) as a Vehicle to Customer Satisfaction

World Class Enterprise is a technique that can continuously improve the following business and manufacturing processes:

♦ Safety, quality, productivity, & delivery

While reducing:

♦ Lead-time & costs

This technique is implemented through the training, empowerment, and participation of the entire workforce. It is the goal of World Class Enterprise to improve and grow the business by being globally competitive.

The "Traditional" New Equipment Approach to Solving Business Problems

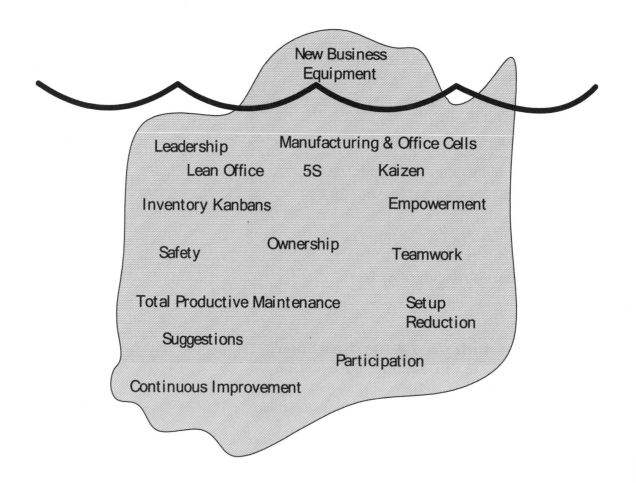

Figure 1.5

Just as the visible portion of an iceberg is supported by a massive underwater structure, new equipment will be only as effective as the "submerged" foundation supporting it. As we begin to develop the Advanced Business Techniques required to achieve World Class performance, it will become apparent that the bridge to World Class Enterprise is 80% people and 20% equipment.

Chapter 2

Implementation "Show-Stoppers," Roadblocks, and Barriers

. . . .

What are the Show-Stoppers?

Before implementation can begin, it is necessary to have completed two prerequisites: top-down implementation leadership and employee empowerment. Without these in place, the show can't go on.

The Top-Down Leadership Prerequisite

The first show-stopper is a lack of top-down leadership.

If we could become world class manufacturers by simply making capital investments in new equipment and technology, GM would have regained its 20 percentage points of lost U.S. market share as a result of their multi-billion dollar facility investments in the 1980s.

IMPROVEMENT

=

CHANGE

Implementing world class manufacturing (WCM) in the traditional manufacturing facility generally requires that every department in the plant do things differently. Only then can we hope to achieve different results.

Undoing twenty to thirty years of bad habits that American manufacturing has accumulated is a very difficult problem because the most difficult part of the WCM journey is accomplished through people—by getting people to change how they "think." When people start to change how they think, they will start to do things differently. This can be a very challenging task for even the best leaders/managers.

Adjusting people's mindsets can be accomplished only by leadership that begins at the top levels in the facility. These leaders are also responsible for:

♦ Creating and communicating to everyone the company's vision, direction, and strategy.

♦ Empowering the work force.

♦ Hands-on leadership—on the shop floor support of change and the new ways of doing things.

This top level leadership requirement must be in place before the WCM implementation begins or it is doomed from the start.

Manufacturing Insanity–

is defined as doing the same thing day after day, and expecting different results!

After this leadership requirement is in place, a *supporting management base* can be developed. Like the top level leaders, these leaders/managers must also understand that:

♦ Their manufacturing survival is at stake and can clearly see the results of the elimination of all waste and the development of customer satisfaction.

♦ Communication facilitates teamwork and that, for the team to strive for customers satisfaction, they must all have a copy of the "playbook" that top management has.

♦ They must be prepared to repeat any message and instructions the four to ten times it will take for everyone to understand the message.

♦ A "gut wrenching" 24-hour-a-day desire is required to develop a world class operation and they must be willing to model and facilitate the performance required to become world class.

♦ The vision of a long-term payback by a WCM implementation prevents them from being tempted to "make the month" or "pump up" the numbers for a short term payback. (Many companies have started down the road to WCM and later aborted implementation when they realized, in the short term, that profits may suffer, as upfront training causes additional training expenses and training time reduces production time. See Figure 2.0).

> They watch your feet — not your lips.
>
> TOM PETERS
> NOTED AUTHOR AND MANAGEMENT CONSULTANT

The Long Term Vision Required for a WCM Implementation

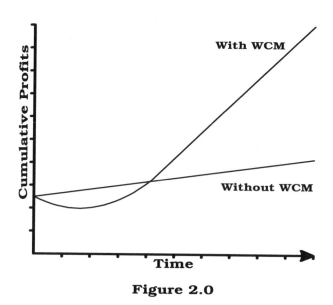

Figure 2.0

Warning! Warning!

If you want to implement world class manufacturing in your facility, reread the preceding paragraphs about leadership requirements. If these comments do not apply to you and the top manager in the facility, do not attempt to implement WCM. Without a "total" commitment, your attempt to implement WCM will be another short-term management fix-it program like MBO's, Zero Defects, Quality Circles, etc., and your attempted implementation will add to the waste in your facility.

The Empowerment Prerequisite

The second show-stopper is employee empowerment.

The goal of empowerment is to have the entire team moving and pulling in the same direction with one agenda. Empowerment gives employees the opportunity to influence the results while developing a sense of accountability and ownership.

The question to ask yourself about empowerment is this: Do you want a few people in the plant making improvements or do you want the power and potential of everyone in the plant making improvements? The "bottom line" is this: plants do not become world class without everyone in that facility driving and pulling toward that goal. Empowerment is the vehicle that allows that to happen.

Empowerment occurs in an environment where the following situations exist:

- ◆ Leadership versus management.

- ◆ Employees are recognized as the most valuable resource.

- ◆ Teamwork.

- ◆ Decision-making is delegated.

- ◆ Openness, initiative, and risk taking are promoted.

- ◆ Accountability, credit, responsibility, and ownership are shared.

**IMPROVEMENT
=
CHANGE**

> The person that figures out how to harness the collective genius of his or her organization is going to blow the competition away.
>
> *Walter Wriston*
> *Former Citibank CEO*

Empowerment Barriers

Once top management has committed to creating an environment where empowerment can develop, everyone must be aware of the barriers in the facility that can restrict or stop this development along the way. These potential barriers are:

- **Lack of trust.** A poor relationship between management and labor in a facility will slow or prevent acceptance of empowerment and WCM. Agree to "start over" or have a "new beginning."

- **Poor communication.** Poor communication supports a lack of trust in an organization. Additionally, it can lead to unclear expectations. When a group has unclear expectations, they revert to the previous known way of doing business. Communicate often, and about everything! Do not leave any communication to chance.

- **Fear.** People fear the unknown and therefore resist change. A clear and constant reminder of the vision, goals, and how everyone fits into those goals is required. People need to feel secure about their jobs. They also need to feel secure about asking questions, reporting problems, and submitting ideas.

♦ **Lack of training.** Inadequate training leads to confusion, frustration, and anger for employees who are asked to change but not given the tools. Baseline the needs of the team and measure their progress after training. This is discussed again later in this chapter.

♦ **Lack of measurements.** As expectations for the facility change, the team will be anxious to see how they are doing. Measure and post in the plant the status of every change that needs to be accomplished. Remember, what gets measured, gets done!

Empowerment is an evolutionary change, not revolutionary. Figure 2.1 shows the stages of the empowerment evolution.

Employee Empowerment Evolution

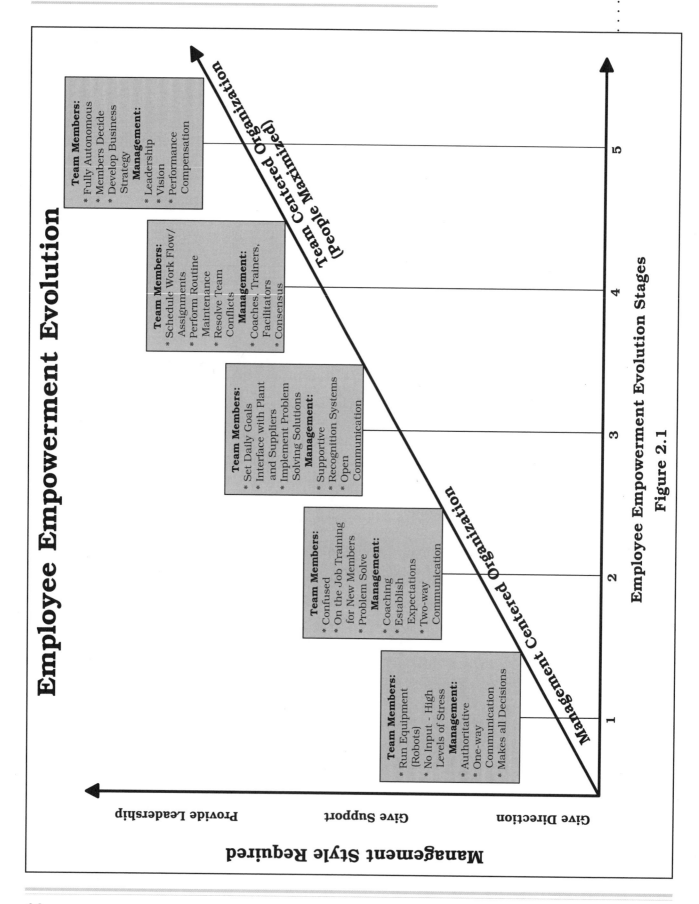

Figure 2.1

Where Did Traditional Manufacturing Management Fail?

Our definition of a traditional management system is basically one that measures direct labor efficiency. Attributes of this system are: keep all machines running, and produce parts without regard to customers' orders, inventory, or waste. Scrap and rework are considered a cost of doing business. Producing direct labor hours via parts production is the manufacturing managers prime directive. Low factory wages are imperative to the survival of the business. The management style is autocratic. There is no leadership. Only top management is asked to think in the performance of their jobs. There is no empowerment.

Many managers will ask the question "Why should we change when our traditional management methods made America the #1 manufacturer in the world and produced American prosperity in the '50s '60s and early '70s? It worked before, why shouldn't it work now?"

The answer is simple and thought provoking. If traditional management focus had been on customer satisfaction through the elimination of all waste, our prosperity during those periods would have been greater and we would still be the #1 manufacturer in the world for all major products. Think about it! Our traditional methods produced a standard of living *less* than what it could have been! A simple comparison will prove the point. Compare your plant's traditional financial measurement—Return on Sales, Return on Investment, Return on Assets, etc.—with:

♦ "0" scrap and rework costs

♦ "0" warranty costs

♦ "0" obsolescence costs

♦ The effect of 80–90% reduction in equipment downtime

♦ The effect of "0" lost time accidents (workmen's compensation insurance and claims)

♦ The effect of at least a 75% reduction in inventory and the associated carrying costs

♦ The effect of at least a 50% reduction in required manufacturing floor space

For anyone who would say that approaching these levels of performance is impossible, see Figure 2.2. It shows the performance levels of companies currently considered world class versus the World Class Performance Goals. Since these companies practice continuous improvement, their current levels of performance change daily. Motorola, for instance, has the goal of reducing its scrap and rework rejections from their current WC levels shown in Figure 2.2 to 3.4 parts per million (PPM).

Column three of Figure 2.2 allows space to write the actual performance figures for your facility. If you have a traditional manufacturing plant, many of these goals are probably not even measured, a good indication that a WCM implementation is necessary.

Assuming all costs (waste) from column three, Figure 2.2, have been properly assigned and allocated, the comparison can be rather dramatic.

World class companies use leadership, empowerment, and the advanced manufacturing methods discussed in this book to lower their manufacturing costs. These companies, with their lower cost structure, have the option of matching competitors prices and earning greater profits, or reducing prices and gaining market share. Most companies go after market share.

However, since American manufacturing has been unable to control manufacturing costs, the answer to improved profitability had always been to raise the selling price. The recession of the early '80s gave us our first lesson in global market control of selling prices.

Caterpillar, for example, went through a decade-long period, beginning in 1984, of being unable to raise the list prices on their construction equipment products. Any attempt to raise prices sent their customers to their competitor, Komatsu-Dresser. In 1997 American car manufacturers were in a similar position. Some car models carried their price rebates right into the 1998 new-model year.

Unfortunately, traditional American management would rather blame our current lack of global competitiveness on low foreign wages, culture, unions, old equipment and facilities, etc.

Managers at world class companies have been known to say that if Japan wasn't around, someone should have invented them because, as our competitors, they make us better!

World Class Manufacturing Performance Levels

World Class Performance Goals	Current World Class Performance (Motorola, Toyota, Others)	Fill in Your Plant's Current Performance Levels
-0- Scrap	10–25 Parts Per Million (PPM) or 0.0010%	_____ PPM $ _____
-0- Rework	10–25 PPM	_____ PPM $ _____
-0- Setup Time	All Machines Less Than 10 Minutes	_____ Average Setup Time
-0- Inventory	1/2–3 Days	_____ Days
-0- Unplanned Downtime	212 Minutes/Month	_____ Min/Mo.
-0- Lost Time Accidents	-0-	_____
100% Participation	32 Suggestions Per Employee Per Year	_____ Suggestions
100% Throughtime	30–60%	_____ %
100% Customer Satisfaction	Measured by % Market Share	_____ % Market Share

Figure 2.2

Implementation Roadblocks

The road to WCM is littered with roadblocks of concrete mindsets and years of bad habits: "We've always done it that way!"

Again, implementing WCM in the traditional manufacturing facility requires that every department in the plant do things differently. Only then can we hope to achieve different results.

The length of time required to complete an implementation obviously depends on the current operating conditions in the facility, the ability to commit resources to the job, and how well stockholders or other owners are prepared to live with a short-term reduction in profitability, as shown in Figure 2.0.

Once training begins the question becomes: How quickly and how thoroughly will people absorb, understand, and change how they do things? How long it takes depends considerably on the plant's "culture" or personality which has developed over the years. This personality partially results from your training and hiring practices. If the plant already has "in-house" training, then a new training program could be well received. If the best available people have always been hired, the training may be accelerated. If hiring is based on who will work for the rate of pay you are willing to pay, and there are no formal training programs, conversion time will be longer.

Unfortunately, many American managers seek the benefits of WCM only when their businesses are in desperate straits and they fear the action of the shareholders or owners. The dip in profitability during implementation can mean the difference between making and losing money. This requires them to manage the bottom line and to make changes in their facilities simultaneously. This scenario can cause managers to generate a credibility gap as changes are made in how the facility does business. If only we could have had these improvements when America was still in charge of the global economy! Alternate implementation strategies as a means of tuning this curve to your requirements are presented in Chapter 3.

As we previously noted, to change the direction of a facility, "people must think differently, so they will work differently." This new thinking requires a reeducation of the workforce. This reeducation can be broken into two components: *soft education and hard education.*

Soft education. The training which is designed to help people understand why change must be made in the way we work. These soft-training sessions, Chapter 1 - Why Implement World Class Manufacturing or "Proof Of The Need" to change, and Chapter 5 - Team Building, are designed to change the way we think. If we change how we think, then we are inspired to do things differently, and only then can we hope to obtain different results.

Hard education. Once we are receptive to "doing things differently" through changes in mindsets, the hard-training can begin. These training courses, Chapter 4 - 5S, Chapter 6 - Total Productive Maintenance, Chapter 7 - Manufacturing Cells, Chapter 8 - Setup Reduction, Chapter 9 - Inventory Kanbans, and Chapter 10 - Kaizen are the "nuts and bolts" of manufacturing and the elimination of all waste.

What About Unions?

Many managers make excuses with this one. Fortunately they are just that—excuses. To their credit, many current union leaders know as much about the global economy and the need to eliminate waste and be competitive as does any manager. Managers must understand that a facility cannot successfully make the WCM journey without an effective partnership between management and the union. But how does a facility, which never had a partnership, develop this new relationship? Actually, to the leaders committed to the change necessary for improvement, this part is easy. Follow these guidelines and the facility will be headed in the right direction.

♦ Partnerships are based on trust which is built over time through open and honest communication. If trust does not exist in the facility today, management must take the initial steps to developing this relationship. Communicate frequently and about everything. Consider having a union representative sit in on management staff meetings. Nothing happens if the facility cannot get through this step.

♦ Treat everyone with dignity and respect. Change will not happen without a few disagreements. Consider all disagreements as opportunities to improve communications and relationships.

♦ Ask for the union's participation from the start. They should be involved in all implementation planning and the top local union official should be at the "podium" when the plan is discussed with all the employees for the first time.

♦ Both union and management leaders must be committed to the future. Remember, world class manufacturing is not a program, but a new way of life, and in the typical manufacturing organization this requires at least a five-year commitment.

IMPROVEMENT = CHANGE

People—Most Valuable Asset/Largest Implementation Roadblock

Tailoring the courses to fit your facility, and actually accomplishing the training is as simple as the two-step soft and hard education process we have presented. But, unfortunately, this drastically understates the problem. The actual length of time it takes to get ready for the nuts and bolts of the training can be as long as one to two years, and the reason has nothing to do with the instructor, or the length of the courses. The reason is people learn at different rates, have different lengths of service, and varying degrees of old habits. Additionally, each person perceives things differently. Some people may even question the real reason for WCM implementation, suspecting, perhaps, that it is just another management scheme to make everyone work harder. People are the most valuable, yet most underutilized manufacturing asset. They are also the biggest barrier to a WCM Implementation. This includes both labor and management people.

There are two ways to break down or eliminate this barrier. The "Despain Method" is one approach. Jim Despain is now an upper level manager at Caterpillar. At one time he was the Plant Manager at Cat's fork lift truck manufacturing facility in Monterrey, Mexico. Jim filled the plant with people fresh out of school. In Jim's mind, these people, who generally had no previous work experience, came to work at Cat with no bad habits or preconceived notions about quality. His comment was, "They don't know you can't build a perfect fork lift, so everyday they go out there and try." People who didn't believe that you could build a perfect fork lift truck were replaced in an on-going cleansing of the system.

For most existing businesses, firing and then hiring all new people at the current location, or moving facilities to a new location where people with no bad habits could be hired, is not a feasible alternative! In most cases swapping out people becomes a "Catch 22"; the people with the bad habits are also the most experienced who understand the ins and outs of the manufacturing processes.

The second approach to this implementation barrier is to retrain, retrain, retrain, retrain, and then never stop training in continuous improvement techniques.

Other Visible and Invisible Barriers

It is extremely important to understand that, within the broad scope of people being an implementation roadblock, there exist three other barriers once the retraining begins. Two are potentially "invisible" barriers and the third one is a very visible barrier. Any of these three can delay the completion of the soft educational efforts and actually prevent a successful completion of the nuts and bolts training.

Plant Baselines

The first invisible barrier is called the plant's "baselines." Before any training can begin in a facility, testing, developing, and understanding both the educational and cultural baselines of the group to be trained is essential. Professional educators call this a "needs assessment." Understanding the cultural and educational baselines allows tailoring the starting point of the courses to the actual needs of the people.

The concept of baselining is important in implementing all phases of WCM. If you decide to take a trip in your car, road maps could be used to guide you to any location in the country, but road maps work as guides only if you know your starting position. The same is true for a WCM implementation. You must know your starting position and then constantly measure the changes (improvements) along the way.

For Lack of a Baseline....

Story #1.

We went to a facility that was having major product delivery and quality problems. We quickly discovered that the product assembly department was not using any type of drawing to verify the assembly process. In fact, no drawings or process sheets were supplied to the assemblers with their work-order package. Assembling products without the current engineering print is extremely dangerous (to quality) and a totally unacceptable practice. We thought we were on the right track. We quickly put together a plan to make sure all work orders would contain the most current engineering assembly prints and all relevant process sheets. We met with all the assemblers and told them to build it "to the print." We gave the assemblers "line stopping" authority if they encountered a quality problem. Any questions?? None. Proceed to assemble!

We went on to solve another problem in the plant, but the quality problems in the assembly department persisted. On further investigation, we discovered that assembly drawings not being included in the assembly work-order package was only a symptom of the actual problem. The "root cause" of the problem was that the people who worked in the assembly department could not read blueprints. Over the years, and by always working in the same department, these people memorized the assembly process. If we had immediately done a needs evaluation in the plant, we could have established a baseline and not wasted some precious time.

Story #2.

We taught a course in inventory kanbans. The course is taught in one day and lasts about nine hours. The first half of the course is spent discussing the decline of the U.S. manufacturing base and the need to do things differently if we want the results to change. We discussed how Setup Reduction and Quality Programs like SPC and Quality @ the Source are extremely important to the success of kanbans. We thought the course was a success. Two days later, one of the people in the class came up to me and said, "Would you tell me what SPC means?" I answered Statistical Process Control. The reply was, "Thanks, I asked several other people in the class and they didn't know either." My heart sank. When I asked why the students didn't ask the question in class, the response was typical for a student—they didn't want to appear dumb. Further questioning indicated that our class did not understand the function of SPC or how to use this process.

Again, a baseline would have prevented us from teaching at a level for which they were inadequately prepared.

Continuous Communication

The second invisible barrier is the number of times we are willing to communicate the WCM message. For most managers, giving instructions once is considered sufficient. But for an implementation to overcome the numerous years of bad habits in our facilities, it will take good continuous communication, modeled by its messenger, before it becomes self-sustaining in the workforce. Everyone involved in the implementation must be prepared to "hold out" for the time it takes for this barrier to be broken down. The patience will be worth it when people become empowered and energized.

Middle Management Conversion

You probably have noted already (or you will) that this book is written in a "repeat the message" style. We have found this method to be effective for those who take the longest to convert and have the highest conversion failure rate—middle management.

Middle-management conversion to WCM philosophies is the third barrier we wish to expose. This barrier is another reason a top-down implementation is an absolute requirement for success. Unfortunately, traditional American management taught our middle managers and supervisors to be enforcers and cops. Additionally, these supervisors were raised or promoted in a system that made producing pieces the first and only order of the day. Problem-solving and teamwork were given lip service, if they were mentioned at all.

In WCM, managers and supervisors need to be team builders, coaches, facilitators, trainers and then, ultimately, to turn their people loose. This conversion is unacceptable to some because they enjoyed the old way of managing for all the wrong reasons. They wanted to be supervisors/ managers because it was a power or ego thing. Others will view the WCM pushdown of responsibility to the floor as a threat to their authority, their current job, and possibly their existence at the facility. Since implementing WCM will allow the facility to perform with fewer layers of management, these fears are well founded and may drive these supervisors to directly or indirectly fight the changes. This fighting to save their jobs may ultimately cost them their job.

The supervisors/managers who understand the importance of WCM philosophies will show commitment by working hard to eliminate their own jobs. This level of commitment is indicative of the people you will want to keep at your facility in order to keep your continuous improvement program moving.

Our suggestions are these: Keep the middle managers and supervisors involved from day one of the implementation. Have separate manager/supervisor meetings on a regular basis with this group to openly discuss the changes that are occurring. External WCM-related seminars and visits to other facilities which have already converted, or are converting to WCM, will help the group adjust to the changes that are occurring everywhere in manufacturing.

The cold hard facts are that it has been our experience that all of the middle managers/supervisors will not survive the transition regardless of the amount of training, counseling, and coaching. Some will leave on their own within the first year. Others will stay on the job and remain managerial brick walls to the process of getting the people to think and work differently. Ultimately they will feedback their resistance and discontent to the people they are supposed to be empowering. These people will have to be let go. No organization can allow a few people to put the survival of the facility at risk.

It speaks poorly of American manufacturing management that we have allowed the management ranks to become overstaffed. While we have always been concerned about value-adding direct labor and non-value adding indirect labor on the shop floor, we have never attempted to force management people to address this concept in the office. The Tom Peters comment that management people must "Think like a consultant" is appropriate here. Every person in the office should be required to measure his or her contribution to customer satisfaction goals everyday. All management people must understand: If you can't measure your contribution to customer satisfaction, like the consultant who is not contributing daily, your job (or the consultant's stay with the company) is at risk. The days of "gold watches after thirty years" just for showing up everyday are gone. Jobs are no longer an entitlement!

As we noted earlier, corporations sometimes recognize this excess in people when the economy slows and they are forced to have major layoffs. Unfortunately, these companies and the people who are laid off never search for the root cause of the problem and this cycle is then doomed to repeat itself.

> "If American business is going to prevail, and be competitive, we are going to have to get accustomed to the idea that business conditions change, and that survivors have to adapt to those changing conditions. Business is a competitive endeavor, and job security lasts only as long as the customer is satisfied. Nobody owes anybody else a living."
>
> SAM WALTON
> WALMART STORES

Implementation—How Long Does It Take?

Figure 2.3 is presented here as a way to determine the approximate length of time required for a WCM implementation. Remember that WCM is a journey without an end. The time-required reference refers to when the facility has successfully implemented all of the advanced manufacturing techniques noted in this book and is in the continuous improvement mode. The definition of successful implementation is that the use of all these advanced techniques is self-sustaining.

This table allows a facility to determine its starting point on the implementation by comparing the five baseline operating environments on the table (plant wide communications, employee empowerment, quality, shop floor management, and training) to its current plant environment.

To further put the implementation challenge and commitment in perspective, an article from *Industry Week* magazine (republished with permission) is included after Figure 2.3. This article, covering a Dana Corporation plant in Bristol Virginia, was part of *Industry Week's* 1996 annual salute to what it considers are the best manufacturing plants in America.

As a former Dana employee, I can attest to Dana's corporate driven culture of leadership and employee empowerment. Before this plant was constructed, Dana's corporate culture had already laid the proper foundation for a smooth WCM implementation. If you think an implementation should be completed in one to three years, read on!

Implementing WCM—How Long Does It Take?

Which descriptions fit your facility?

	Traditional Facility	Facility In Transition	World Class
Plant Wide Communications	None, unless to blame the factory people for a problem or to announce a lay-off.	Plant-wide meetings with top local management at least monthly.	Plant-wide and departmental meetings as often as daily.
	All communication is one-way.	Visual communication of plant vision, goals, and performance has started.	Two way communication. Goals and performance are understood and known by everyone.
Employee Empowerment	None; generally an adversarial relationship, characterized by blaming and finger pointing.	Employees are expected to "manage" their work area.	Work force feels like owners.
	No one on the shop floor is expected to use anything other than "arms and legs" in the performance of the job.	Everyone is encouraged to participate, but middle managers and supervisors are roadblocks.	Integrated self-managed work teams.
		Employee suggestion system started.	Improvements implemented without direct management involvement.
Quality	Quality less important than costs or schedules.	SPC program in place with QA Department as the enforcer.	Everyone has "line stopping" capability.

Figure 2.3 - continued on next page

Quality (Cont'd)	Emphasis is on detection of errors. Everyone thinks quality is the responsibility of the Quality Control Department.	Supplier certification program in place.	Error proofing prevents defects from occurring. Employees treat all downstream operations like customers. Quality measurements only meaningful in parts per million (PPM).
Shop Floor Management	Supervisors used as cops in direct labor reporting system. Idle machines viewed as a problem. Scrap, rework and downtime are considered a cost of doing business.	Supervisors feel threatened as responsibility and accountability is pushed down to the people on the shop floor. Cop management mentality is replaced with trust and respect.	Supervisors converted to trainers, coaches, and facilitators. Machine operators give plant tours to customers.
Training	No formal training except as required by law.	Some training available to management.	Continuous and on-going training in place and available to everyone. Training requirements established for everyone.
Time Required to Implement WCM	5–10 years with committed management.	3–8 years with committed management.	Continuous improvement techniques (kaizen) must be in place to hold position. Benchmarks for world class performance change daily.

Figure 2.3 - continued from previous page

DANA CORP.

At A Glance

- **Average first-pass yield of finished product: 99%.**
- **Scrap and rework 0.7% of sales.**
- **Annual inventory turns up from 64 five years ago to 120.**
- **Work-in-process turns up to 130.**
- **Average number of days parts remain in inventory down from 3.8 in 1991 to 2.6 last year.**
- **Cycle time for the plant's major product— journal crosses for light-duty-vehicle drive shafts—down 55% from 1991 through '95.**
- **Customer-reject rate improved 75%.**
- **Productivity up 28%.**
- **Machine availability—an estimated 60% only a few years ago—now up to 98.7%.**

BRISTOL, VA.

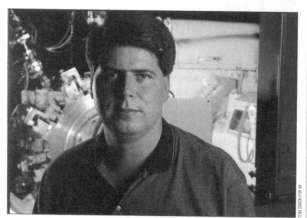

Plant manager Mike Bowersock (above) says the key to Dana-Bristol's success is balance—"We do everything *well."*

BY WILLIAM H. MILLER

ASK MANAGERS AT MANY MANUFACTURING PLANTS what they are most proud of at their facility, and they'll snap out a ready, unhesitating answer. But that's not the case at Dana Corp.'s Spicer Driveshaft Div. plant in Bristol, Va. Ask the question there, and managers ponder a bit. They furrow their brows, turn the query over in their minds, then give varying replies. Some mention the plant's employee-involvement (EI) program. Others, its statistical process control (SPC) system. Still others, its inventory control, its predictive maintenance, its heat-treating operations, or other areas.

It takes Mike Bowersock, the plant's tall, soft-spoken plant manager, to put the differing answers in perspective. "We think we do *everything* well," he explains. "There are plants that are better at employee involvement than us. There are plants that are more environmentally sound. There are plants that are further along with predictive maintenance. However, there are

the plant to adopt from the very outset the cornerstones of the "Dana style" of management: a lean staff, flat organizational structure, extreme decentralization, and an emphasis on employee involvement and teamwork.

The payoff has been Dana-Bristol's performance. It is dazzling. Consider a few statistics: First-pass yield averages 99%; scrap and rework are a minuscule 0.7%; annual inventory turns have climbed from 64 five years ago to a sizzling 120; work-in-process turns have risen to an even higher number—to 130.

Meanwhile, the average number of days parts remain in inventory has fallen from 3.8 in 1991 to 2.6 last year—even in the face of a 150% increase in sales. Cycle time for the plant's major product— journal crosses (a machined component of drive shafts) for light-duty-vehicles—went down 55% during the same period. The customer-reject rate has improved 75%. Productivity is up 28%. Machine availability, which foundered at an estimated 60% only a few years ago, is up to an impressive 98.7%.

The plant's excellence hasn't gone unnoticed: In 1995 it received the U.S. Senate Productivity & Quality Award for the state of Virginia.

ALTHOUGH DANA-BRISTOL MANAGERS STRESS their facility's all-around balance, it's obvious that EI is a source of special pride. Deservedly so. Not only do production employees make their own on-the-job decisions—they're directly responsible for their own quality, for example—but also fully 90% of them serve voluntarily on teams. Brandishing names like "Knight Raiders," "Sleeve Slingers," "Cell Mates," and "Bad Company," 22 of the teams are permanent, meeting on at least a weekly basis. In addition, temporary teams—80 of which currently exist—continually are forming to address specific problems; more than half of these teams are created by production employees themselves in response to problems they—not management—have identified. The teams' solutions, which the plant calls "quick kills," numbered 1,100 last year, ranging from paperwork reduction to design of a new switch for a riveting machine.

All team members receive eight hours of training in problem-solving, while team leaders get 40 hours of leadership training. These courses are part of the deep commitment to off-the-job training that the plant considers indispensable to its EI success. In each of the last two years, training provided to each employee has averaged 35 hours. Included is a specially designed in-house course, called "Business 101," that instructs employees in profit ratios, profit-and-loss statements, overhead allocation, and other basic facts of the business—all brought down to the plant level. "Our aim is to get our people engaged in achieving our plant's goals," explains Holt. "The course emphasizes the little things that employees can control—the use of gloves, for example."

The number of training hours Dana-Bristol provides will increase even more this year, putting the facility close to achieving Dana's ambitious corporate-wide goal of 40 hours annually per employee. The plant recently launched an initiative with local technical colleges to offer courses to employees on such topics as math, metrology, problem-solving, business concepts, and effective presentations.

Ingrained as EI is at Dana-Bristol now—with fully 5.5% of employees' time spent away from equipment—that hasn't always been the case. "Initially, our EI was like quality circles, or like elementary school. It operated at the ground level," describes Quality Assurance Manager Roger Anderson, who has

few plants that we are aware of that have maintained the balanced approach to running the business that we have."

Indeed, Dana-Bristol—as the plant is known—possesses commendable overall balance. And it's a balance of excellence.

The 280-employee facility, located in the outskirts of Bristol in the mountainous southwest corner of Virginia, manufactures machined components for drive shafts, primarily for pickup trucks and sport-utility vehicles. The plant is an internal supplier to sister Spicer Driveshaft plants, shipping its products on a just-in-time basis.

Opened in 1988, the plant has capitalized on the luxury of its relative newness. Unlike many older plants that have had to make difficult transitions to new operating cultures, Dana-Bristol was able to incorporate many of the elements of its present success on day one. Nothing has been more important than its meticulous selection of employees, more than half of whom have post-high-school educations. "We reject 'loners,' people who have no focus, and people who are not 'finishers,'" says John Holt, manager of human resources.

This elite workforce, which is all salaried, made it easy for been with the plant since its opening. "At first our EI was management-directed. Now it is *employee*-directed."

The transition to today's sophisticated implementation of EI didn't happen overnight. "It took me a while to adapt to our way of doing things," admits Mike Artrip, a coordinator in the plant's journal-cross department, who left a job in a local machine shop to join Dana-Bristol shortly after the plant opened. "When I came here, it was a whole different world for me. There are no time clocks. You schedule your own breaks. You make your own decisions on the job. The trust they [management] give you is amazing."

Corroborates Lauren Stieh, also one of the plant's early production employees: "It took the EI concept a while to jell. Many of the employees came from the old school, where there was a distinction between 'bosses' and 'workers.' But most people jumped into the new way."

Recently promoted to division-level quality-assurance engineer at Spicer Driveshaft Div.'s headquarters in Toledo, Ohio, Stieh reflects fondly on the atmosphere at the Bristol plant. "As long as I could back up my decisions, I had no fear of reprisal," he says.

To Robert A. Fessenmyer, general manager of the Spicer Driveshaft Div., Dana-Bristol's marriage of EI and training is the key to the plant's success. "Their [the plant's] number of hours of training leads the division, and their [use of] EI teams is well up there," he reports. "The plant started the right way—with an emphasis on team building. And they're continuing that culture."

Although he singles out Dana-Bristol's EI and training for praise, Fessenmyer provides testimony to Plant Manager Bowersock's claim of overall balance by talking of the plant's other strengths.

For one, the division chief cites Dana-Bristol's pioneering work in predictive maintenance, a 1½-year-old program that has dramatically increased machine uptime to the current 98.7% figure. Fully 100% of the plant's production equipment is subjected to vibration analysis and ultrasonic inspection, carried out by two full-time predictive-maintenance technicians.

"We can now predict two months ahead of time when a gearbox, for example, will go out," says John Stines, facilities manager. Such advance knowledge is essential; because the plant operates with minimal inventory, any unplanned machine downtime could quickly lead to out-of-stock conditions among customers.

In addition, the plant has been a leader in SPC. "Dana-Bristol was one of the first plants in our division to have direct feedback of data from machines," Fessenmyer indicates. He describes the plant's data-collection system as a "key shop-floor management tool" that provides inventory levels and machine-performance information to production employees in real time.

The SPC technology implemented at Dana-Bristol has been extended to its sister Spicer Driveshaft facilities. Many of the plant's predictive-maintenance techniques will be similarly extended.

In emphasizing predictive maintenance and SPC, Dana-Bristol is capitalizing on manufacturing concepts and technologies that are rapidly gaining footholds elsewhere in industry. But that doesn't mean the plant is bereft of ideas of its own. Far from it.

Truly original ideas regularly pour out of Dana-Bristol's teams. A prime example: the plant's "college student" program that Bowersock believes is unique in industry.

The program was conceived four years ago when it became apparent the plant was having difficulty keeping pace with production requirements. Even though the facility had always operated on a three-shift, seven-day workweek, a steady rise in orders made it increasingly necessary to ask employees to work overtime. The overtime requests were so frequent, in fact, that the quality of employees' home lives began to be threatened—not to mention the plant's quality performance. Management turned the problem over to a team.

After a few weeks of deliberation, the nine-member team responded with a suggestion: Why not hire students from local technical colleges to fill in on Saturdays and Sundays? Management agreed to the idea. Today, in the third year of the program, 41 college students now help cover weekend production. The students, who otherwise might be performing minimum-wage jobs flipping hamburgers, gain valuable manufacturing experience. They receive a minimum of 40 hours of training before starting their part-time jobs and make their own decisions on the job. "They're even empowered to shut down machines," marvels Joyce Smith, engineering design and records coordinator who led the employee team that came up with the idea. The plant also benefits from the arrangement. Besides getting help for its production crunch, it gains an experienced pool of potential employees. Twenty of the plant's current full-time employees started as temporary workers in the program.

SO WHAT ELSE IS NEW?

Excellence is so pervasive at Dana Corp.'s Spicer Driveshaft Div. plant in Bristol, Va., that it sometimes seems taken for granted. For example, a visitor to the plant notices a trophy case at one end of the large conference room off the lobby. The case is crowded with awards and plaques, but one particularly large trophy stands out. Closer inspection reveals that it is for winning the 1994 Virginia state championship in the Men's Industrial Slow-Pitch softball league.

"Oh yes, *that*," Plant Manager Bowersock acknowledges dismissively when asked about it. "We won the state championship. Our team went to the nationals in Florida."

Solid as Dana-Bristol's current performance is, the plant is not resting on its laurels. Employees talk enthusiastically of raising their already-sparkling statistical performance to even higher levels, thus exemplifying the facility's self-developed vision statement: "Empowered people interacting in a creative team environment using problem-solving and prevention skills while displaying a passion for continuous improvement."

The plant currently is focusing on gaining QS 9000 certification. That hadn't been a priority because, as Bowersock explains, "we are a second-tier supplier." But now the plant wants the certification—not only as confirmation of its quality excellence, but also because the Spicer Driveshaft Div., which *is* a first-tier supplier, is seeking it. In order for the division to get certification, each of its 16 plants must be individually certified. Dana-Bristol is undergoing the assessment process for certification, which is expected next spring. Certification will be just another chapter in Dana-Bristol's eight-year history of balanced excellence.◄

Chapter 3

Tuning the Implementation to the Needs of the Facility

Financial Implications

As mentioned in the previous chapter, initial and ongoing costs which will affect the bottom line are a result of the training involved to implement these advanced manufacturing techniques. These financial implications can be minimized or distorted by implementation roadblocks as discussed in Chapter 2.

Since the primary goal of every company is to make money, it would be naive to believe that all companies have the independent financial control (or ability) to install WCM without continuing to manage the "bottom line." The short-term financial requirement of "making the month" can conflict with pulling production operators off the floor for two or three days of implementation training. Therefore, under these conditions, it is necessary to budget and financially forecast the cost of the implementation.

The Four Times Rule

It is a commonly held principle in advertising that people must see an advertisement at least four times before they understand it. The same fundamental applies here. The WCM message and training must be continuously repeated until there is clear evidence that it has become self-sustaining.

Implementation Cost Curve

Unless you have an existing training budget that can be used to fund this program, the training required to educate everyone in WCM concepts will revise your cumulative profitability curve similar to the curve shown in Figure 3.0A - Normal Implementation Curve.

The financial impact of the elimination of waste begins to significantly change the slope of your past performance. The downward trend of the cumulative profits as shown in Figure 3.0A is broken as improvements begin to be implemented as a result of the training already completed. These improvements have the effect of funding the remaining training. Depending on the facility and the training schedule, the downward trend in cumulative profits can be broken in a 12–24 month time period.

Tuning the Implementation Cost Curve

This chapter also presents variations in the implementation path that can be used to suit your particular needs and budgets. There is no way to avoid the training costs of an implementation, but using improvements to fund additional training can modify the implementation cost curve shown in Figure 3.0B.

Modifying the implementation cost curve can be achieved by accelerating the implementation of those modules that have an immediate impact on the performance of the facility. The two modules used in this strategy are Machine Setup Reduction - Chapter 8, and Inventory Kanbans - Chapter 9. These modules can be used to provide early and quick successes for the plant, the program, and the customers.

Implementation Costs

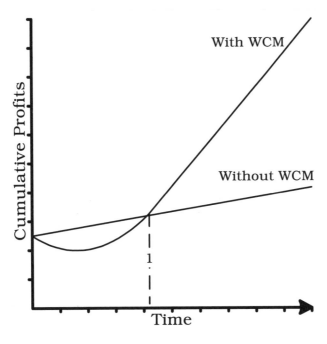

Figure 3.0A
Normal Implementation Curve.

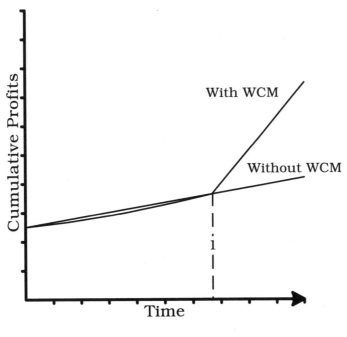

Figure 3.0B
Modified Implementation Curve.

The Black and White Syndrome

We did a WCM implementation at a facility that had numerous quality problems. These problems were largely related to poor Purchasing and Quality Department practices. Parts that did not conform to the engineering print specification had been accepted from their suppliers, put in the stockroom, and ultimately delivered to the assembly department. After the people were taught Quality @ Source and given line-stopping authority, we immediately ran into another problem. Those trained wanted to immediately find and scrap all the discrepant material. The financial impact of such a move would have been about $200,000.00 for a facility that was at break-even.

Instead, we chose to segregate all the suspect material and return it to the suppliers, sort and rework it as needed, or scrap it. This process took about a year and cost the facility approximately $40,000.00. The goal of improving product quality was accomplished by removing all the suspect parts from the shop floor, thereby preventing them from being delivered to customers.

Purchasing and Quality Department practices were changed, and we lost some short term credibility for not immediately scrapping the material. While we felt the situation was professionally managed, it did reinforce how necessary it is to give people a broader management vision and the feeling of ownership in the facility.

It must be clearly understood that this modification does not reduce the cost of an implementation, nor does it represent an effective shortcut. This modification, however, does reduce the dip in cumulative profits at the cost of an extended length of time required to reach the cross-over point. This cross-over, shown as line #1 in Figures 3.0A and 3.0B, represents the point at which the benefits of a WCM implementation begin to exceed the implementation costs. The expression "No pain, no gain" applies to implementing WCM.

Before we discuss the actual modification of Figure 3.2, we will make the assumption that the facility being discussed has both manufacturing and assembly operations. If your facility has only one of these operations, it will be apparent in the following discussions which parts of these instructions do not apply. Also, we will discuss the management groups involved in these areas in the general terms that we have encountered over the years.

Please note that additional implementation guidance is included in Chapters 4–10.

Referring to Figure 3.2, this modification occurs as follows:

TEACH THE ENTIRE FACILITY:
Module #1 (Chapter 1)
Why Implement World Class Manufacturing
- Proof of the Need to Change

Module #4 (Chapter 4)
5S

Module #5 (Chapter 5)
Team Building

As we pointed out earlier, an unproductive inability to communicate develops if everyone in the facility is not educated in the basics of WCM. We cannot stress enough the importance of a complete and thorough implementation of Modules #1, #4, and #5 to the entire facility. The remaining modules use these three modules as their foundation and any attempted shortcuts here will cause extreme cost and unnecessary backtracking later. If your implementation is subject to some form of external review, lack of this foundation could put the entire program at risk due to the lack of results in the forecasted fashion.

After a successful completion of the Modules #1, #4, and #5, teach only the groups specially involved in these areas:

Module #8 (Chapter 8)
Machine Setup Reduction

- **Manufacturing Management and Supervision**

- **Machine Operators and Setup people**

- **Manufacturing Engineering**

- **Quality Assurance**

- **Production Control/Production Planning**

- **Representatives from your top ten suppliers (As you begin the WCM journey, you must make sure your suppliers are travelling the same path. If they are not, you must include them in your own facility's WCM training. This will not only improve their performance to your facility, but it will also begin the development of a partnership between the two companies. Remember, you cannot have a world class company without world class suppliers.)**

Module #9 (Chapter 9)
Inventory Kanbans

- ◆ **Purchasing**

- ◆ **Quality Assurance**

- ◆ **Receiving**

- ◆ **Representatives from your top ten suppliers**

- ◆ **Assembly Department (management and hourly personnel)**

- ◆ **Production Control/Production Planning**

- ◆ **Manufacturing Management and Supervision**

- ◆ **Manufacturing Machine Operators**

Ultimately, everyone in the facility must be taught all the advanced techniques of WCM, but the intent here is to start with the groups who are intimately involved in the areas which can have an immediate impact on the facility and its customers. While it can be successfully argued that techniques like inventory kanbans can even be used to automate the replenishment of office supplies, we believe everyone would agree that a quick analysis of the potential paybacks dictates that you start on the shop floor.

Successful implementation of these modules should have the following immediate impact and payback for your facility:

- Increased manufacturing capacity
- Reduced product leadtimes
- Reduced part shortages
- Reduced inventories
- Improved on-time deliveries
- Paper work reduction
- Improved communication throughout your facility and between your facility and your suppliers

The actual timing of these improvements, after completion of these modules, will vary depending on factors which vary by facility. Typically, the timing is 60–180 days.

It is extremely important that training is resumed for the remainder of the facility when improvements begin to take place.

Learning from Others

In the late 1980's, Dana developed a superb training program called Excellence-In-Manufacturing (EIM). Groups of people from the floor and office (all groups are mixed) are put through five continuous days (40 hours) of in-house training, taught by the plant's facilitator, where they are exposed to WC concepts.

While EIM is a well-prepared, thought-out and leading edge (even visionary) program, some of its effectiveness is lost due to the way it is implemented. The following areas of the program could be improved:

1. While Dana is noted for the amount of training it accomplishes through its "Dana University" programs, 40 hours of continuous training on what might be considered radically new ideas is too intense for most people. It is much too fast for the majority of the people in the class. This led us to develop the modular approach to training on WCM concepts. We believe "you eat the elephant one bite at a time." The modular approach spreads the training time out and allows you to "repeat the WC message." Being able to repeat the message numerous times over the implementation period is an extremely important element in a successful implementation. The message must be repeated until it becomes self-sustaining. The self-sustaining message is one of the measures of a successful implementation.

2. The Dana program was designed to train all people in a facility in one year. At the six-month time period, half the people in the facility had knowledge of WC concepts while the other half had not received any training at all. This led to an unacceptable communication gap between the groups that knew and the groups that didn't know. In addition, while some people in the first group were ready to make changes, they found their untrained peers uncooperative. This situation can be avoided by using the WCM implementation "roll out" model shown in Figure 3.1.

3. Another difficulty inherit in the Dana program, as well as other training programs, is the "black and white" syndrome. Those who are trained in the program and understand the requirement to change want all changes to be accomplished immediately without regard to the financial impact. The key to managing the bottom line during an implementation is to pick a basic implementation schedule and then guide the team through and around the roadblocks, avoiding any time-consuming and costly backtracking.

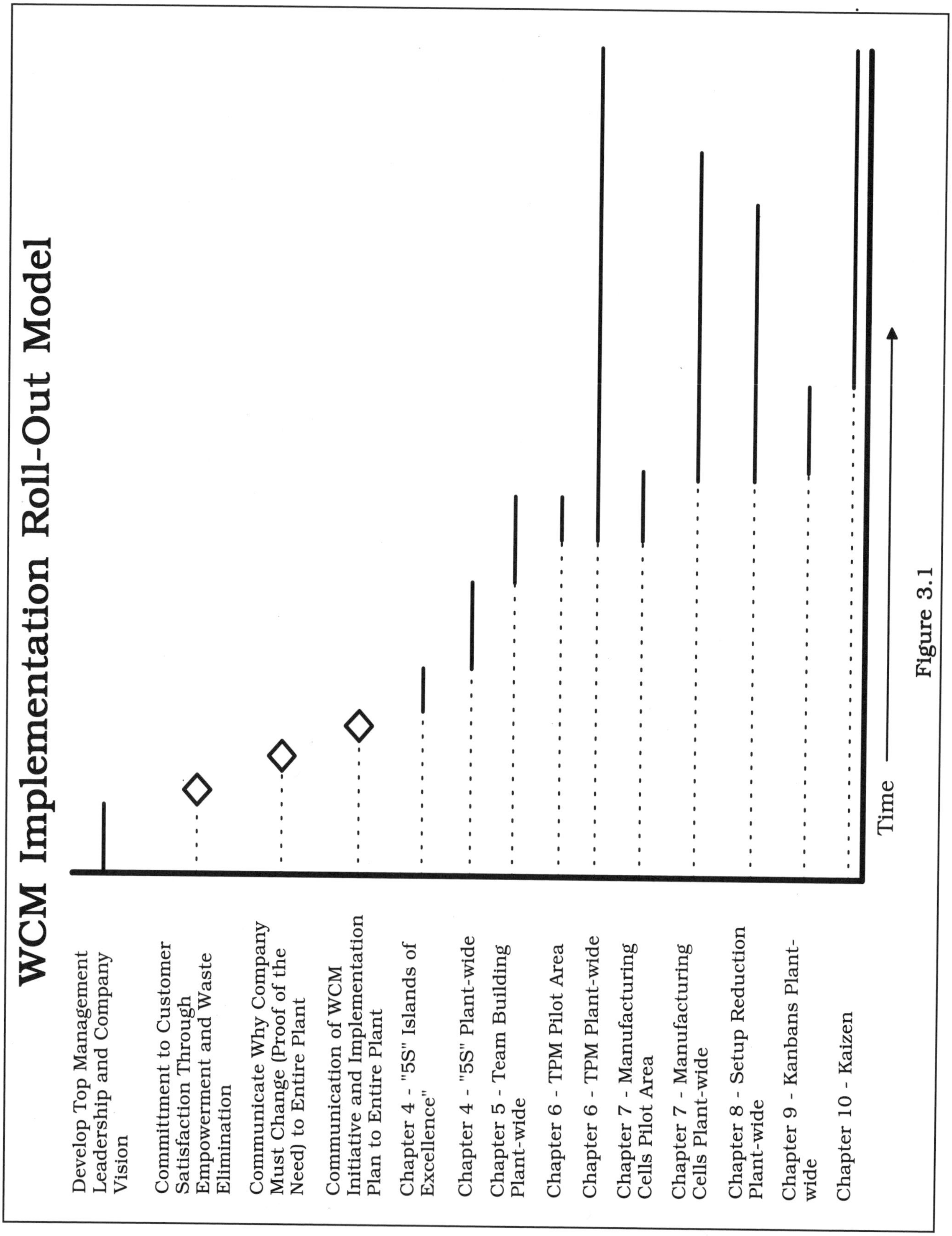

WCM Implementation Roll-Out Model

Develop Top Management Leadership and Company Vision

Committment to Customer Satisfaction Through Empowerment and Waste Elimination

Communicate Why Company Must Change (Proof of the Need) to Entire Plant

Communication of WCM Initiative and Implementation Plan to Entire Plant

Chapter 4 - "5S" Islands of Excellence"

Chapter 4 - "5S" Plant-wide

Chapter 5 - Team Building Plant-wide

Chapter 6 - TPM Pilot Area

Chapter 6 - TPM Plant-wide

Chapter 7 - Manufacturing Cells Pilot Area

Chapter 7 - Manufacturing Cells Plant-wide

Chapter 8 - Setup Reduction Plant-wide

Chapter 9 - Kanbans Plant-wide

Chapter 10 - Kaizen

Time

Figure 3.1

Implementation Path Guidelines/Suggestions

Implementation Path by Course Module	Brief Description with Recommended Timing and Course Length
Chapter 1 **Proof of the Need to Change** **(Why Implement World Class Manufacturing)**	This introduction should be modeled after Chapter 1 and developed specifically for the business environment that exists in the company implementing the training. This is a 60-90 minute introduction and "proof" that must be heard and seen by the entire plant population. This should be presented by top plant management and should occur in one plant meeting if possible (or several meetings on the same day).
Chapter 4 **5S**	Unless your facility in already "World Class Clean," this module must be implemented next after the Chapter 1 "proof." No exceptions! Implementing 5S is an extremely effective, low cost method of improving your facility, and its complete implementation can be proof to everyone that this WCM implementation is not just another "program of the month." This module can be taught in eight hours which must include a shop floor or office exercise. The entire plant must go through this training. The next module, Team Building, can start only when all 5S training in the plant is completed and when the efforts of the initially trained 5S groups becomes self-sustaining, therefore insuring a plant-wide 5S implementation success.
Chapter 5 **Team Building**	No facility will attain manufacturing greatness because of this book or as a result of one person in the facility. Manufacturing greatness occurs when all of the people in a facility are working together as a team and doing great things for the customer. This book will outline the strategies and procedures that can be used to develop this greatness, but the plant team must execute them for customer satisfaction. The objective of "staying focused on the task" while working together cannot be accomplished without training. This module can be taught in twenty four hours and should include at least two team-building exercises. As people complete this training, they may begin training in another module.
Chapter 6 **Total Productive Maintenance**	Maintenance in American Manufacturing is one of the most relied-upon, yet also the most neglected asset. Because it has been neglected, it generally requires the most training, upgrading, and time (2-5 years) to bring it to world class standards. While the investment payback takes time, TPM also has one of the largest potential paybacks of all the WCM modules. Additionally, TPM affects the ultimate performance levels of all other modules. The training to redefine the roles of manufacturing and maintenance and to develop a manufacturing/maintenance partnership can be accomplished in a 3-5 day TPM event per work site.

Figure 3.2 - continued on next page

Implementation Path Guidelines/Suggestions—Cont'd

Implementation Path by Course Module	Brief Description with Recommended Timing and Course Length
Chapter 7 Manufacturing Cells	Manufacturing cells will reduce the required manufacturing floor space and give your team an opportunity to "own" and operate a part of the business. Manufacturing cells combine and move all the equipment required to make a family of parts into one area. People being trained in cells should have completed modules 1, 4, and 5. No exceptions. Training can be completed in twenty four hours, and should include an actual shop floor cell design.
Chapter 8 Setup Reduction	Setup reduction is a simple method that can be the fastest way to improve your manufacturing capacity and reduce your lead-times. While the thought of setup reduction will have universal appeal and support throughout a facility, unfortunately, the common perception will also be that it is impossible! This perception changes during the setup reduction class, and full understanding and support will develop quickly during the class because everyone hates long and difficult setups. This class can be taught in sixteen hours and should include a shop floor reduction exercise.
Chapter 9 Inventory Kanbans	Kanbans are wonderfully useful inventory replenishment tools that exemplify, like setup reduction, the simplicity of the world class methods. They are easily understood, can be quickly implemented, and give your team the opportunity to take more responsibility for the operation of their area and the plant. A small or partial kanban implementation can be used to show the power of the world class methods to any high-level doubters that may exist in the organization. However, their full potential for improving the plant operations is only achieved when all the other modules are in place. Kanbans can be taught in an eight-hour class which should include suppliers if external (to the plant) kanbans are being developed.
Chapter 10 Kaizen	Kaizen is a Japanese word that means continuous improvement. This module will consider the use of two different kaizen techniques, kaizen as on-going continuous improvement and the kaizen event. In the kaizen event, a team of people are sent to a shop floor area to radically change the performance of the manufacturing area, usually because of cost problems or major changes in customer requirements. The pre-production kaizen event is designed to make sure that all world class methods are in place before a new part or product goes into production. To ensure success, these continuous improvement techniques or events must involve people who have completed all the previous modules. Kaizen events can last from 3-5 days.

Figure 3.2 - continued from previous page

Chapter 4

5S

Paving the Approach to World Class Enterprise

What are the "5S's"?

The 5S's are the keys to workplace organization, housekeeping, and visual management. While some people tend to dismiss the 5S concept because of its simplicity, this concept consistently produces an organized workplace, resulting in:

♦ An increase in quality

♦ An increase in productivity

♦ A cleaner workplace which creates a safer workplace

♦ A reduction in required floor space

♦ Earlier identification of abnormal business situations

WASTE

Waste is anything other than the MINIMUM amount of people, time, equipment, material, parts, and space required to ADD VALUE to the product.

The 8 General Types of Waste

Scrap/Rework /Remake

Transportation

Motion

Waiting Time

Inventory

Overproduction

Overprocessing

Underutilized Human Resources

Where do the 5S's Apply?

The 5S's apply to everything within the four walls of a facility.

♦ All office areas

♦ All manufacturing or processing areas

♦ Warehouse areas

♦ Job shops

The simplicity of 5S implementation is not a fault. It is actually the "magic" that makes it so successful. As you will see with the other WCM modules, simplicity is the reason they work.

Ultimately, housekeeping and workplace organization are directly linked to achieving discipline in business. World Class Enterprise cannot be achieved without the discipline and culture of 5S in place.

When leadership and empowerment are in place, there is a very natural tendency to want to jump to more tangible improvements like TPM, Setup Reduction, Manufacturing or Office Cells, or Kanbans. We incorrectly perceive that these will produce more quantitative results. However tempting this leap is, avoid it! There are no shortcuts. Deviations from the recommended path will almost certainly cause the implementation time line to be lengthened. You cannot build the bridge in random sequence or with randomly selected components. As some of the younger members of our team would say—been there, done that!

The reality is that 5S does produce "shop-floor" quantitative results. For example, probably 50% or more of the time saved in the Setup Reduction Module is achieved by externally "organizing" and being ready with everything in its place to do the setup. Simple and low cost!

With the opportunity to take ownership of their area of responsibility, through leadership and empowerment initiatives, the team must now develop a working environment that will be safe to work in, one they can be proud to own, and one that customers can use as an example to their suppliers.

The wonderful news is that 5S, like the rest of the WCM initiatives, will result in a safer, more satisfied workforce while reducing costs and improving productivity. If you doubt this statement, have your teams log how much time they waste looking for and getting things they need to do their job: tools, forms, paperwork, gloves, wiping cloths, gauges, fixtures, etc. If your plant is typical, there is a lot of waste! What about worker's compensation costs? Is a minimum 50% cost reduction significant?

For any financial types who want to do a "pay back" analysis, the implementation cost of this module is almost nothing!

"World class facilities develop beginning with the 5S's, and facilities that fail, fall apart beginning with the 5S's."

HIROYUKI HIRANO
5 PILLARS OF THE
VISUAL WORKPLACE

You never get a second chance to make a first impression!

5S Success Precedes World Class Development and Lack of 5S Precedes Failure

Comparison of two manufacturing plants: Plant "A" above, and Plant "B" to the left. The photo from Plant "B" is from the maintenance area. How well was the equipment in "B" maintained if the maintenance area looked like this? How long did it take to find repair parts when the equipment failed? Which plant would a customer choose to do business with? Note: Plant "B" was eventually closed because it could not effectively compete.

The Origin of 5S

The 5S's were created in the Western World based on the Japanese organization and housekeeping system that contained five words that all began with the letter "S."

Step #	Japanese Word	English Translation	5S Word
1	Seiri	Proper Arrangement	Sort
2	Seiton	Orderliness	Straighten
3	Seiso	Cleanliness	Sweep
4	Seiketsu	Cleaned Up	Schedule
5	Shitsuke	Discipline	Sustain

Basic Definitions of the 5S's

1. **SORT.** Proper Arrangement. Remove from the workplace any item that is not needed for current production or the current day's assignment. Keep only what you need today. Add anything that is needed but not there.

2. **STRAIGHTEN.** Orderliness. Arrange items so they are easy to use. Mark and label these items so they are easy to find and put away. Use a consistent labeling system. Have a designated place for everything. Store everything close to the work site.

3. **SWEEP.** Cleanliness. Sweep the floors, wipe off equipment, paint if necessary, and in general, make sure everything in the plant and offices stays clean. Inspect while cleaning to prevent breakdowns.

4. **SCHEDULE.** Cleaned Up. Standardize and maintain the use of sort, straighten, and sweep.

5. **SUSTAIN.** Discipline. Practice and repeat these procedures until they become a way of life throughout the entire business.

5S Implementation—Paving the Approach!

In addition to the benefits previously mentioned, a 5S implementation will pave the approach to the bridge built with the remaining WCM modules:

♦ Pride in the workplace supports team development (Chapter 5, Team Building)

♦ Sorting out means removing paperwork, parts, tools, and fixtures that are not used in producing the product. This prevents the possibility of these items being used to create a defective part (Chapter 5, Team Building/Error Proofing)

♦ Clean equipment allows operators to notice equipment problems before they become breakdowns (Chapter 6, Total Productive Maintenance)

♦ Sorting retains only what is needed to produce a product. The remaining office and manufacturing space is smaller, resulting in less wasted motion needed to produce the product (Chapter 7, Manufacturing Cells.) Additionally, it is easier to visualize the process when unnecessary items are not in the way.

♦ Reducing setup times is dependent upon being organized. With everything in its place, search time is eliminated (Chapter 8, Setup Reduction.)

♦ Sorting out means eliminating unnecessary raw material and work-in-process inventory in the facility (Chapter 9, Kanbans)

LACK OF **5S**'s

1. **Hides safety problems**

2. **Creates waste**

3. **Limits a company's ability to satisfy their customers**

IMPLEMENTING 5S

5S Implementation Steps Outline

Prelaunch

    STEP #1. Form, Train, and Develop the 5S Grading/Recognition Teams.

    STEP #2. Develop the 5S Models using the Grading/Recognition Teams.

Launch

    STEP #3. Announcement of 5S Initiative by Top Management at Plant Wide Meeting.

    STEP #4. Train the Plant in 5S.

For many team members, the goals of 5S implementation will be an exciting opportunity and a journey on which they will want to embark immediately once the program is announced. These early implementers are important to the success of the entire initiative; therefore, it is extremely important that the 5S support systems (Steps #1 and #2) be fully in place on the day the 5S initiative is announced.

STEP #1. FORM, TRAIN, AND DEVELOP 5S GRADING/RECOGNITION TEAMS

Forming the Grading/Recognition Teams

As discussed in Chapter 2, every organization has top performers. Whether you have 1% or 50% depends on your organization's hiring practices and culture. But you do have some. These are the people with the "gut wrenching desire" to participate, take ownership, and be successful. They are the passionate, committed champions of the projects they are assigned to today. By definition, a project champion is a person who has, or can develop, an occupational hobby.

If you have a 100-person company, find six people to volunteer for the Grading/Recognition part of this initiative. A member of top management should be a member of the Grading Team. Divide these six people into two teams (Grading and Recognition) of three each, with each team having a champion. Remember that people do best at what they like to do!

5S Implementation Rule #1

Leaders must lead! Everyone must be involved without exception! 5S applies to the office and shop floor and it "paves the approach" necessary for all other improvements which are the long-term hope for a company's survival.

5S Implementation Rule #2

Everyone must be trained in 5S. Remember the advertising axiom: A person must see an advertisement at least four times before they understand it! Establish 5S "Model Areas" so that everyone can have a point of reference for what their own area should look like.

Training the Grading/Recognition Teams

As noted earlier, 5S training begins with the Grading/Recognition Teams. The success of the 5S initiative, and the speed at which this success occurs, depends upon properly trained, committed champions who have the total enthusiastic support of upper management. This training must include the following:

- A clear understanding of the company's overall vision for the future and how the 5S initiative is the start of making the vision reality. These team members will help communicate this vision to the rest of the plant team. If there is not a clear vision, do not begin any World Class Enterprise initiative until one has been developed.

- A thorough understanding of this chapter.

- Visits to other companies, preferably competitors, who are benchmarks for 5S activities. (See box on following page.)

- Participation in the design, development, and implementation of the Islands of Excellence as defined in Step #2.

- Review of the 5S Office Area Guidelines and Manufacturing Area Guidelines (beginning on page 89), as well as the Master Scoring Criteria Guide (pages 93 & 94). Revise these guidelines, as necessary, to meet the needs of your facility.

A person who knows and doesn't act - doesn't really know.

If you are unsure of how to locate benchmark companies in your area, contact one of the following organizations. These organizations are involved in WCM or lean manufacturing kaizen events, seminars, books, and plant evaluations:

Association for Manufacturing Excellence
380 W. Palatine Rd.
Wheeling, IL 60090-5863
847/520-3282

Productivity Inc.
101 Merritt 7
Norwalk, CT 06851
800/966-5423

Industry Week
Best Plants
1100 Superior Avenue
Cleveland, OH 44114
216/696-7000

Developing the Grading Team—The Grading Team's responsibilities has five parts:

1. Participate in and contribute to the development of the Islands of Excellence concept (Step #2).

2. Set the initial grading standards for the factory and offices using the results of the Islands of Excellence experience.

3. Proceed with 5S training for the rest of the facility (or train the trainers). Train the trainer instruction should include, as a minimum, the following:

   ♦ Review the company's vision (what we have been calling "proof of the need to change")

   ♦ Visit other companies, preferably competitors, who are benchmarks for 5S activities

♦ Review of the 5S Office Area Guidelines and Manufacturing Area Guidelines (beginning on page 89), as well as the Master Scoring Criteria Guide (pages 93 & 94)

♦ Review the Models concept, Step #2

4. Participate in setting up the Red Tag Staging/Parking Lot Areas. The Red Tag System is explained in Step #4.

5. Perform periodic grading of the entire facility and publicly post the results. To make sure these results get the right visibility, review them at departmental or plant-wide meetings.

At the end of this chapter are 5S application guide sheets for both the office and manufacturing areas, as well as Master Scoring Criteria Guidelines and blank scoring sheets. These documents provide the team with a starting point from which to make changes, thereby improving the process to better fit the facility.

Developing the Recognition Team—The Recognition Team has the following responsibilities:

1. Develop a campaign of meetings, signs, posters, and visual messages to preface the 5S initiative.

2. Help develop the 5S Model Areas (Step #2).

3. Develop a plant-wide 5S recognition and rewards program. Determine criteria and milestones for area awards and plant-wide celebrations. "T" shirts, hats, and jackets are appropriate awards at plant meetings.

4. Develop criteria for determining when the 5S program can be regarded as self-sustaining and the recognition team can be disbanded.

STEP #2. DEVELOP THE 5S MODELS: THE "ISLANDS OF EXCELLENCE" USING THE GRADING/RECOGNITION TEAMS

> "You will achieve the level of safety that you demonstrate you want to achieve."
>
> *Dupont*

This Dupont expression applies to 5S also (see office pictures on page 70).

To complement the implementation training using this manual, we strongly suggest setting up 5S "Islands of Excellence." Islands are areas of the plant developed as 5S models for the rest of the facility to use as a guide. Islands will jump-start your people on the 5S learning curve and set the initial benchmark. These islands should represent all areas of the facility. As a minimum, one factory area and one office area should be represented. The previously worst-kept department or space in each area is preferable.

The islands that are selected should be areas that are owned (supervised) by the champions or members of the Grading/Recognition Teams if possible. This gives the team members "hands on" 5S knowledge and experience, allowing them to set the standard and prevent comments like, "nothing is impossible for the person who doesn't have to do it." This also gives them valuable 5S application and scoring experience.

Top management must be involved in setting up the benchmark islands and ensuring participation by every area in the plant. Remember: do not propose perfection when you start your 5S initiative. Continuous improvement and the pursuit of perfection applies to 5S. Your current 5S standards will not be acceptable in one year, just as your current quality levels will not be acceptable to your customers in one year. However, if you are the average American manufacturing plant starting a 5S implementation, telling your team that you want "an operating room environment" will thoroughly frustrate your people and kill the initiative. The islands should represent the current acceptable standard that is attainable by everyone. (It can be a considerable stretch, but it must be attainable!) The establishment of 5S islands must be complete before moving to implementation Step #3.

One last comment on islands—take lots of before and after pictures so that no one forgets where they started and what they have achieved.

Examples of the lack of 5S's in the office. The 5S implementation will be a failure unless management properly demonstrates the level of 5S that is to be achieved.

STEP #3. KICK OFF THE 5S IMPLEMENTATION: TELL YOUR ENTIRE TEAM ABOUT THE IMPORTANCE, GOALS AND VISION OF 5S.

If your operation is not currently having plant wide meetings (as a minimum by shift), kicking off the 5S implementation is a good time to start. It is extremely important that the entire team hear the 5S kick-off message and the questions and answers that occur as a result of this message. Have the Grading/Recognition Teams at these meetings present visuals that show the 5S training schedule. The meeting should contain the kick-off message, the training schedule, plus the following as minimum:

♦ IMPORTANCE OF 5S: Establishing the plant wide discipline and organizational baseline that supports all improvement activities necessary to secure the future of the business. 5S is a common theme among all world class organizations.

♦ GOALS OF THE 5S IMPLEMENTATION: Improve safety and improve pride in the work place. Become a model supplier for your customers. Improve quality and productivity.

♦ VISION: How do 5S and the "Islands of Excellence" fit into the vision of the future for the whole plant? Why the need to do things differently? What's next in the pursuit of World Class Enterprise?

STEP #4. TRAIN THE ENTIRE PLANT IN 5S

All individual team training should begin with a review of the Importance, Goals, and Vision as stated in the Step #3 kick-off meeting. This should be given by the same person who led this discussion in that meeting. After the review, train in the principles of 5S below.

1. SORTING

Review the definition of Sort—Proper Arrangement. Remove from the workplace any item that is not needed for current production or the current day's assignment. Keep only what you need today! Add anything that is needed but not there.

Store frequently used items, those required in the next 30-day production schedule, in the work area. Infrequently used items should be stored away from the work area and items that are not needed anywhere in the plant should be disposed of.

What We Will Accomplish Using the Sorting Process

- ◆ **Improved safety**. When unnecessary items are removed, the work area becomes less crowded and easier to work in. Potential problems are easier to spot.

- ◆ **Improved communication between team members working in the same area**. Removal of unnecessary items eliminates visual and verbal barriers between people.

- ◆ **Smoother work flow**. Work areas, with unnecessary items removed, now require less space and can be redesigned for improved work and production flow.

- ◆ **Improved quality and productivity**. Quality improves because of improved communication among people in the same work area. Smaller work areas mean less work-in-process inventory which hides problems. The removal of unnecessary items prevents the substitution of the wrong material, tools or fixtures to produce the product. Productivity improves because less time is spent looking for items. Now that the work area is smaller, there is less wasted motion in producing the product.

5S Implementation Rule #3

Facility environmental, health, and safety procedures must be followed at all times in the cleaning, moving, and disposal of equipment and material.

Sorting Using the Red Tag System

The Red Tag System is a method used to identify items that are found in the work area, but their use and need are unknown.

One of the problems that arise when you start sorting what you need from what you don't need is the "identification" of all the items in your work area or department. If you have worked in one area of the plant since the facility was built, you probably can identify every item that surrounds you and how often it is used, if at all, and how many are needed. But how many of us have worked in one area of the facility since the plant was built? Very few! That leaves us scratching our heads, wondering what some of the stuff is, what job is it used for, and whether we should move it, store it, or throw it away.

Here's where the Red Tag strategy comes in. The Red Tag System allows you to use the knowledge and experience of the whole plant to answer the following questions:

- ♦ What is this?
- ♦ Should I keep, store, or dispose of it?
- ♦ If I need it, how many should I keep?

5S Implementation Rule #4

The Red Tag System is for one-time use only; it is not an on-going crutch for future clean ups. Make sure all inventory, equipment, tools, fixtures, and jigs are clearly labeled by suppliers before being brought into the plant. Develop visual arrangement storage areas which clearly indicate where items are stored and how many are stored there.

Red Tag Implementation

As an area is sorted, fill out a Red Tag (see Figure 4.1) for each item that is unidentifiable. Attach the Red Tag to the item and, if possible, prominently display the item in the area. The idea is to get other team members to take a look at the item as they pass by.

All sorting and tagging should occur in each work area within two days of the 5S class or you will lose the momentum of the training. Red Tag unidentifiable items and also, items that will not be needed for production within the next thirty days. All shifts in a work area must be involved.

EXAMPLE RED TAGS:

5S RED TAG

Name: _____ Date: _____

Item Found (Description): _____
_____
_____
_____

Work Area: _____ QTY: _____

Reason for Disposition Request (circle as appropriate):

1) Not Needed in Next 30 Days
2) Not Needed in Known Future
3) Defective
4) Surplus
5) Not Needed Now (Service Only)
6) Need Identification
7) Other _____
_____
_____

5S RED TAG

Sort Request Disposition Target = 30 Days

Filled Out By:	**Quantity:**
Date:	**# of Units:** **Value: $**
Plant/Office Location:	**P/N:** **Customer:**
Item Name or Description:	**Reason for Disposition Request (circle as appropriate):**
Category (circle one): 1) Raw Material 2) Work-in-Process 3) Finished Goods 4) Tools or Fixtures 5) Customer Tools or Fixtures 6) Surplus Equipment 7) Maintenance or MRO Supplies 8) Office Equipment or Supplies 9) Company or Customer Files 10) Unknown 11) Other _____	1) Not Needed in Next 30 Days 2) Not Needed in Known Future 3) Defective 4) Surplus 5) Not Needed Now (Service Only) 6) Need Identification 7) Other _____ _____ _____
Disposition By: **Date:** **Disposal By:** **Disposal Date:**	**Disposition:** 1) Scrap (With Paperwork) 2) Scrap (No Paperwork) 3) Return to Supplier 4) Move to Red Tag Area 5) Move to _____ Storage Area. 6) Store in Work Area _____ 7) Other _____ _____ _____

Figure 4.1

Red Tag Staging Areas (Red Tag "Parking Lot")

Most people (and we hate to admit that this includes us) feel uncomfortable throwing things away unless positively sure they will not need them in the future. Sometimes we know we do not need an item in our work area, but we are not really sure what it is, or whether to store or dispose of it. In some cases, disposal or scrapping may include financial consequences (write off) that we need to consider. The Red Tag Staging Area is an open space in the plant set aside for placing unneeded or unidentified Red-Tagged items from each area. This additional disposition review of items which should not or cannot be disposed of by the individuals in a work area gives the financial people an opportunity to explain to owners or investors, in advance, why these items are being written off and removed from the company's list of assets. This "safety net" of review in the staging area/parking lot usually calms the concerns of people who are afraid of getting rid of things indiscriminately. (See Figure 4.2).

Whether you have one centralized Red Tag Area or ten departmental Staging Areas depends on the size of your facility and your ability to focus experienced people to look at the items. If you have a 100-person plant, one central area will work. If you have a 1,000 person plant, you probably want departmental or functional Red Tag Staging Areas.

How Long Should the Red Tag System Cycle Take to Complete?

We like the 30-30 plan: thirty days maximum stay in the work area after red tagging, thirty days maximum length of stay in the staging area. If it takes longer than 60 days to complete this cycle, you probably have not placed the proper *sense of urgency* on it.

Please note that the Red Tag System cycle is designed to be a one-time event. Develop visual labeling and storage areas which support this goal. Everyone must be trained in 5S so that they can develop the ownership and discipline necessary to prevent unneeded or excess items from ever entering their work area or the plant again.

Other things to remember!

♦ One Red Tag per item. A box full of miscellaneous stuff should be tagged individually.

♦ Items which are difficult to move to the Parking Lot/Staging Area can be Red Tagged and left in place. It is important that everyone understands that the person who wrote out the Red Tag becomes responsible for seeking disposition of that item.

♦ If you Red Tag and Stage an item, and no one in the facility needs it or knows what it is, throw it out!

When are We Finished Sorting?

At this point in the training, it is appropriate to review the 5S Master Scoring Guidelines (located at the end of this chapter) as well as the standard set by the islands. Each facility must determine whether the sorting target is based on the islands concept, the 5S scoring check sheet (grading a score of 5 for example), or both.

One last sort comment: unnecessary items often become invisible to the people who are around them every day. As the final sort step, when you think you are finished sorting, ask your manufacturing or office neighbors to review your area.

5S Implementation Rule #5

Continuous improvement applies to all aspects of 5S and WCM. Without continuous improvement, your 5S grade of 5 today may only grade out as a 2 or 3 in the future.

RED TAG PARKING LOT EXAMPLES

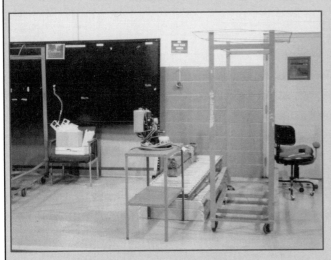

Figure 4.2
Typically 60% - 70% of all items put in the Red Tag Parking Lot are junk.

2. STRAIGHTEN

Review the definition of Straighten—Orderliness. Arrange items so they are easy to use. Have a designated place for everything which is close to the work site. A place for everything, and everything in its place is the expression that really defines straighten.

Organize and standardize the way necessary items are stored so that anyone can find and use them. Try to use a common storage system (in part number sequence or alphabetically by customer for example) for all inventory items throughout the plant.

Paint, mark or label all necessary items so they are easy to find and even more importantly — easy to put away. See Figure 4.3 & 4.4.

Develop/purchase a labeling system that can be used throughout the plant so that all labeled items have the uniform look of a common labeling system. See Figure 4.7.

What We Will Accomplish Using the Straightening Process

♦ Improved safety. Organized storage prevents items from being left in areas where they might be a safety hazard.

♦ Improved quality. An organized and standardized storage system prevents the location of similar parts from being switched without the knowledge of the people at the point of use.

♦ Improved productivity. Productivity improves significantly because there is significantly less time spent looking for items.

Visible Arrangement Storage

Once you have sorted, straightening must be used to prevent the reoccurrence of unacceptable housekeeping conditions. One of these straightening techniques is visible arrangement storage, also known as the signboard strategy. Visible arrangement storage is clear identification of an item (by name, part number, ID number, etc.), and where this item is to be stored. This is accomplished by using a location label on the item or putting the item's storage location on it's nameplate, and having similar markings on the storage area. See Figures 4.5 and 4.6. Make sure suppliers clearly label all inventory, equipment, tools, fixtures, and jigs with their storage location before these items are brought into the plant. See Figures 4.8 and 4.9.

Items such as tools, dies, fixtures, inventory, etc. will need to be stored in your plant. Without a good visible arrangement storage system, the Red Tag System will not become a way of life because items will end up being stored in the first available space.

Other things to remember!

♦ Straighten applies to offices and desktops also. See Figure 4.10

♦ You must develop a visible arrangement storage location marking system that is understood by everyone, not just by the people who developed it. Put a prototype on the shop floor and test it.

♦ Items which are used in several locations in the plant should be stored in one central location for inventory control.

♦ Items which are used together (for the same job or to produce the same part) should be stored close to each other.

When are We Finished Straightening?

Again, at this point in the training, it is appropriate to review the 5S Application and Scoring Guidelines for the straightening process as well as the standard set by the islands. Each facility must determine whether the straightening is based on the islands concept, the 5S scoring check sheet (grading a score of 5), or both. Remember that continuous improvement applies to all aspects of 5S and WCM. Without continuous improvement, your straightening grade of 5 today may only grade out as a 2 or 3 in the future.

5S Implementation Rule #6

Use a "ceiling-down" strategy. The first "straighten" and "sweep" begins with the ceiling, walls, and floor.

Note for advanced application: Develop a cross reference of tools, fixtures, gauges, etc. required to produce each product. When a product is discontinued, you can easily identify and dispose of all equipment dedicated to that product.

Visible Arrangement Storage — Items are Easily Found and Easily Put Away!

Figure 4.3

Green aisleway painted markings in the left picture allow eye wash station to easily be found. The right picture shows this same type of marking applied to fire extinguishers (painted red).

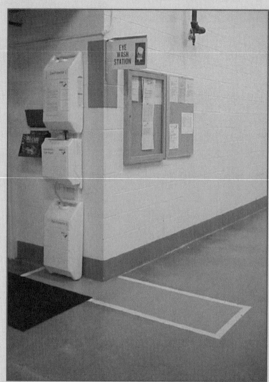
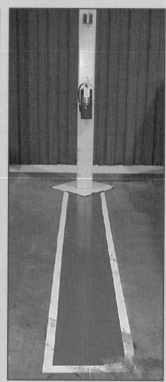

Figure 4.4

Everyday examples of 5S activities. On the left, airliners at airports can move safely into and out of passenger loading gate areas because there is "a place for everything and everything is in its place." In this case refueling trucks at Chicago's O'Hare airport. On the right, enhanced safety and parking space utilization occurs when "lines" clearly define where to park at shopping malls and other parking lots.

Visible Arrangement Storage

Figure 4.5

Fixture/tool storage rack (left) and hand tool storage board (right) with tool locations clearly marked. The storage locations are also referenced on the tools themselves.

Figure 4.6

Hand tool storage rack with foam tool outlines make it easy to identify missing/out or position tools.

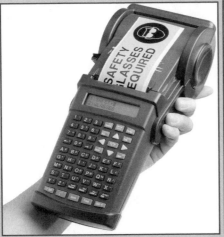

Figure 4.7

Brady Handimark makes it easy to label everything throughout the facility.

Brady Company (800) 635-7557

Visible Arrangement Storage

Figure 4.8

Figures 4.8 and 4.9 show examples of good visible arrangement storage systems. Suppliers send inventory in with clearly marked location numbers on them. This clear identification system assures correct location storage. Additionally, when the location size is matched to the required inventory levels, over-shipments from suppliers (no open location to store it) or under-shipments (too many open locations) become more visible. The floor storage system shown in Figure 4.9 left works well as a "spot on the floor kanban" that is discussed in Chapter 9. An empty spot becomes the "kanban" or signal to produce more material. Figure 4.9 right is explained below. (The labelling system shown in these photographs is available from JEKA USA Services, Inc., Long Beach, CA 562-983-8047)

Figure 4.9

Right photograph illustrates a container kanban. Each plastic tote holds 15 completed circuit boards. As the internal customer (assembly) for this product requires additional boards, full containers are removed and the empty containers are placed in the "empty container" spot. When the empty containers stack reaches the black line on the wall, this becomes the "signal" to produce more circuit boards.

Visible Arrangement Storage

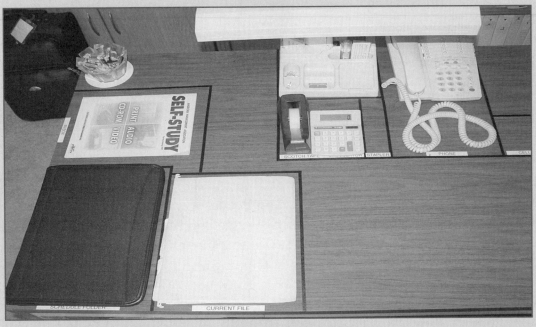

Figure 4.10

5S workplace organization applies to desktops and all office areas also!

Figure 4.11

5S workplace organization includes making operator instructions really visual. As shown, instructions are visually displayed in front of the operator's normal working position (not in some notebook or in a computer somewhere) and are a combination of both pictures and text. Part and product quality is assured when operators perform each operation the same way every time.

3. SWEEP

Review the definition of Sweep—Cleanliness. Sweep the floors, wipe off equipment, paint if necessary, and, in general, make sure everything in the plant and offices stays clean.

Part of the sweep strategy is to develop methods and ways of preventing the accumulation of dust, dirt, chips, and shavings. See Figures 4.12 & 4.13.

If equipment is repainted, it should be repainted with a "light" color, for example beige or white. This allows future problems, such as oil leaks, to be exposed immediately when they occur.

What We Will Accomplish Using the Sweep Process

♦ Improved safety. Even safety glasses cannot prevent flying dust, dirt, chips, or shavings from filthy work areas from getting into an operator's eyes. Additionally, clean floors reduce the possibility of slipping and falling injuries.

♦ Improved team morale and ownership. No one wants to work in or own a messy, filthy work area.

♦ Improved quality. It is very difficult and costly to deliver a clean, high quality product which was produced in a filthy environment.

♦ Reduced equipment downtime. When equipment and machines are kept clean, there is an opportunity to notice problems such as oil leaks and new noises when they first develop and before they cause the equipment to fail. This gives the maintenance department an opportunity to prepare for the repair during a "planned" equipment downtime period.

Other things to remember!

♦ Consider the ceilings, walls, and floors as the first opportunity for sweep.

♦ Establish specific areas where cleaning and sweeping supplies will be kept. See Figure 4.14

5S Application and Scoring Guidelines for Sweep

Review the 5S application and scoring guidelines for the sweep process as well as any dirt prevention ideas set by the islands. Each facility must determine whether the sweep target is based on the islands concept, the 5S scoring check sheet (grading a score of 5 for example), or both.

Sweep — Preventing Things from Getting Dirty

Figure 4.12   **Figure 4.13**

In Figure 4.12, metal scrap and off-all is ejected down a chute of a punch press. The metal tote container catches some scrap while other pieces land on the floor. At the end of the shift, the operator must both empty the tote and sweep the floor. In Figure 4.13, a metal guide is added to the tote container which prevents any material from landing on the floor. Now at the end of the shift the operator must only empty the tote, the floor does not get dirty,

Sweep — Providing an Area Where 5S Supplies are Kept

Figure 4.14

Clearly defined locations indicate where cleaning supplies are stored. Behind a manufacturing cell (left) and on a wall (right). A defined 5S supplies location for all individuals and teams within the facility should be provided.

4. SCHEDULE

Review the definition of Schedule—Cleaned up. Standardize and maintain the use of sort, straighten, and sweep.

Develop 5S activity checklists for all manufacturing and office areas. See Figure 4.15. Whenever possible, checklists should include a picture of what the area should look like when the checklist is complete.

Clean up while the task is small – by shift, daily.

What We Will Accomplish Using the Schedule Process

♦ Improved safety.

♦ Improved team morale and ownership.

♦ Pave the path to Step #5, Sustain. Unless 5S is on a regular schedule, it is impossible to make it a habit in your facility.

♦ While your team will be happy that housekeeping has improved, maintaining this level of housekeeping depends on your diligence in supporting the development of a regular 5S schedule. Keep in mind that, for the most part, your team has been trained to clean up only for special visitors or circumstances and that maintaining a 5S level of housekeeping has not been accomplished before.

5S Implementation Rule #7

Have regular inspections and grading by top management as part of the Grading Team. Remember that continuous improvement applies to 5S also. Pursue perfection; don't expect it at the beginning.

Remember that the 5S initiative cannot be successful without a schedule that becomes part of your facility's culture.

> How does a facility measure its 5S improvement progress?
> One measure: Eliminating special clean ups for customer
> visits — always being tour or visit ready.

5S Implementation Rule #8

Set up a recognition and rewards program. Have celebrations as conditions improve.

EXAMPLE 5S SCHEDULE CHECKLIST:

American Licorice Vertical Jar
5S Activities Checklist

Vertical Jar Position	Perform Daily	Perform on: (as noted)	Initial When Complete	Activity
P/S #1 Feeder	X			Blow out scales, sweep, clean platform area. Discard all debris (see area #1).
P/S #2 Feeder	X			Move all full scrap containers to designated area. Replace all containers.
P/S #3 Pan Stacker	X			Sweep, clean jar bander area. Put away all excess supplies. Remove all empty cardboard.
P/W #1 Jar Packer	X			Sweep, clean tray conveyor floor area.
P/W #2 Jar Packer	X			Clean all packaging jar tables.
P/W #3 Jar Packer	X			Sweep, clean jar packaging floor area.
P/W #4 Jar Packer	X			Remove all excess jar supplies, and any items not needed. Setup following shift with supplies.
P/W #5 Scrapper	X			Make sure all cleaning supplies are put back in their designated area.
Team		Weekly		Thorough cleaning of scales, platform, and feeding tube
Team		Weekly		Thorough cleaning of the jar packing conveyor and frame
Team		Weekly		Thorough cleaning of the tray conveyor and frame
Team		Weekly		Thorough cleaning of the bucket conveyor and frame
Team		Weekly		Scrub down all floor areas in vertical line

Remember: Everyone is done when the Vertical Jar team is done!

Figure 4.15

5. SUSTAIN

Review the definition of Sustain—Discipline. Practice and repeat these procedures until they become a way of life throughout the entire company.

Housekeeping must be built into, and become a part of, every process. The plant's ability to continue making improvements and survive in the future depends on it. Sustain means making the first 4S's a habit and part of the plant's culture.

Sustain also means having the Grading Team hold 5S audits throughout the facility using the audit form shown on the following page. After the audit, the graded audit forms should be displayed in a very visible area of the facility—in a highest score to lowest score format. At the facility's monthly plant-wide meeting, top management will recognize the people/areas which received the highest scores.

What We Will Accomplish Using the Sustain Process

♦ Improved safety through better housekeeping.

♦ Improved team morale and ownership. Everyone feels good about themselves when they know they have developed the discipline to conquer a problem.

♦ Reduced overhead costs. Long term, improved safety means reduced worker compensation costs.

Remember that "sustain" is the discipline (rope) that ties the other 4S's together!

5S Implementation Rule #9

The plant team is not ready to move to the next module of WCM until there is enough knowledge and discipline in place to make the 5S implementation self-sustaining. A lack of discipline will only carry over to the next module and prevent it from being fully implemented.

5S AUDIT CHECK SHEET

5S Score	Improvement(s) Required to Achieve a Score of 5
Sort	
Straighten	
Sweep	
Schedule	
Sustain	

5S Total Score = _____

Score Divided By 5 = _____

Previous Score = _____

Scored By: _____

Location: _____

Date: _____

5S Implementation Rules

1. Leaders must lead. Everyone must be involved. No exceptions! 5S applies equally to the office and the shop floor and is the "paving of the approach" required for all other improvements. All of these improvements are necessary for a company's survival.

2. Make sure everyone is trained in 5S. Remember the advertising axiom: a person must see an advertisement at least four times before understanding it! Establish 5S "Islands of Excellence" areas so everyone has a point of reference to pick up ideas for their own area.

3. Facility environmental, health, and safety procedures must be followed at all times in the cleaning, moving, and disposal of equipment and material.

4. The Red Tag Sort System is for one-time use only; it is not an on-going crutch for future clean ups. Make sure all inventory, equipment, tools, fixtures, and jigs are clearly labeled by suppliers before being brought into the plant. Develop visual arrangement storage areas which clearly indicate where items are stored and how many items are stored there.

5. Continuous improvement applies to all aspects of 5S and WCM. Without continuous improvement, your 5S grade of 5 today may only grade out as a 2 or 3 in the future.

6. Use a "ceiling-down" strategy. Your first "straighten" and "sweep" should begin with the ceiling, walls, and floor.

7. Implement regular inspections and grading by top management as part of the Grading Team. Remember that continuous improvement applies to 5S also. Pursue perfection; don't expect it at the beginning.

8. Set up a recognition and rewards program. Have celebrations as conditions improve.

9. The team is not ready to move to the next module of WCM until there is enough knowledge and discipline in place to make the 5S implementation self-sustaining. A lack of discipline will only carry over to the next module and prevent it from being fully implemented.

5S Manufacturing Area Guidelines

Sort Location	Evaluation Criteria
All	All unnecessary items (equipment, work-in-process, raw material, tools, fixtures, gauges, partitions, files) are removed from the work area.
Bulletin Boards/ Production Boards	All displayed notices are necessary. Production board information is current.
Documents	Only documents which will be used today are in the work areas.
Floors/Aisles	Only process related items are on the floor. Aisles are not blocked. There is easy access to all emergency equipment, electrical panels, and exits.
Straighten Location	**Evaluation Criteria**
All	All equipment, partitions, furniture, and storage cabinets are arranged neatly and conveniently.
Bulletin boards/ Production boards	All notices are displayed in a straight and neat manner. All notices hang within the frame of the board. No torn or soiled notices are displayed.
Documents	Documents and binders which will be used today are stored in a neat and orderly fashion. Document binders are clearly labeled as to content and responsibility for control and revision.
Equipment	Equipment controls are correctly labeled and critical points for daily maintenance checks are clearly marked. Equipment check sheets are up-to-date, clean, and neatly displayed.
Floors/Aisles	Aisles are clearly marked and there is no storage in the aisles or on the markings. Objects are always placed at right angles to the aisle lines. No raw material, work-in-process, finished goods, tools, or gauges are stored directly on floor. No items block electrical cabinets, fire extinguishers, or emergency exits.
Shelves	Shelves are marked so it is clear where things are stored and where they should be returned. All shelves are in good repair and properly supported.
Storage	Nothing is stored on top of equipment or cabinets. Storage of boxes, totes, and containers is always neat and at right angles to the aisles and parallel to each other. Cleaning supplies are stored in an identified location, in a neat manner, and are readily available when needed.
Tools, Fixtures, & Gauges	Equipment must be arranged and stored so that it is easily accessible to the operator, depending on its use to monitor quality or for tool changes. The storage location must also keep the tools, fixtures, and gauges clean and protected from damage.
Walls	Anything hung on the walls (bulletin boards, drawings, process sheets, pictures etc.) is hung at the same distance from the ceiling. Everything is displayed in a frame or holder.

5S MANUFACTURING AREA GUIDELINES - CONT'D

Sweep Location	Evaluation Criteria
All	All equipment, tools, fixtures, gauges, partitions, table tops, furniture, and file cabinets are kept clean. Work surfaces and glass are kept clean and polished.
Floors/Aisles	Floors are clean and free of dirt.
Tools, Fixtures, & Gauges	Tools, fixtures & gauges are clean and free of residual magnetism. Critical areas are protected to prevent damage.

Schedule Location	Evaluation Criteria
All	There is evidence that a schedule exists to maintain all Sort, Straighten, and Sweep criteria. Cleaning methods and frequencies are identified.

Sustain Location	Evaluation Criteria
All	There is evidence that people are committed and becoming disciplined to continuously keeping 5S at highest possible levels. 5S audits are performed regularly with results posted.

5S OFFICE AREA GUIDELINES

Sort Location	Evaluation Criteria
All	All unnecessary items (furniture, equipment, partitions, files, records) are removed from the office area work stations.
Bulletin Boards	All displayed notices are necessary. No outdated, torn, or soiled notices are displayed.
Documents	Only documents which will be used today are on the work stations or desktops.
Floors/Aisles	Aisles are not blocked. No documents or files are stored on the floor or underneath desks or work stations.
Straighten Location	Evaluation Criteria
All	All furniture, equipment, partitions, and cabinets are arranged neatly and conveniently.
Bulletin boards	All notices are displayed in a straight and neat manner. All notices hang within the frame of the board. No torn, outdated, or soiled notices are displayed.
Documents	Documents and binders which will be used today are stored in a neat and orderly fashion. Document binders are clearly labeled as to content and responsibility for control and revision.
Shelves	Shelves are marked so that it is clear where things are stored and where they should be returned. All shelves are in good repair and properly supported.
Storage	Nothing is stored on top of cabinets or equipment. Storage of boxes and containers are always neat and at right angles. Cleaning supplies are stored in a neat manner and are readily available when needed.
Walls	Anything hung on the walls (bulletin boards, drawings, process sheets, pictures etc.) is hung at the same distance from the ceiling. Everything is displayed in a frame.
Equipment	Controls are correctly labeled and critical points for daily maintenance checks are clearly marked. Equipment check sheets are up-to-date, clean, and neatly displayed.

5S Office Area Guidelines - Cont'd

Sweep Location	Evaluation Criteria
All	All furniture, equipment, partitions, file cabinets, and table tops are kept clean. Work surfaces and glass are kept clean and polished.
Floors/Aisles	Floors are clean and free of dirt.
Equipment	All equipment is clean and free from contamination or moisture.

Schedule Location	Evaluation Criteria
All	There is evidence that a schedule exists to maintain all Sort, Straighten, and Sweep criteria.

Sustain Location	Evaluation Criteria
All	There is evidence that people are committed and becoming disciplined to continuously keeping 5S at highest possible levels.

5S MASTER SCORING CRITERIA

Sort Points	Description
5	Unneeded items have been completely disposed of.
4	All unneeded items are in Red Tag parking lot (awaiting disposition).
3	It is easy to distinguish between needed and unneeded items.
2	It is difficult to distinguish between needed and unneeded items.
1	Needed and unneeded items are mixed together. It is not possible to determine the difference between needed and unneeded items.

Straighten Points	Description
5	All tools and gauges are identified and in their proper location. Supplies and raw material areas are clearly marked for part number and quantity per location.
4	Color coding, outlining, or other methods are used to facilitate placement of tools, gauges, supplies, and materials. Quantity per location not marked.
3	Location and item indicators are used for tools, gauges, supplies, and raw materials. Aisles are clearly marked. Some items may be out of place.
2	It is difficult to distinguish what goes where and in what quantities. Some items and locations may be marked.
1	It is not possible to determine what goes where and in what quantities. No items or locations are marked.

Sweep Points	Description
5	Cleaning tasks have been combined with dirt prevention methods. Tools, fixtures and gauges are free of residual magnetism.
4	Cleaning tasks and cleanliness inspection checklists have been combined.
3	The work area is cleaned daily but cleaning tasks and cleaning methods are not clearly defined.
2	The work area is cleaned, but not on a daily basis.
1	The work area has not been cleaned in a long time. Dirt and dust are evident everywhere.

5S Master Scoring Criteria - Cont'd

Schedule Points	Description
5	A periodic schedule/methodology exists to maintain the first three steps of 5S at the highest possible levels for the entire facility.
4	The first three steps of 5S have become a habit in most of the facility or area.
3	Cleaning schedules are followed throughout the facility or area daily.
2	Cleaning schedules are followed in some areas.
1	No cleaning schedules or methodology exist, or existing schedules are not followed.

Sustain Points	Description
5	A disciplined system of control and maintenance is in place to assure that sorting, straightening, and sweeping are maintained at the highest possible level. Management is committed and responsible. 5S is part of every job.
4	5S practices and audits are in place throughout the facility. Improvements are identified and implemented. Management provides recognition and rewards in support of 5S.
3	5S audits are performed throughout the facility. Improvement areas are identified but not yet implemented. Management actively supports the 5S process.
2	5S training has occurred for all associates. 5S activity is apparent in some areas. 5S audits performed in some areas.
1	5S training has begun, but there is no other evidence of a 5S activity.

Chapter 5

Team Building

Unleashing the Power of Your Workforce

With contributions to Value Stream Mapping by Ron Crabtree

Why Teams?

As we study the tools of World Class Manufacturing, one thought should become very clear. This is a lot of work! The WCM techniques affect every area of the organization and every part of the business. How, then, will we make the sweeping changes needed in a limited amount of time so as to remain competitive? The answer is Teams.

Teams provide many benefits to the organizations who implement them and to the individuals who work within the team environment. Properly developed and supported, teams will enable both organizations and people to grow and prosper. We will evaluate the benefits for both.

Individuals

Most working people today have been subjected to so many improvement programs that it is easy to understand why they think WCM is another "program of the month." When it comes to teams, the most common question people have, whether they ask it or not, is, "What's in it for me?" The answer to that question is "Plenty!"

The three major benefits for individuals in teams are as follows:

♦ Members learn new job skills. As the team studies their work process the members learn each of the jobs— essential if the team expects to make significant improvements. Members also learn problem solving techniques that help them evaluate the information and data they collect and make informed decisions.

♦ Members participate in the decisions affecting their jobs. As the team members become more aware of the strengths and weaknesses of the process, they make decisions, as a team, about what actions to take to improve the operation, meet team goals, and resolve issues. It is the team's decision how the work will flow, how to handle late deliveries, who will perform each assignment, and so on. No one person on the team has more influence than anyone else. All members contribute to the decision making process.

♦ Members feel like the valuable member of their company that they always have been. The team's control over their work environment shows each member that their individual contributions are valued by the organization and their peers. No longer are they stuck at the same desk or machine, day after day, with their suggestions for improvements falling on deaf ears. Team members control their own destiny.

In addition, teams get people talking—not just the members of the team to each other but to management, with all employees sharing the vision and goals of the company. This is important if the teams are to make informed decisions about how to best support the organization. Not only do teams make decisions but they also find better solutions and implement corrective action much more quickly than managers who are farther away from the process. The team's knowledge of the process and the goals of the organization provides the speed and flexibility needed to respond to customer demands.

A fully trained, self-directed work team operates very much like a self-contained business. The members set goals, assign work, track progress, communicate with suppliers and customers, manage inventories, and work within their operating budgets. Basically, the team members are empowered to take over many of the traditional responsibilities of the supervisor, while supervisors become team coaches and technical resources. Everyone on the team shares in the results.

Organizations

Organizations benefit from the use of teams in three major areas:

- ◆ Increased Quality — Teams empower the people closest to the customer to make the changes needed to improve the process. Furthermore, they can do it very quickly. The team's daily contact with customers and suppliers (either internal or external) keeps them informed on the incoming and outgoing quality of the product or service. Timely communication within the team and with other teams highlight the quality issues enabling the team to correct the problem right away. Teams typically reduce defects by 50 to 100%.

♦ Increased Productivity — If the team is not producing defects, their production is obviously increased. But that is not the only way a team increases productivity. As the group analyzes the process, it sees ways to improve the work flow, eliminate excess handling and moving of material, and balance the time needed for each job. The team's activities result in productivity increases of 50% or more and reduced lead times of as much as 90%.

♦ Reduced Cost — Although the team dramatically improves quality and productivity, it typically does this without adding people or more work steps. The focus on eliminating waste within the process drives costs down with every improvement made. See figure 5.1. A well-developed team (which takes time, by the way) does not need constant supervision, which eliminates excess layers of management. The team is multi-skilled and cross-functional, which reduces the drain on your support resources, the number of job classifications, and job complexity. Since the team makes so many of their own decisions, their response time to problems is reduced.

All of this translates to some impressive improvements in customer satisfaction. Why is this so important? Competition! Even as you are reading these words, your competitor is plotting ways to steal your customers from you. Someone out there is developing a process to deliver your goods or services better, faster, and cheaper. Technology is changing at an incredible rate and your state-of-the-art manufacturing equipment is already outdated. Information on your newest product is available to your competitor the instant it leaves your shipping dock. On top of all this, your customers are demanding faster service and cost reductions.

How Does Implementing Teams Improve Productivity?

By working smarter! Converting the team's time spent on waste:

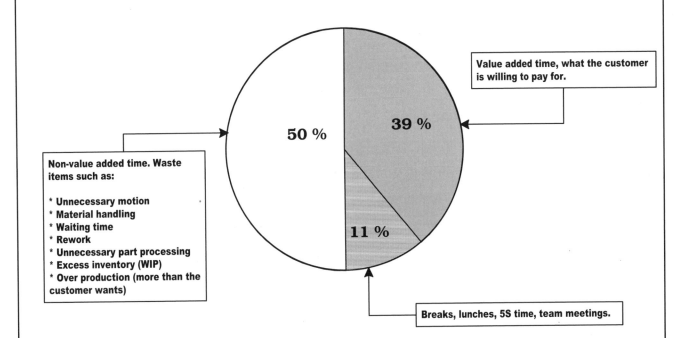

Value added time, what the customer is willing to pay for.

50 %

39 %

11 %

Non-value added time. Waste items such as:

* Unnecessary motion
* Material handling
* Waiting time
* Rework
* Unnecessary part processing
* Excess inventory (WIP)
* Over production (more than the customer wants)

Breaks, lunches, 5S time, team meetings.

To value-added time:

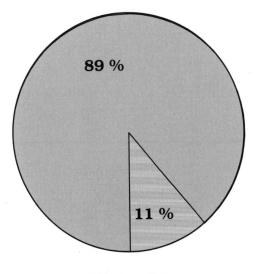

89 %

11 %

Figure 5.1

Studies have shown that individuals participating in empowered teams have much higher morale, participate more in decision making, and experience a higher level of satisfaction in their jobs than their non-team counterparts. Empowered teams attract and keep the best employees in the job market. With management support and appropriate training, companies see teams achieving remarkable results.

Summary — Benefits of Teams

♦ Teams are more flexible than larger groups in reacting to sudden change. They effectively delegate work and are flexible in work assignments.

♦ Teams increase the knowledge of every member as ideas and concepts are shared and discussed, resulting in a better trained and more aware work force.

♦ Teams take advantage of the knowledge and skills of several people, providing a better decision than any one person could make.

♦ Teams help people communicate.

♦ A well-trained team dramatically increases customer satisfaction by focusing on eliminating waste. This results in quality, productivity, and cost improvements.

♦ Teams focus on what is best for the entire group (or company), not just one individual.

♦ Highly developed teams eliminate the need for direct supervision. Supervisors serve as coaches and advisors.

♦ Team members experience a higher level of self-worth than employees not involved in teams, resulting in lower employee turnover rates.

♦ Teams build trust within the organization by building trust in people.

♦ Committed teams achieve outstanding results.

Requirements for Teamwork to Occur

There are four requirements within the organization for teamwork to effectively occur. These are:

♦ High levels of two-way communication throughout the organization. Communication can dramatically increase productivity by keeping everyone aware of the mission, vision, goals and strategy of the organization. Some chief executive officers spend as much as 40% of their time communicating this vital information to their organizations.

♦ Team members from diverse backgrounds. Diversity helps teams approach problems from a variety of angles, thus ensuring an effective resolution.

♦ Common purpose/motivated by mission. A strongly developed vision and mission for the organization helps all team members make the right decisions and saves time in the decision making process. One has only to ask "Does this decision support the goals of the organization?"

♦ Common goals/measurements. Teamwork is enhanced when all team members understand the goals of the team and the organization, and common measurements, understood by everyone, are used to assess the progress made.

The History of Teams

Throughout this book, we note several differences between American and Japanese companies. Team development is another area where there are stark contrasts between the two cultures. In Japan after World War II, General Douglas MacArthur administered the allies' occupation. One of his economic reforms was to force the recognition of Japanese labor unions on industry. Ironically, the sides united because "neither one of us has anything so let's work together for our mutual prosperity." Supporting the Japanese in team development were their Buddhist and Shinto religious beliefs. Buddhism teaches grouphood over selfhood—the goals of the group are more important than individual goals. The Shinto teachings include beliefs that human nature is essentially good—easily supported in a 99% ethnically pure population—and that work is part of life. With these shared beliefs among virtually everyone in the work environment, there was little to stop the acceptance of common goals within the team. Americans, on the other hand, have limited their support of teams to their favorite sporting events.

At the turn of the century, the work environment in this country began evolving into repetitive jobs supporting mass production. The individuals instrumental in this evolution were Frederick Taylor, the father of modern industrial engineering, and Henry Ford, the father of mass production. However, the workforce at that time supported their concepts. The majority of factory workers were immigrants who were poorly educated and spoke little English. In this environment, it simply made sense to make the jobs as simple as possible and use supervisors to direct the work as needed, based on the decisions of upper management. Anyone desiring advancement out of the ranks of hourly employee had to individually excel.

Unfortunately, the simple-task production line eliminated individual worker independence. People lost freedom, power, control, and ownership of their jobs. These precious commodities were held by a privileged few. The end result was a passive and uninterested workforce.

As the Japanese became an increasingly competitive threat to many U.S. industries, Americans became interested in how the Japanese were able to achieve such outstanding growth in their manufacturing plants. Investigation led to the discovery of the one major difference between us: teams. Quality Circles, modeled after the Japanese concept, became popular during the 1970s. Some were successful and some were not but the ground had been broken. Americans knew that teams were a powerful tool to solve problems and set about finding the best way to use them in manufacturing operations.

Japanese industry does not hold the patent on the use of teams to improve the "quality of life" of its workers. In the early 1950s, research conducted on British coal miners working in teams revealed that these workers had higher levels of job satisfaction and productivity as their control over their work increased. They were also more flexible in responding to changing market conditions.

Several companies in Sweden, from automobile to appliance manufacturers, have successfully eliminated the moving assembly line from their production facilities. They have noted remarkable increases in not only employee morale but also production levels by using teams to completely assemble major components or, in some cases, the entire unit.

Although teams have been developing around the world since the middle of the century, this country did not begin wide-scale team implementation until the mid-1980s.

Team Building Rule #1

Identify the areas where the first self-directed work teams will be formed. Use the "Islands of Excellence" as the first teams.

What is a Team?

Before we continue our discussion of team development, it is necessary to define the term "team." Some people think strictly of sports when they hear the word. Others simply envision a group of people sitting around a table in the company's conference room. In reality, the teams we have in mind in this chapter are much more complex than these simple examples. While we have seen many definitions of "team," the one that best reflects our intent is from *The Wisdom of Teams: Creating the High-Performance Organization.*

> "A team is a small number of people with complementary skills who are committed to a common purpose, performance goals, and approach for which they hold themselves mutually accountable."

If we examine the definition closely, the reasons teams are so important today become clear.

Flexibility

The small size of the group—from 3 to 15 people—allows the team to be flexible. This group can convene on a moment's notice, if necessary. Since changes are made on a daily basis because of customer demands or evolving technology, the performance flexibility provided by teams allows an organization to react quickly.

Skills

The team must consist of individuals with a mix of skills since this base provides team synergy. By definition, synergy means combined or cooperative action. Synergism, in medicine, means the joint action of drugs that, when taken together, increase each other's effectiveness. The same principle may be applied to groups. **The ability of**

the team to make a strong, workable decision will always be greater than the ability of its strongest team member.

The specific skills needed by team members will depend on the project the team is undertaking. The term "skill" means not only technical but also social or "people" skills. For example, a team working on reducing defects on a particular product would include members from quality, manufacturing, process engineering, and possibly maintenance. However, someone on the team should be comfortable speaking before a group as this will probably be necessary when the group summarizes its findings for management. Others in the group (ideally everyone) should be able to sense if someone on the team has quietly withdrawn from a discussion and help that person express his or her concerns. As we will see, there are many issues to consider when developing teams.

Commitment

Each member of the team must be totally committed to the purpose, goals, and approach of the team. This is a tall order indeed! However, as previously noted, there are top performers in every organization. These individuals will have no problem making the commitment because they can visualize the final outcome. They also recognize and appreciate the special talents and skill of others. This group will not generally have problems as a team.

Do not limit your team members to this small percentage of your workforce. The balance of your employees may be developed into effective team members. It is very easy within a group, especially a group that does not agree with our ideas, to stop participating in the action. How easy to divorce ourselves from the group and say, "I told you it wouldn't work!" This type of behavior will destroy the team. Until each member has committed full, good-faith support to the team, the team will not develop to its full potential. We will provide some tips on how to obtain commitment later in this chapter.

Not only is the commitment of each team member critical to the success of the team, management's support of the team process is also critical. The teams must be empowered to take action and make things better. These are active roles. If management is deciding to "get involved with this team thing" because it seems like the current "quick fix," we can tell you right now your efforts will fail.

> "The most successful teams have strong upper management support, demonstrated partly by the CEO's commitment to the team process and expressed confidence that success is achievable. Team building begins with a decision at the top to encourage, and even require, employees to operate in teams. Lack of management support is the number one cause of team failure."
>
> DEBORAH HARRINGTON-MACKIN
> THE TEAM BUILDING TOOL KIT

Mutual Accountability

Mutual accountability springs naturally from each team member's commitment to the purpose, goals, and approach of the team. This is why the commitment process is so critical. Mutual accountability is also why teams are so effective. Everyone accepts personal responsibility for making the team work. The group proceeds as if with one mind toward a clearly understood goal with a consistent approach to the project. Team members not committed to the team will hold back and not participate in the group's efforts. Basically, these people lack trust.

Trust cannot be provided on demand. Trust comes from a history of promises made and promises kept. It comes from acknowledging successes and failures. It comes from taking action in the best interest of the group, not of the individual. When trust is built, carefully and over time, team members will exhibit higher and higher levels of commitment to the team and accountability will naturally follow. Remember: The opposite of trust is fear.

Creating an environment where all the components of a successful team can grow is the first step in developing high performance teams.

Types of Teams

There are essentially only three types of teams: leadership or steering teams, project teams, and self-directed or high involvement work teams.

Leadership Teams

Leadership or steering teams:

- Include upper management personnel

- Determine the company's vision and, from there, set short-term and long-term goals

- Are permanent in the organization although members may change periodically

There are no reasons why hourly personnel cannot be part of this team. Companies may choose to select their steering teams from across all levels of the organization. This provides input about the vision and goals from a larger cross-section of employees. (Larger organizations may have leadership teams within major departments such as Engineering or Quality.)

Once the vision has been developed and the goals determined, the team meets regularly to determine progress and resolve issues related to the vision and goals. This team must be in place with a clearly defined vision established before the other types of teams are developed. As noted previously, common purpose and performance goals are key elements of successful teams. Individual team goals must be developed in line with the company's overall vision and goals.

Project Teams

Project teams:

- ♦ Include volunteer members from different departments and levels of expertise depending on the project

- ♦ Form to work on a specific project

- ♦ Disband when the project is complete

Project teams are just what the name implies. Examples of projects could be solving a specific quality problem or developing a paper recycling program. Although it sounds as if these teams quickly complete their project and move on, they still go through all the development stages the other teams experience.

Self-Directed Work Teams (SDWT)

Self-directed work teams:

♦ Include *all* members who work in a specific department on a specific shift

♦ Are responsible for an entire work process

♦ Are permanent teams who have control of and responsibility for all aspects of the work in their specific area

This type of team is the focus of our attention in this chapter. They deliver a service or product to a customer—either internal or external. If an area operates on two or three shifts, there will be a separate team on each shift. The term "self-directed" can be so threatening to some members of the organization that we frequently see the name altered to high performance work teams. The concept is the same. Once the company's vision and goals are determined, self-directed teams will be the most powerful tool for achieving and exceeding those goals.

For teams to become "self-directed," a great deal of training and management support is required. As a result, successful self-directed teams develop over a period of time. How much time is needed depends on the attitudes of the individual team members and the frequency and quality of the training. This training is critical to the success of the team. Too often we select a group of highly motivated individuals to form a team, then leave them to fend for themselves. We provide no training, management support, or experienced team facilitator. Without these, the team will most assuredly falter and almost certainly fail, much to their mounting frustration. Recovering from such failures is extremely difficult.

Team Building Rule #2

Conduct plant-wide information meetings explaining the concept of self-directed work teams and identifying the target areas.

Team Building Rule #3

Identify individuals in the organization with the skills to be strong team facilitators. Provide training in the skills, if necessary. Explain to the facilitators their role in the development of self-directed work teams. Clearly describe the expected development level (how self-directed the teams will be) and the expectations for the teams (how much quality, productivity, and cost improvements are expected).

What is a Team Facilitator?

Although the roles within each team are defined later in this chapter, one of these roles will be referenced repeatedly before that point. It is important to understand the nature of the team Facilitator before we continue.

A Facilitator is an important resource for a developing team who helps the group overcome obstacles and demonstrates team behavior. (The word *facilitate* means to make easier; move forward.) The Facilitator contributes to the development of the team process. However, this person does **not** contribute to the team's task. The Facilitator's concern is more with <u>how</u> decisions are made than with <u>which</u> decisions are made. The Facilitator acts as an outside observer as the team works together as a group. This neutral, objective observation provides a source of feedback when the team experiences difficulty or becomes blocked.

A Facilitator helps a team obtain resources for accomplishing their task. This is mostly accomplished by making suggestions or helping the team brainstorm solutions. Although the Facilitator does not participate in making decisions about the project, he or she should be very informed about the task and familiar with the process the team is studying.

The Facilitator will also train the group in the team process, problem-solving tools, and the scientific approach to problem-solving, along with helping the team stay focused on its task. He or she is a technical person with excellent training and people skills.

Based on this information, we can see that selection of the Facilitator is very important. Facilitators themselves, must work at acquiring the skills necessary to be effective in this role. Some of the specific skills this person must possess or be willing to develop are:

♦ Effective presentation skills and ability to train others to be effective presenters
♦ Teaching ability in statistical methods
♦ Excellent communication skills
♦ Extensive knowledge of the team development process
♦ Strong team-building skills including how to resolve conflict, provide feedback and listen
♦ Effective meeting skills
♦ Project planning skills
♦ Thorough understanding of the team's project
♦ Data gathering and statistical skills

Ideally, the Facilitator will be on good terms with everyone on the team. The group should see the person as neutral and fair. If an organization has a pool of such people to draw from, the team could even select its own Facilitator.

Team Dynamics:
Learning to Work Together

It might seem odd that a group of people, who have worked side by side for years, must learn *how* to work together; yet this is exactly what must happen. The history of the industrial workforce in this country simply did not allow team working relationships to develop. Working *beside* someone is not the same as working *with* someone.

The most important element in any team is communication. Yet we find that many communicating people have very poor skills. The teams will progress through the development stages as quickly as each team member is willing to learn <u>and</u> <u>apply</u> strong communication skills. Therefore, continuous feedback regarding communication must be provided by an experienced team facilitator during every team meeting.

Team Building Rule #4

Meet with the people who work in the target areas to review the self-directed work team concept, explain why their areas were chosen as "Islands of Excellence," and encourage questions from the group. Introduce the team facilitators and establish the first meeting dates and times. (One team per facilitator.)

During the course of numerous Kaizen workshops conducted in factories across the country, we often learned facts about individuals who worked in the departments we were studying. It was alarming how often we discovered that two people, within this 1,000 square foot-area, had not spoken to each other in two, five, ten *years* or even longer! You can imagine the turmoil in the group as we began the work of breaking down the barriers. If everyone on the team is not on speaking terms with everyone else on the team, the team will fail.

Stages of Team Growth

There are four stages of team growth. Unfortunately, there are no shortcuts through the stages. You cannot leap from stage one to stage three without going through stage two. Each stage has specific developmental skills which must be learned before the group may proceed to the next level. There are no "bad" stages of team growth. All are very important and will strengthen the group. Be sure, during your team training, to let the team members know that they will encounter these four stages and what to expect in each stage. They will experience some strong emotions and significant changes during their journey. Knowing what to expect and that their feelings are normal will make the transition easier.

To help remember the stages of team growth, just think of the word "TEAM".

T–tentative

E–emotional

A–attainable

M–masterful team

Team Building Rule #5

Train the team members in the four sequential stages of team development.

Stage 1 – Tentative

This stage can most closely be related to attending a neighborhood party where you know only a few people. How do people react in this situation? They smile politely, exchange names, make small talk, then move on to the next person or group. The conversation remains very shallow. If a person says something others do not agree with, it is unlikely that person will receive a strong challenge from anyone in the group. The others will nod, look thoughtful, and say "Hmmmm," even while they are thinking "What a jerk." No one in the group would consider saying anything like that out loud, no matter how strongly they wanted to. If someone does challenge the speaker, the others in the group will listen very attentively but will not likely take a stand on the issue.

This is how a team begins to form. The members talk about various topics, form opinions about others in the group, but generally keep their thoughts to themselves. (If the group is a Self-Directed Work Team (SDWT), the opinions, most likely, already exist.) Deeper concerns may exist for those who have little or no experience working within a team. A team facilitator is essential to assist the team through this very important stage of development.

During the tentative stage of team development, the members must receive training in the following:

- ◆ Team Development – Team members are taught the stages of team development, how to establish guidelines, team roles and responsibilities, overcoming obstacles, the importance of a mission statement, and goal setting. This helps everyone understand up front what to expect of others and what is expected of them as the group develops.

STAGE 1 – TEAM BUILDING EXERCISE

During this stage, each member of the team will have the same questions: "Can I trust you?", "Do you trust me?", "How do I fit in this group?", and "What's in it for me?" Each person will be seeking the answers to these questions while guarding themselves very carefully. Therefore, the team environment must be established as a "safe" place. It is particularly helpful to have the group determine team behavioral guidelines as the first step in creating the safety zone. These guidelines establish acceptable behavior within the group and answer many of the unasked questions about what is expected of the team members. This exercise allows everyone on the team to see that, stated or not, they all have the same concerns and needs. (See "Establishing Team Guidelines" on pages 134-136.)

♦ Effective Communication Skills – It is ironic that most people think they are very effective communicators when, in fact, they are very poor listeners. Here it is helpful to use several interesting and fun exercises that develop these skills. (Samples are provided free upon request to info@wcmfg.com) Once the skills have been explained and demonstrated, it is the responsibility of each team member to help every other team member use the skills *all the time*. Good communication skills should not be saved for the team meeting.

♦ Openness to the Ideas of Others – Most people believe they already are open-minded. They do not realize how strongly they hold their own beliefs. Here it is useful to challenge the team with exercises needing creative solutions and a change in individual belief systems. This activity helps team members see how others view a given situation and frequently opens their eyes to their own doubts about new experiences. See the Stage 1 – Team Building Exercise in the side-bar box.

♦ Team Building Situations – These are followed by discussion about what they observed and what they were thinking and feeling during the exercise. This sharing allows the team members to observe that they are not the only ones experiencing some discomfort. They also see that others experience things differently and why that is so. This opens everyone up to recognizing the similarities and differences between them as individuals and tapping into that range of viewpoints when making decisions. Recommended resources are given in the bibliography for Chapter 5.

Stage 2 – Emotional

We are warning you in advance, Stage 2 is a very difficult stage. It can most closely be related to the uncertainty and upheaval of adolescence. It is characterized by in-fighting, control behaviors, frustration, jealousy, and general chaos. It is normal. (We don't call it emotional for nothing!)

The issues team members face during this stage are:

♦ "I feel uncomfortable with my team." Do not let the surfacing issues within the team discourage you from proceeding with team building. Every group of people working on a project experiences these growing pains. Church groups, the PTA, Little League coaches all deal with the same issues. This stage is where individuals are trying to find their place in the group and establish control.

♦ "Not everyone on the team agrees with me." When working alone, this doesn't matter. If you disagree with me, that's your problem. In a team, however, the disagreement is everyone's problem. This naturally makes people feel that if everyone on the team is not in constant agreement, they are failing as a team. Nothing could be further from the truth. The lack of disagreement does not necessarily mean agreement. It may indicate apathy. Teams gain more from disagreement than agreement. The key is to know how to handle the disagreements. Again, this is why every team needs a skilled facilitator as part of their development process. The facilitator will keep the disagreement focused on the topic and not let it shift to personalities.

> ## A Word of Encouragement
>
> We have watched more than 150 teams develop over the past few years. They have experienced intense struggle, loud arguments, and total frustration. There were times when even their facilitators expressed doubts about the possibility of their success. Most of these teams produced excellent results. Not only were their results superior, but they were also a real team. The degree of struggle the team faces is directly related to the degree of success the team achieves. The weakest team performances came consistently from the teams where there was little or no evidence of disagreement or struggle.

♦ "We aren't getting anything done!" Because team members will be either trying to win the group over to their side or not participating at all, the group will feel that they are not making any progress. They will change direction frequently, feel confused about the project, and set unrealistic goals. As a result they become frustrated. The saying "It is always darkest before the dawn" is very appropriate here. Just when the team thinks they are hopeless, the breakthrough occurs and spirits soar. They have arrived at the other side of stage 2. The keys to success are staying focused on the task and communicating.

Stage 3 – Attainable

The shift from Stage 2 to Stage 3 is not always clear cut but it generally occurs as a result of the team deciding to make the team task or team goal the "boss." Often, the team is not even aware of the change. This stage is characterized by:

♦ A gradual decrease in the degree of frustration, disagreement, and confusion

♦ A gradual increase of the feeling "We can do it"

♦ Resolution of disagreements to the satisfaction of everyone

♦ Members listening more to each other and expressing their ideas openly

♦ An understanding of the strengths and weaknesses of fellow team members

♦ Everyone participating on some part of the project

♦ Attachment between group members and friend-ships forming

♦ Relief that progress is now being made

The team no longer relies so heavily on its facilitator. The group uses its communication skills to resolve its own issues. As obstacles arise, the team develops its own plan of action. However, it is not unusual for the team to slip back into Stage 2 behaviors when faced with a crisis. This, too, is normal although the team may become quite upset by the step backward. Some direction and encouragement from the facilitator usually gets the team back on track. It is during this stage that the team makes some real progress on its project.

Stage 4 – Mastery

This stage is the most rewarding for the team. It is now that team members notice how much they have person-ally changed as the result of the team process. This stage is characterized by:

♦ Team member's skill at working through group problems or preventing them altogether

♦ Each person genuinely interested in the ideas of others and willing to listen to both sides of an issue

♦ The group using the strengths of individual mem-bers and helping each other overcome their weak-nesses

♦ Completing a large amount of work in a short pe-riod of time

How Long Do Each of the Team Development Stages Last?

The answer to this very common question among those new to team development is that there is no "correct" time limit. Much depends on the personalities of the individual team members, the strength of the team facilitator, how often the team meets, the project the team is working on, and a host of other factors. For example, a newly formed self-directed work team, consisting of members who see each other daily and have a reasonably good working relationship established, may not spend any time at all in stage one. On the other hand, a project team, consisting of representatives from several departments who do not know each other, may spend several weeks being tentative. In addition, if a member is added to a team in Stage 3, it is not uncommon for the team to return briefly to Stage 1 while the new member gets comfortable. The team should not concern itself with the amount of time spent in each stage. The focus should be on developing strong communication skills and learning how to work together toward a common goal.

Final Thoughts on Team Development

Understanding the stages of team growth will relieve team members' fears about the process. However, teams should be aware that the path to success is never smooth. There will be times after a success or two that the team will feel that it cannot lose. Other times, an unexpected setback will cause the team's mood to plunge. In general, attitudes will be good when the team feels it is accomplishing something. Attitudes will be poor if the team feels it is blocked or not making progress.

Team members should strive to keep a positive attitude all the time, but, lacking this ability, they should be prepared to help each other as much as possible. It is unlikely that everyone will be in a down mood at the same time (except at the beginning of Stage 2). During those times, the members who are feeling positive should encourage their team mates. This period will not last and the team will soon be moving forward again. As the team develops through Stages 3 and 4, they will learn to avoid the problems which result in bad feelings.

Although we have discussed the stages of team development at length, the team should not focus on the stages or even on the development process. Team development is not the goal. Teams are a way of accomplishing improvements in the work place. **The focus of every team must always be the task**. Teams are just another tool to be used. Like the other WCM techniques, it is important to understand the tool so that it is used wisely.

Building Your Team

Now that we understand the stages of growth that teams go through, the next step is to identify the skills teams need to reach their highest performance level. These skills are:

- ◆ Developing Communication
- ◆ Conducting Effective Meetings
- ◆ Identifying Team Roles and Responsibilities
- ◆ Resolving Conflicts
- ◆ Establishing Team Guidelines
- ◆ Establishing Team Mission and Goals
- ◆ Making Group Decisions

No, the team will <u>not</u> spend months in training before they can begin working on improvement projects. For the most part, the training is brief and the concepts quite simple. The difficult part is practicing the concepts every day and making them new habits. The self-directed work team uses its improvement project as the training ground and the team facilitator for feedback on how the group is progressing. There is no better way to learn than by doing. The group will begin to solidify as a team by establishing guidelines, mission, and goals.

In fact, by the time the team completes these activities, it will probably be entering Stage 3 in the development process. Training in specific problem-solving techniques should be presented only when the team is ready to use the technique. In this way, practice immediately follows the learning experience. This helps the team become skillful with the tool and more likely to use it on its own for other improvement projects. Specific problem-solving tools are discussed later in this chapter.

Team Building Rule #6

Train the team in communication, effective meetings, conflict resolution, and group decisions skills.

Developing Communication

Communication is one skill that everyone can learn and practice anywhere and that will benefit any situation. The reason many team building exercises focus on communication is that it is so important to the team process. During the team's development, use communication exercises often to help the team practice good communication skills.

The first step in developing these skills is to understand where weaknesses exist. Everyone has at least one weakness in the ability to communicate. Knowing what that weakness is enables a person to work on overcoming the problem. Below is a summary of the most common problems related to both speaking and listening.

Speaking. Part of communication is effectively verbalizing our ideas. Communicating ideas verbally is something we all do on a daily basis and doing it properly is essential in the team environment. Thinking about what to say before saying it helps this process immensely.

Below is a list of effective speaking skills.

- Use vocabulary appropriate to the listeners. This means do not speak up or down to them.

- Avoid terms understood only by those in a specific line of work. Avoid slang terms that may not be understood by everyone in the listening audience.

- Speak clearly and at a pace the listeners can follow comfortably

- Speak loud enough to be heard by the individual or group being addressed. Adjust your volume to your location—conference room or shop floor.

- Share all information available with everyone on the team. Keeping back information does not make for trusting relationships.

All of these factors affect your being understood. If you are unsure of your verbal communication skills, ask someone on your team to give you feedback. Heed suggestions for improvement and ask for updates on your progress every so often.

Using Speaking Skills Effectively

The participants in an improvement seminar in Monterrey, Mexico, were all locals who had learned English as a second language. The seminar was conducted in English but we used special care not to use American slang or other words that would not be understood by the class members. We also slowed down the presentation to allow the listeners time to literally translate the English words into their native Spanish. Although this lengthened the class, the group was able to learn the material well and effectively participate in the work site improvement projects.

Listening. Listening is a critical part of communication, yet it is often neglected. Do you sometimes find yourself forming a response before the speaker has even finished? If so, you are not alone. Listening is not a skill in which most of us have been trained. Good listening can be improved with practice. How do we improve our listening skills? The old saying that goes "Seek first to understand, then to be understood" is excellent advice for listeners because it places the focus of attention where it belongs—on the speaker. When we listen, we must put aside our personal opinions about what the person is saying and listen to the words. Too often, we assume we know what the speaker has to say and we start arguing before hearing the entire message. This is true especially if we expect the speaker to disagree with some of our ideas. (Many of us seem to experience this daily.)

As you practice listening, you become aware how difficult prolonged listening can be. Most of us are so used to TV or radio noise that we can "tune out" quite easily. While most of this background noise is worth tuning out, it is not a good idea to tune out a face-to-face conversation. We do, however, because the mind can process more words per minute than most people speak. This gives us time to form responses or even let our minds wander a bit. Many of us have this experience during meetings, lectures, and even chats with family members.

Here are some practical rules for listening effectively.

♦ Focus on the speaker. Make eye contact so nothing distracts your attention. Do not continue any other activities while the speaker is talking. Such distractions imply that you do not consider the message or the speaker very important.

♦ Hear the entire message before you begin to form your response.

♦ Rephrase what you think the speaker said and ask if your understanding is correct. If the speaker says no, ask him or her to repeat what was said. Continue until the speaker says you have understood correctly what was meant.

♦ Observe the nonverbal signals that will give you more information. Notice how the person is standing or sitting. Listen to the tone of voice. Determine if the speaker is relaxed, tense, excited, sad, frustrated. You can listen to their "body" language.

Practice good listening with everyone and you will be amazed at how much this will improve your personal and working relationships.

Other Communication Tips. Shown below are several other factors that affect good communication. Mostly these are common courtesies. Treating others with respect goes a long way toward opening communication.

- ♦ Avoid interrupting the speaker.

- ♦ Do not have side conversations when someone else is talking. This is extremely rude.

- ♦ Do not state or even hint that what someone is saying is ridiculous, foolish, or not worth your time. (This includes rolling your eyes, deep sighs, shaking your head, or muttering to yourself.) Hinting that the speaker's message has no value may cause the speaker to be very hesitant about offering ideas in the future. It may also make the speaker angry, defensive, or frustrated.

- ♦ Acknowledge all comments or ideas made by team members. Lack of response says the speaker's message is not important.

- ♦ Ask for clarification if someone says something you do not understand.

Communication skills should be practiced all the time, not just in team meetings. When team members notice that the rules for effective communication are not being followed, they need to address the issue right away. At first, the facilitator may be the only one noting violations. Soon, however, all the team members will notice when someone breaks the rules. Eventually, good communication will be standard in every meeting.

Conducting Effective Meetings

The cornerstone of an effective meeting is having—and using—an agenda. An agenda is a clearly written document that states exactly what will happen in the meeting and how long it will take. Ideally, the agenda for the next meeting is established as the last item of business during the current meeting. Schedule no more than five minutes at the end of each meeting for this activity. The agenda must identify the starting time of the meeting, each item to be discussed, who will participate in or lead each discussion and for how long, and the ending time of the meeting. In order to keep track of the time, a timekeeper is identified for each meeting (See the next section "Identifying Team Roles and Responsibilities.") An agenda will look something like the following model.

Dept. 47 Team Meeting Agenda

Time	Item	Who	Duration
1:30 PM	Opening remarks and sign-in	John	5 min
1:35 PM	Maintenance problems on Machine #4	Arnot	5 min
1:40 PM	Possible solutions to problem	Team	10 min
1:50 PM	Review presentation for Steering Team	Team	15 min
2:05 PM	Department quality summary	Maria	5 min
2:10 PM	Discussion of effects of project on quality	Team	15 min
2:25 PM	Set agenda for next meeting	Team	5 min
2:30 PM	End		

> **NOTE:** Changes to the agenda are not permitted without the agreement of every team member. If an item takes less time than assigned, move on to the next topic. If the discussion will take longer than permitted, the team must decide to table the discussion for later or keep going. Continuing the discussion may be the right thing to do but it will obviously affect the rest of the agenda. The team must address these issues as they occur.

Note the general format for team meetings.

- Problems that affect the outcome of the project – these must be dealt with right away. If a problem is major and demands immediate attention but is not on the agenda, the team must make a new agenda and reschedule the old agenda items for another meeting.

- Planning issues (the presentation for the Steering Team)

- Information sharing (effects of the project on quality)

- Establish the next agenda

Being prepared for the meeting also helps ensure the meeting is effective. Members prepare for each meeting by referring to the previous meeting minutes and completing the items they are responsible for. The minutes are a complete summary of the meeting. They are most effective when published immediately after every team gathering. (The exact time limit for distribution is determined by the team.) The minutes:

- Summarize the discussions that took place

- List the actions that will be taken

- Note who is responsible for each action

- Include the meeting agenda for the next meeting

The minutes document the progress of the team and serve as a historical account of the team's activities. Someone on the team should be responsible for bringing previous minutes to each meeting in case they are needed for reference. Team members must have the minutes to prepare for the next meeting since they specify the agenda items and what each member is responsible for providing.

Simply having an agenda and complete minutes does not guarantee effective meetings, however. They only provide the possibility for a good meeting to take place. Another skill needed for effective meetings is the ability to stay on track. Staying on track means that the team members keep their conversation focused on the current topic. For example, if you notice that you are suddenly discussing the company picnic during the time scheduled for reviewing the presentation for the Steering Team, you are not on track. Wandering off track is very common. Every team member should remain focused on the topic and redirect the conversation if it wanders. Initially, the team will rely on the facilitator for this, but eventually everyone will notice when the team is off track.

Other skills such as identifying team roles, resolving conflicts, and making group decisions also contribute to the effectiveness of the team's meetings. These are discussed separately below.

Identifying Team Roles and Responsibilities

Within the team, members will perform certain roles to help the team accomplish its goals. These roles help keep the team organized and on track. Each role has specific responsibilities which everyone needs to understand. Team members rotate roles every so often so that each person has the opportunity to perform all of the activities. This prevents a panic situation if one of the members performing a specific function is not present for a meeting. The roles and their related responsibilities are listed below.

Team Leader. The team leader, a participating member of the team, has several administrative duties. The leader:

♦ Ensures that a meeting place or alternate location is available for the time and date the team wants to meet

♦ Arranges meetings between the team and others from either inside or outside the organization

♦ Is notified if members cannot attend a meeting for reasons acceptable to the team

---

How Supervisors Fit into a Self-directed Work Teams Environment

Some organizations use the supervisor as the leader of the self-directed work team. While it may seem the supervisor will maintain order and provide direction during the team's development, there are several reasons this is not a good idea. The supervisor's presence as the leader in the team meeting signals to the team that, despite assurances the team will control the work environment, nothing has really changed. The team still reports to the same person and that person is still in charge. Members often go along with the supervisor's suggestions because they believe they have no other option. Even more common is the fear of speaking up during a meeting where the supervisor is present, especially if the supervisor has been with the group for a long time.

We recommend that supervisors be used as administrative and technical resources for the team. The supervisor should identify for the team the general nature of the company's goals but not how to reach them. The supervisor should be invited to attend meetings as an observer and always receives copies of the meeting minutes. He or she must let the team know when it is losing sight of the project and provide encouragement and support to the team in all its activities. Supervisors should also be informed of the company's expectations for their participation in the changing organization. Management must be very clear about the supervisor's new duties and responsibilities.

♦ Opens and closes meetings, summarizes discussions, organizes decision making options, and tests for agreement among the members

♦ Observes the team process to ensure everyone is participating and using good communication skills throughout the meeting

Scribe. The scribe or recorder is a participating member of the team responsible for taking complete notes during the meeting and publishing the minutes after the meeting. The minutes may be handwritten if necessary but must be readable. The scribe ensures that:

♦ All topics discussed in the meeting are summarized

♦ Responsibilities and deadlines are noted

♦ Decisions the team made are recorded

♦ Minutes are distributed to the team members. (How distribution is made is a topic for team guidelines.)

Timekeeper. The timekeeper:

♦ Participates as a member of the team

♦ Announces the start of the meeting

♦ Keeps track of how much time remains for each agenda item during the meeting. This is most important during brainstorming sessions or general discussions

♦ Lets everyone know when 2 to 5 minutes remain in order for the discussion to be completed and summarized

Team Member. The responsibilities of the individual team member are the most important for the success of the team. Each member is expected to:

♦ Accept that management is committed to the success of the team

♦ Participate fully in the team project

♦ Report on time to the meeting place prepared to discuss all the items on the agenda

♦ Actively participate in the discussions and activities of the team

♦ Help other team members who are hesitant about participating

♦ Respect each other and not gossip either in or out of the meetings

♦ Offer to assist the leader, facilitator, timekeeper, and scribe in their roles

♦ Willingly take on the work required to benefit the team's performance

♦ Complete all assignments on time

♦ Participate in the decision making process and then support the decisions

Facilitator. The facilitator's responsibilities are described at length on page 110. You may want to review the information again.

As the team members rotate through the roles of team leader, scribe, and timekeeper, they will begin to practice those responsibilities on a regular basis. Everyone becomes more aware of the team process and works toward making the project, and the team, a success.

Resolving Conflicts

It is expected, during the course of the project, that team members will not always agree with each other. As noted earlier, disagreement is not necessarily a bad thing. It only becomes bad when the conflict moves away from the issue and starts to focus on personalities or when members refuse to address the problem. Training in the stages of team development can ease the fear of disagreement. But what do you do when the disagreement starts to get out of hand?

First, the team must stay task focused. That is, everything it does needs to be directed toward accomplishing the goal. Each team member should recognize that every other team member has something of value to offer toward reaching the goal. If necessary, have each team member identify one special skill that each of the other team members has that is contributing to the team's success. It is hard to stay angry at someone who has just said something positive about you.

Second, have the team review its team guidelines (see page 134). Is everyone following the guidelines as they are trying to resolve the conflict? Are the team members maintaining respect for each other even in the midst of disagreement?

Third, keep the lines of communication open. Do not resort to flinging insults or being closed and distant. It is not acceptable to storm out of the room or say "Forget it. Do what you want. I don't care." These statements indicate the person cares very much but has given up on being heard. Listen to what is said and paraphrase what is heard until the speaker indicates he or she has been understood. Once both sides understand each other, the discussion may continue. If necessary, use the team facilitator to arbitrate and/or to meet with the disagreeing parties individually.

Fourth, provide constructive feedback as a way to criticize an action but not the person. Some things to think about before using constructive feedback are:

- ◆ Acknowledge the value of feedback. Feedback can clear the air or praise a team member for a job well done.

- ◆ Understand the events that led to the situation under review. Try to understand what the other person was thinking when he or she took the action.

- ◆ Provide feedback when the time is right. Feedback should only be provided with the welfare of the other person in mind, not to inflate our own egos. Never criticize a person in the presence of non-team members. (You may praise them in that situation, however.) Do not criticize someone if you do not know much about the circumstances surrounding the action or if the person is powerless over the situation.

- ◆ Be specific when providing feedback and focus on the action—not the person. Follow the Feedback Guide (following page) to ensure the process is done well.

Fifth, try to prevent conflicts in the first place. Practicing good communication skills, treating each other with respect, and establishing team guidelines will all help avoid conflicts by preventing the misunderstanding that leads to them in the first place.

Feedback Guide

There is an effective method for providing feedback which can go a long way toward resolving conflicts. This method allows both parties to express their views about the behavior causing the problem and avoids judgment of personalities.

1. Start with a description of the offensive behavior, being careful not to be judgmental.
2. Explain how the behavior makes you feel.
3. Explain why the behavior makes you feel that way.
4. Discuss the situation and allow the other person to question anything he or she does not understand.
5. Describe what you would like the other person to do differently.
6. Explain why you believe this new action will eliminate the problem.
7. Ask for the other person's opinion. Be prepared to discuss alternate solutions.

Following this outline as soon as the problem becomes clear forces both parties to carefully review their feelings about the matter. It prevents a buildup of frustration and resentment which often results in a personal attack. Avoid using statements that accuse ("why must you be so selfish") or exaggerate ("why do you always..."). These will only make the other person defensive and look for proof that you are wrong. This moves attention away from the original problem and a possible settlement.

Team Building Rule #7

Use the guidelines and goal setting exercises as opportunities to practice communication, effective meetings, conflict resolution, and group decisions.

Sixth, recognize that every conflict between two or more team members is a group problem. It is impossible for a conflict between individuals not to affect the entire team. Also recognize that the conflict is most likely the result of poor overall team skills and not the result of one person being a trouble maker. Examine why the problem was able to develop in the first place and repair the process.

Last, keep your reaction to the conflict appropriate. Do not get hysterical over a minor incident and do not ignore major problems. Both of these reactions cause frustration among the team members and take the focus away from the team's task.

We cannot overstress the fact that conflicts will occur, but they do not have to be a serious problem for the team. In fact, the team's ability to successfully resolve conflict will strengthen the group and increase its productivity.

Establishing Team Guidelines

It is important that the team establish a set of behavior guidelines so that everyone knows what is and is not acceptable behavior in the group. The guidelines must be:

♦ Written

♦ Provided to every team member

Taking the time to establish and write down these guidelines helps prevent misunderstandings and bad feelings between group members. Everyone on the team is expected to participate in the establishment of the guidelines and live by them when they are complete. Some of the more common guidelines are as follows:

TEAM GUIDELINES

1. Establish when and where the teams will meet and for how long. It is best if both the time and location are consistent every time the team meets. Self-directed work teams generally meet every week or every other week for one hour. Identify a method for notifying members of changes to the meeting place or time if any should occur.

2. Establish rules for punctuality. Time is very valuable. Determine that you will respect others by starting and ending your meetings on time. Discuss issues such as how to deal with late-comers or members who leave early.

3. Establish rules for attendance. Decide on acceptable reasons for missing meetings. Determine how absence from a meeting will be communicated to the team leader.

4. Establish the expectation that everyone will participate. Showing up for the meeting and participating in the meeting are two different things. Determine how the group will ensure that everyone contributes to every meeting.

5. Establish the rotation of team roles. Determine how long the rotation period will be and how the new roles will be decided.

6. Establish guidelines for courtesy and confidentiality. This is critical to the establishment of trust among team members. Determine that members will listen to each other without interrupting and how the team will handle side conversations. Establish what information must stay within the group and what topics may be discussed outside the group.

7. Establish rules for breaks and interruptions. Will there be a break during the meeting, how long will it be, when will it be? When is it acceptable for the meeting to be interrupted?

8. Establish rules for other behaviors such as smoking in the meeting room, cursing, addressing offensive comments, etc.

As you can see, the guidelines are very broad and cover many areas. Do not be fooled into thinking that everyone on your team has the same expectations for team behavior. Take time to discuss these issues, and write down the agreements made by the team members to prevent problems later. If the guidelines do not seem to fit after the team has worked together for awhile, change them. The important thing is not so much what the guidelines are but that everyone on the team agrees to live by them.

Establishing Team Mission and Goals

Many teams benefit from the creation of a team mission statement. This statement, created to support the corporate vision and mission statement, will help keep the team focused on its goals. A mission statement is not the same as a goal. Goals are specific and measurable. The mission statement is more an expression of the team's overall objectives and values. It should have emotional, inspirational appeal for the team members. A self-directed work team may include in its mission such statements as "provide superior customer service," "continuously improve our process," "through the use of teamwork we will...." These statements define the commitment the team is willing to make to achieve its goals. The team is responsible for developing its own mission statement. All of its activities and goals should support the overall mission.

Goal setting is another very important team activity. Initially, management will outline for the team their expectations of what the team will accomplish. How the team will make this happen is up to the team to decide. The original objective provided by management should be specific enough that the team is able to develop a plan of attack. For instance, management should not advise the team that their task is to improve their work area. This does not provide enough information and the team may take weeks just trying to figure out where to start. If management tells the team they want an increase in productivity of 30% without adding people, the team has a specific goal to meet.

While the initial goal is provided by management, the team will take over the goal setting task after they have completed the first project. Team goals must support the corporate vision. The team will select its next project before the current project is complete, allowing time for the team to present this goal to the Steering Team for review. Once the team is experienced with goal setting, review by management may not be required.

The team also needs to clearly understand the extent of its responsibility and authority. How much money does the team have to use as it sees fit? Can the team decide to work overtime? When is approval required before the team moves ahead? Answering these questions as the team is forming will prevent disappointment and frustration later. As the team gains experience in making improvements, it is expected that its level of responsibility and authority will increase.

Making Group Decisions

As teams work through their projects, they need to make many decisions. Ideally, these decisions reflect the ideas and opinions of everyone on the team. We already know that team members will not always agree. How, then, will they be able to make effective group decisions? The techniques we suggest are brainstorming and consensus.

Brainstorming is a valuable tool for starting discussions, collecting lots of ideas, and getting everyone's creative juices flowing. Before the team can actually make a decision about a specific course of action, it should make sure that all possible choices have been studied. Brainstorming is where synergy (building on other people's ideas) really comes into play. Team members with different skills and experiences each provide a unique outlook on the problem. By pooling all the suggestions, the team develops a solution to satisfy everyone's concerns. Since self-directed work teams are generally made up of the employees from one department, they may need input from other areas during their brainstorming session. For example, a manufacturing SDWT may want to include delegates from quality, manufacturing, engineering, or maintenance. These people should be familiar with the area and the process being studied.

The key to a successful brainstorming session is creativity. No idea is foolish. The team may want to conduct a simple brainstorming warm-up before the real session begins. This will not only help people to start thinking creatively but will also relax the group. Once the group is ready to go, follow these simple steps to conducting an energetic brainstorming session.

1. State the problem in the form of a question. "What are the contributing factors to our daily downtime?" "Where can handling damage defects occur?" "How can we increase production by 35%?" (Avoid starting the question with "who" as this will be seen as trying to place blame.) Write the question in large letters on a piece of flip chart paper or a white board and keep it in front of the group for the entire session.

2. Allow everyone a few silent minutes to think about the question and jot down their ideas. This step may actually be done a few days before the brainstorming session. Everyone comes to the meeting ready to give ideas.

3. Go around the room and invite each participant to provide one idea. When everyone has had a turn, start around the room again. Continue in this way until everyone has provided all of their ideas. List each idea only once.

4. Write all ideas on a flip chart and keep the entire list in front of the group. If you fill up a page, pull it off the pad and tape it on a wall.

For brainstorming to be effective, the ideas must be free-flowing. For this reason, there can be absolutely no judgment of any idea. This includes rolling eyes, laughing, groaning, or facial expressions. During the brainstorming session, discussion about ideas is not permitted—not even to ask for clarification. That will come later. Often, participants will think of additional ideas as the result of hearing the other ideas. This is encouraged. Add these ideas to the list. When everyone has all their ideas listed on the flip chart, give the team a few more minutes to review the list and see if any new ideas develop. When the team remains silent for several minutes, the session is complete.

A unique way to record the ideas is to write them on separate pieces of paper and stick them to the flip chart. After all the ideas are collected, the slips of paper are arranged into categories or grouped together. Similar ideas are combined, if the people who had the ideas agree, thus shortening the overall list.

Consensus is the second technique for making group decisions. A consensus means that everyone on the team finds the decision acceptable enough that they will support it. No one opposes the idea outright. Consensus does not mean that everyone is totally satisfied, nor is it the result of a majority vote or unanimous decision. Consensus means that every team member will support the idea and do all they can to ensure its success.

Reaching a consensus requires much discussion by the entire team. A consensus decision is usually the result of creatively combining two or more individual ideas. It is highly unlikely that the consensus plan exactly matches the idea of one person on the team. (If this happens frequently on your team, you may have a dictatorship rather than a team.) When the team leader believes the group has reached consensus, he or she should test for consen-

---

Beware of This Consensus Trap

We have seen one mistake made on many occasions when a team is testing for consensus. The team leader or scribe summarizes the decision and asks "Does everyone agree with that?"; directing the question to the group in general but not to each specific team member. Around the table we see some heads nodding up and down while others are completely still. We also see nonverbal behavior such as heads down or crossed arms which may indicate uncertainty or disapproval. It is always best to go around the table to each person, say their name, and ask if they can support the stated decision. ("The group has decided to monitor the salt bath for one week and review the results at the next meeting. Do we all support this? Ted? Mary? Alice? Tom?") If a team member does not respond, or agrees by saying "Oh, all right!" - STOP! Ask them to explain their concerns about the decision. Review the decision again including these new concerns. Ask the hesitant team member what needs to be included in the decision to make it acceptable to them. Once this is done, restate the decision and test for consensus again. Do not use decisions that are not supported by everyone on the team. Do not dismiss someone's concerns as silly. Either of these actions will cause frustration and hard feelings among team members.

sus by stating the decision and asking each person if they can support it. Clearly summarizing the decision ensures that everyone understands which decision is being tested. After intense discussion, team members may each have their own understanding of what the group has decided. Only when every member on the team states their support of the decision has a consensus been reached. See box on page 140.

Prioritizing tasks is an important skill for the team to master. Most teams do not have a problem finding things to work on. In fact, they usually brainstorm so many ideas that they have a problem selecting one. Several techniques are available to help groups determine their starting point.

One way to determine which task from the brainstorm list to select is by potential cost savings, the primary reason companies begin improvement projects. Your company probably has cost information already available on lost time accidents; rework, repair or scrap; machine downtime and overtime; etc. Get this information for the topics on your list and determine your highest cost item. Your priority has just been determined.

Another method for determining priority is by time or frequency. If your team is trying to decide which machine to select for setup reduction, knowing how much time each machine takes to setup will help make the decision. However, a machine that does not take the most time to setup but is setup more frequently than the others may be the best choice. Gather the information your company currently has and use it to help decide what to work on first.

Other choices the team has to make may not have cost or time details available. Sometimes the cost or time results are so close that it is difficult to decide where to start. In the case where several options are available to the team, a technique called multivoting may be used.

Multivoting helps the team to focus on fewer items on its list and determine the importance of each of these items. Simple multivoting just counts up the number of votes a particular item receives. It works best with long lists. Weighted multivoting assigns an importance factor to each vote and works best with shorter lists. Let's look at both of these methods.

Simple multivoting means each person on the team votes to prioritize one third of the items on the list using the following four steps:

1) Write out all the options on a flip chart and number them.

2) Allow each team member five to ten minutes to decide which items they feel are most important. Everyone does this quietly, without discussing their choices with anyone else.

3) Have each team member read off the items which received their votes. (Encourage team members not to change their own selections as the votes are read.) Total up the number of votes for each item and make a new list starting with the item(s) that received the most votes and working down to the items with one vote.

4) Review the results with the team and determine if the group is satisfied with the number one selection (test for consensus). In the event of a tie for the

number one item, determine if the team can select between the items or conduct weighted multivoting to break the tie.

In weighted multivoting, each member of the team assigns a value of importance for each item.

1) Make a list of all the items on a flip chart and numbering each item.

2) Team members select the 3 to 5 items they want to work on first by specifying his or her number one choice, then number two choice, etc. The number one choice will receive the highest number of points. For example, if the team is choosing 3 items, the team member's number one item is worth three points, the second item is worth two points, and the third is worth one point. If the team is selecting five items, the team member's number one choice is worth 5 points and the values go down from there. This ranking is done without discussion within the group.

3) Team members read off the items they selected and the point values they assigned. These are written on the flip chart next to each item (use a different colored marker). The item receiving the most points becomes the top priority item. (It is possible that the item receiving the highest score was not selected by anyone as their number one item.)

4) The team must agree to the results before accepting the top priority item (test for consensus.)

A variation of weighted multivoting is simply giving each team member a specific number of points and allowing distribution of those points to the items the person selects. For example, the team is trying to select the top five items from a list of 15. Each team member is given 15 points but can select no more than 5 items. Maria decides that one item is very important and several others are much less important. She gives her important item 7 points and the four less important items 2 points each. This totals her 15 points. Joe, on the other hand, thinks two items are very important and three others very unimportant. He assigns his two very important items 6 points each and the three unimportant items 1 point each totaling his 15 points. This allows all team members the opportunity to express their own personal opinion about the relative importance of the items selected.

While multivoting provides the team a way of prioritizing a long brainstorm list, it does not remove any items from the original list. All the ideas are kept and, as projects are completed, new projects are selected from the original list. You may find that during work on one item, another item was fixed. In that case, note in the team's meeting minutes that the item was completed and place the item on the team's completed project list.

How All the Components of Making Group Decisions Work Together

You are one of eight members of a self-directed work team in a manufacturing area. Your instructions from management are to improve the profitability of the area. This directive is a bit unclear, so the team proceeds with a *brainstorming* session. The problem is stated as the question "How can we make our area more profitable?" The following list of (13) ideas is created:

Reduce scrap and rework	Eliminate accidents	Hire more people to work more
Reduce downtime	Reduce setup time	Increase PM
Limit supplies to area (paper, pencils, etc.)	Reduce headcount	Don't move material so much
Combine operations	Run larger batches	Reduce inventory
Work more overtime to make more parts		

After some discussion to clarify each of the ideas, the team decides to use *simple multivoting* to determine the top four items to keep. The results are as follows:

Reduce scrap and rework	8
Reduce downtime	6
Eliminate accidents	4
Combine operations	3
Reduce setup time	3
Hire more people	3
Reduce inventory	2
Eliminate changeovers	2
Don't move material so much	1

The team members discuss the results and decide to keep any items with 3 or more votes. They also decide that hiring more people may not be necessary if they are successful in the first 5 items. This idea is placed on the list with the items that received fewer than 3 votes and will be reviewed at a later date. The team is left with 5 items to prioritize.

The team then requests cost information for these items in its area only. It learns that the cost for each item is approximately $18,000 per month except for item number 4. There is no cost data available for combining operations.

The team members must now decide which project to attack first. They use *weighted multivoting* to prioritize the list. In this case, each person determines the top three items and assign them values of 3, 2, and 1 in descending order. The results are as follows:

Reduce scrap and rework	8
Reduce downtime	17
Eliminate accidents	16
Combine operations	2
Reduce setup time	5

Finally the team must *test for consensus* that it will work on reducing downtime as the first project.

By this time, the team should be ready to produce some results. The members understand the team process and the stages of development. Their communications skills are improving, team guidelines and goals have been established, and they work at resolving conflicts. Meetings are productive and the group is gaining confidence in its decision making skills. It is now ready to be given the specific tools needed to identify and analyze problems.

Problem-Solving Tools

Once the team has identified the specific project it will address, it must identify and analyze the overall problem. Some tools are designed for teams to clearly identify the problem they are trying to solve. Other tools help the teams analyze the data or information they have collected. Some tools can be used for either purpose. The benefit of most of the tools is they provide the data in easy to understand picture form. In this section we will identify the tools and how they are used.

Root Cause Analysis—Ask Why Five Times

The most important step teams can take in solving problems is to identify the root cause of the problem. Most companies have problems that just don't go away. Despite repeated efforts to eliminate these problems, they come back again and again—often on a fixed cycle. This recurrence indicates that the problem was never truly identified in the first place. Instead of solving the problem, the team was treating a symptom. As the team uses the tools for identifying problems, it must always be sure to identify the true root cause of the problem. One excellent tool to ensure the team has identified the root cause and not a symptom of the problem is to ask the 5 Whys.

Are you pulling weeds?

Anyone who has ever tried to get rid of a yard full of weeds knows how difficult this can be. If you cut the plant off at the surface of the ground, you will find a new plant growing in the same place several days later. Not only is there a new plant but it is stronger and healthier than the one it is replacing. The way to get rid of a weed is to pull out or kill the entire root of the plant. The 5 Whys tool is used to sort through the surface issues and get to the root of the problem. Only by removing this root can the problem be eliminated.

The "Operator Error" Myth

It is common practice in some organizations to accept "operator error" as the cause of a defect. This is never acceptable. An error on the part of an operator is always a symptom of a deeper problem. Typically, other factors caused the problem and the operator was just following orders. Using the "operator error" excuse not only prevents a true solution to the problem from being developed but it also creates fear and mistrust within the organization.

Here is how the **5 Whys** work. Let's say the team has identified a problem with a part that has the same defect again and again. The defect is a missing hole.

> **#1 Why** is the hole missing?
> **Answer**: Operator error.

> **#2 Why** did the operator make the error?
> **Answer**: He wasn't inspecting the parts as required.

> **#3 Why** wasn't he inspecting the parts?
> **Answer**: The supervisor told him we are behind in the shipping schedule.

> **#4 Why** are we behind in the shipping schedule?
> **Answer**: The raw material was late in arriving.

> **#5 Why** was the raw material late in arriving?
> **Answer**: The supplier underestimated the lead time.

In this case, if the team stopped after the first or second why, it would direct the effort toward making the operator do a better job. However, the problem was not with the operator. The operator was reacting to a direct order from his supervisor to make more parts. And the supervisor was only trying to do his job and meet the customer's requirements. The real problem was the supplier's lead time. If the team wants to ensure that the operator performs the inspection as required, the issue of receiving material on time must be resolved. If not, the next time material is late, the operator will receive the same instructions from the supervisor and missing holes will be the result. (Another example of using the 5 Whys technique is shown in Chapter 8.)

To test how effectively a problem has been solved, answer the following question. "Will the corrective action we have taken guarantee this problem will not come back?" If you cannot answer with an emphatic YES, the problem has not been completely solved. (See the section on Error Proofing later in this chapter.)

Identifying problems

In the above discussion about how group decision-making tools work together, the team decided to work on reducing downtime first. The total downtime in the area is most likely the result of downtime in several parts of the process. If there are several machines, each one may have its own downtime problems. Downtime may be caused by machine failure, or a lack of parts, or poor quality parts that need to be sorted, or untrained operators. There are many things to consider.

How does the team evaluate this problem and others like it? Several tools are available.

Brainstorming

The first tool, brainstorming, has already been discussed in the section on Making Group Decisions. In the above example, the team members could identify all of the locations where downtime occurs or all the various types of downtime for their process. Since each team member is familiar with different parts of the process, downtime for every part of the process will be identified. Encourage the free flow of ideas from everyone to get the most benefit from brainstorming.

Multivoting

Multivoting has also been discussed in the section on Making Group Decisions. Remember that this tool helps the team determine the priority of its projects and, as a result, identifies the problem it will work on first.

Process Flowcharting

A flow chart is a picture of what happens first, second, third, and so on, in a process. The flow chart identifies all steps in the process: where decisions are made, what happens if the decision is yes or no, which steps add value to the product or service, and how long it takes to complete the process for every unit produced. The flow chart is used to identify all the value added and non-value added steps in the process so that the team can eliminate as much non-value added work as possible.

Value added work is any work that physically changes the part or advances the product toward completion. Without value added work, the part cannot be produced. Examples of value added work are machining, heat treating, welding to assemble parts, painting to provide a protective or cosmetic finish, assembly, plating, etc.

Any work that does not comply with the definition of value added work is *non-value added* work. Examples of non-value added work are inspection, moving, counting, re-work/repair, removing burrs, welding to repair a machining error, painting to repair a cosmetic defect, storage of material, etc.

Completing a flow chart is a good idea for a newly formed self-directed work team. The benefits of flow charting are that it will:

♦ Make the actual process clear for everyone

♦ Provide a before picture of the process when the group started

♦ Make it easy to track improvements over time

♦ Quantify the improvements made

A flow chart for a manufacturing process is quite simple. (Refer to the sample flow chart in Figure 5.2.) Most teams experience nearly all their difficulty with this procedure in defining the beginning and ending cutoff points of the process. For self-directed work teams, the process begins when the parts arrive at their work site and ends when the parts leave their work site.

Starting at the top of the Process Flow Analysis form, name the process (i.e., 2468 Strap Bending or 1234 Housing Drilling). Write in the date the flow chart was developed. Identify the department by number or the location where the process occurs (i.e., department #456 or small press area). Identify which analysis this is. The first time the flow chart is developed the analysis is #1. Later flow charts are numbered in sequence.

The next step is to break down the process into individual steps. Be careful not to make these steps too broad or too detailed. For the sake of discussion, let's use the process of frying an egg as an example. We would not list three steps—get utensils, fry egg, eat—as the process because there is not enough detailed information. However, do not go overboard on detail—extend right hand, grasp handle of frying pan, lift pan 2 inches, move pan toward body 22 inches, lower pan to stove, position pan over burner, etc. This type of detail will only make the flow chart unmanageable. More accurately the process would go something like this: preheat burner, place spatula next to stove, place plate next to stove, place frying pan on burner, get egg from refrigerator, break egg into pan, fry egg flipping once, place egg on plate, eat. In general, major breaks in activity indicate a new step.

List the steps in the process detail portion of the form. Be sure to include steps such as moving the part, removing burrs, inspecting, counting parts, storing material, and waiting. The time it takes to perform each step is also recorded. It helps to take 5 to 10 readings of how much time each step takes. Do not average these times but rather use a time that seems to be the most repeatable. Note, too, how far the part travels during the process. Travel includes handing the part from one person or machine to another, the distance traveled on a conveyor, and moving parts to be stored outside the department between steps. The last type of travel is most common in batch processes. Once all the steps are recorded, number the steps in the far left hand column.

Now comes the tricky part. The team must determine into which of the six categories of activity each step falls. The categories are defined as follows:

- *Process* - Process is defined as any value added work. (All other categories are forms of non-value added work.)

- *Transportation* - Moving the material from one location to another by hand, conveyor, or lift truck

- *Inspect/Rework* - Inspection is any comparison of the part to specifications. This includes testing. Rework deals with any work done to make the part acceptable to the specifications. This includes repair.

- *Delay* - This refers to any time where parts must wait because the machine or operator is not ready for it.

- *Store* - Store refers to long-term storage outside the area where the value added work is performed. It includes when the parts leave the area to be stored between steps and as finished inventory. If parts stay in containers within the work area, the time spent in this condition is considered a delay.

- *Record* - This category includes activity such as recording findings or data entry.

We guarantee that teams will spend some serious time debating whether some steps are value added or non-value added. The perception is that any step which must be performed or the product cannot be shipped must be value added. This is not true. Inspection is very important to many types of products, yet inspecting or testing the part does not physically change the part. The real debate will be over steps such as deburring or resin curing. We maintain that these are <u>not</u> value added and the team should work on eliminating the need for these steps. If the team

Team Building Rule #8

Train the team to use specific problem-solving techniques only when they are needed.

insists, however, that in certain cases a step must be considered value added, then do so. Just make sure you are consistent in your determination of what is and is not value added work.

After each step has been categorized, add up the number of steps for each category. How many steps are process or value added compared to non-value added steps? This is usually a very eye-opening experience for the team. The number of transport, rework, delay and store steps can be staggering—especially when you consider that all of these steps represent waste. The time spent on these activities increases the lead time of the product.

Add all the times recorded in the time column to determine the total time needed for each part to complete the process. This is the Total Processing Time. Next add the times for the value added or process steps only. This is the Total VA Time. Divide the Total VA Time by the Total Processing Time. Multiply that answer by 100 to determine the percent of processing time spent on value added activities. (This formula is shown at the bottom of the process flow form.) We have frequently seen this value less than 1%.

The flow chart represents the opportunity the team has to improve the process. Eliminating non-value added steps, eliminating or reducing the amount of time spent in storage, or combining value added steps streamlines the process and reduces the time it takes to complete the product. If it takes less time to make the part, you can get it into the hands of the customer faster. Eliminating non-value added steps saves your company money. We challenge your team to use this tool to its fullest potential and you will be amazed by the results.

Process Flow Analysis

Page _____ of _____

Process Name _____

Date _____

Dept./Location _____

Analysis No. _____

Step	Process (value-add)	Transportion	Inspect/Rework	Delay (waiting)	Store	Record/Data	Process Detail	Time	Distance
	◯	⇨	◇	D	▽	☐			
	◯	⇨	◇	D	▽	☐			
	◯	⇨	◇	D	▽	☐			
	◯	⇨	◇	D	▽	☐			
	◯	⇨	◇	D	▽	☐			
	◯	⇨	◇	D	▽	☐			
	◯	⇨	◇	D	▽	☐			
	◯	⇨	◇	D	▽	☐			
	◯	⇨	◇	D	▽	☐			
	◯	⇨	◇	D	▽	☐			
	◯	⇨	◇	D	▽	☐			
	◯	⇨	◇	D	▽	☐			
	◯	⇨	◇	D	▽	☐			
	◯	⇨	◇	D	▽	☐			
							Totals		
	Number of Steps								

VA % = <u>Total VA Time</u>   X 100 = _____
Total Processing Time

Previous VA % = _____

Figure 5.2

ADDING VALUE

Any operation or process the customer is willing to pay for. Adding value generally means changing the shape or form of the product.

Value Stream Mapping

What is Value Stream Mapping?

Value Stream Mapping is a method of creating a "one page picture" of all of the processes that occur in a company from the time a customer places an order for a part or product until the customer has received that product in their facility. The goal of this picture is to be able to depict the flow of material and information across and through all of the current process steps (the value stream). Value Stream Maps document all the processes to produce and ship a part or product, both value adding and non-value adding (waste) processes.

The following page shows an example of a basic Value Stream Map (VSM). Process and VSM graphs can take many forms, from simple boxes on paper for simple processes to extremely complex computer models of what is going on in a process across enormous numbers of operations in many companies.

Value Stream Mapping is related closely to Process Flowcharting discussed on page 150. VSM differs from Process Flowcharting in that VSM includes both the material and information flows.

Why Value Stream Map?

During the team creation of a VSM, business and manufacturing wastes that occur in the processes can be easily identified. Paraphrasing Taiichi Ohno, "eliminating business waste is not the problem, finding it is." Finding waste throughout the "picture" reduces the risk of using World Class Manufacturing concepts to create individual processes that are "islands of excellence" without improving the *total system efficiency* or the *total value stream's* capability for customer satisfaction.

Why Value Stream Map?

100% inspection, 10 minutes each

Production of custom widget. 1 hour value added. 10 days in queue

Supplier ships material. 2 days transit time.

Producer Order Processing — order material from supplier — 15 minutes value added. 2 weeks lead-time.

3 minutes — place order over the internet.

I'm placing my order for my custom widget.

Finished goods packaging, stores, and shipping. Ten minutes value added. 2 days in queue

Manufacturer ships widget. 2 days transit time.

Customer receives product — 30 days after ordering it.

I finally got it! Why 30 days?

Elapsed time from order to delivery = 30 days

Value added time = 1 hour, 25 minutes

Why 30 days?

WHY VALUE STREAM MAP?

"Eliminating manufacturing waste is not the problem, identifying it is."

Taiichi Ohno

Additionally, once the "as is" or "Current State" VSM is created, it becomes the baseline for improvement and the creation of a Future State VSM (FSVSM). The FSVSM can then be used as a World Class Manufacturing implementation road map.

The Origins of VSM

Value Stream Mapping has it roots traced back to a number of forward thinking industrial thinkers during the turn of the 20th century. Henry Ford is credited with introducing process mapping as early as the 1920's to graphically display all of the things happening in a series of operations. The Japanese, and Toyota in particular, are credited with refining and perfecting Value Stream Mapping, which they also refer to as "material and information flow maps." In recent years there has been much publicity and focus on Value Stream Mapping as defined by Mike Rother and John Shook in the book *Learning to See*.

VSM - A Team Activity

Ideally the VSM team is cross functional, representing individuals from the process steps depicted and the supporting business functions like purchasing, planning, human relations, finance, engineering, and any other important functional areas.

Remember that Value Stream Maps are scaleable. It is strongly recommended that initial Value Stream Mapping be limited in scope and drawn primarily on paper by hand. Resist the urge to cover every possible detail. Focus on the key elements in logical process steps (remember the egg frying example on page 151?) that represent the logical flow of the value stream. Use simple, easy to understand symbols to depict the processes.

Four Steps to Value Stream Mapping

STEP #1) Pick the product or product family to map (improve).

STEP #2) Create the "Current State" VSM.

STEP #3) Create the "Future State" VSM.

STEP #4) Develop an action plan to make the FSVSM the CSVSM.

STEP #1 - PICK THE PRODUCT OR PRODUCT FAMILY TO MAP (IMPROVE)

The VSM focus should be on the product/product families or series of processes where competitive pressures are high, or where customer satisfaction is low, or for products that represent the largest share of the sales volume. VSM's are the most effective when they begin with an initial goal, such as, reducing product or service lead-times.

STEP #2 - CREATING THE "CURRENT STATE" VSM

A. Form a team and select a team leader.

Ideally the team is made up of people who are directly involved with the products and processes to be mapped along with key individuals from supporting departments, and in some cases from suppliers and customers (see page 104).

The team leader should have previous VSM experience and be a skilled facilitator who can coordinate activities and help break communication barriers (see page 110).

B. Educate the team in VSM Methodology (this can be dropped for experienced teams).

C. Decide the scope of the Value Stream Map. Brainstorm an initial map.

It is not uncommon to find that many members of a Value Stream Mapping team have never physically looked at the product/process from end to end. This is an important first step in opening the team's eyes to the task at hand. It is strongly recommended that the team physically "walk" the entire product/process at the onset. Where it is not practical to do this, there should be a well-prepared description of every product/process with as many visual representations as possible before the Value Steam Mapping team starts it's work.

Create an initial "rough cut" map.

D. Agree upon the symbols, icons, and data to use. The following icons are recommended:

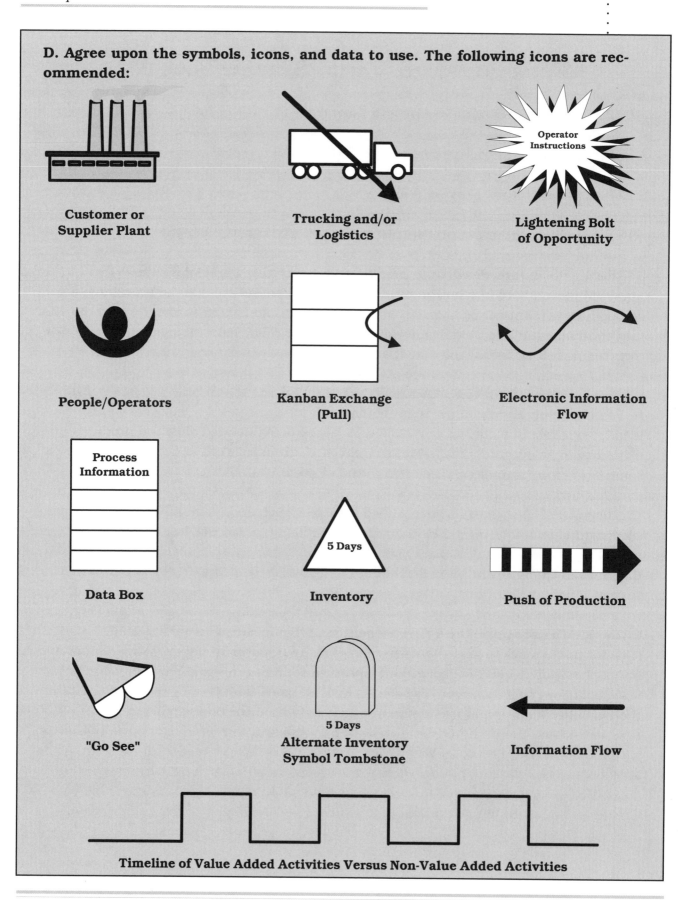

Customer or
Supplier Plant

Trucking and/or
Logistics

Lightening Bolt
of Opportunity

People/Operators

Kanban Exchange
(Pull)

Electronic Information
Flow

Process
Information

Data Box

5 Days

Inventory

Push of Production

"Go See"

5 Days
Alternate Inventory
Symbol Tombstone

Information Flow

Timeline of Value Added Activities Versus Non-Value Added Activities

As a practical matter, we recommend the following types of data be considered for your Value Stream Map:

(a) C/T – Cycle Time
(b) C/O Change Over Time
(c) Uptime (% machine is available, see Chapter 6 for details)
(d) Top Three Reasons for Unplanned Downtime
(e) Production Batch, or Transfer Batch Size
(f) Number of People, by type or classification, at each operation
(g) Number of Product Variations at each operation
(h) Pack Size/Standard Pack Quantity
(i) Operating or Working Time Available (minus breaks, etc. – see Chapter 7, page 293, 294)
(j) Scrap Rate
(k) Rework Percentage
(l) First Time Capability (FTC)
(m)Top Three Defect Causes
(n) Average Days Supply in Inventory between operations
(o) Queue Time between operations
(p) Source of Schedule Information for each operation
(q) Distance between operations
(r) Time for material to travel between operations
(s) Over time worked by operation (average weekly or monthly)
(t) PM's planned versus completed by operation

There are many other types of information that could be included in a Value Stream Map. We recommend you focus on those that can be readily understood by all and keep the list to 20 or fewer initially.

E. Determine missing information the VSM requires.

After brainstorming what the team thinks the Current State VSM looks like, it will usually be evident very quickly that much information needed to accurately reflect the current "as is" condition is missing. The team should work to focus on the important pieces of information needed. Generally, a list of all ideas should be compiled and prioritized by the team to obtain a "short list" that will be addressed by the team in more detail. Review *Establishing Team Guidelines*, (pages 134-146) for suggestions on how to make this activity effective.

As a general rule of thumb, focus on measurable objectives. Focus on data elements that reflect how the process is working (and not on the people). See page 145 for more suggestions.

F. Make assignments to gather and/or create information; go see the process.

Collect as much information about causes of waste as possible. Use Problem Solving tools as needed to fully understand what the root causes of the waste are in the Value Stream (waste prevents flow). This can be the most time consuming part of the team's initial work.

The facilitator has an important role in helping the team decide who will gather needed information. In some cases there will need to be hours of process observation completed to create the data. Great care must be taken to communicate with others in the facility regarding the intent of the data gathering. Remember, the focus in World Class Enterprise is on eliminating waste and improving flow, not finding fault with the people involved.

G. Build the final Current State Value Stream Map

Using agreed upon standard definitions, create a Current State Value Stream Map of your process. A sample of what one might look like (for an imaginary factory) is shown on the following page. It includes the information flows, product flow from suppliers to customers, the Takt time (see page 195), and Value Added time as a percent of total "in plant" time.

STEP #3 - CREATE THE "FUTURE STATE" VSM

Now that the VSM team has built a good understanding of "what is", the Future State Value Stream Map can now be built. Creating your Future State Value Stream Map before beginning the change process provides the basis for prioritizing improvements in the future.

It is strongly recommended that the teams initially set goals that they can achieve without significant capital investment. The focus should initially be on "no cost" or "low cost" improvements. It is not uncommon for a 50 to 95% improvement to be accomplished by teams without large capital investments.

WCM Associates recommends frequently revisiting your Future State Value Stream Map (at least monthly) as you make progress on improvements. As months pass it is very common for the team to discover that new information becomes available and conditions in the business environment occur. The Future State Map should be adjusted periodically as this occurs. If you are successful in meeting the improvement goals set for the Future State Map, it will become your new "Current State", and the baseline for your next round of improvements.

Current State Value Stream Map Example

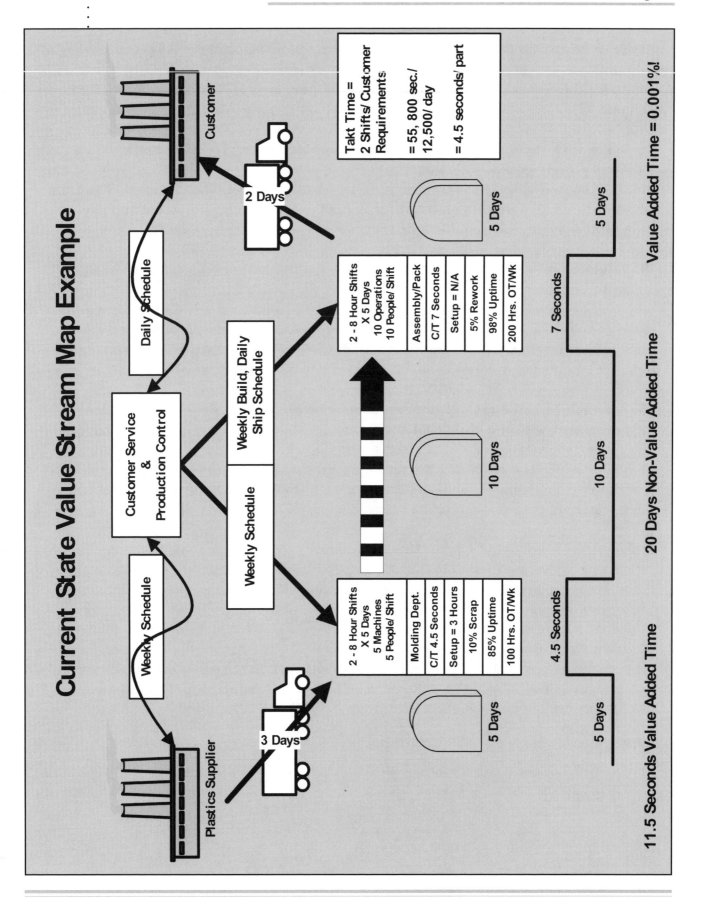

Takt Time =
2 Shifts/ Customer
Requirements:

= 55, 800 sec./
12,500/ day

= 4.5 seconds/ part

Customer

2 Days

Daily Schedule

Customer Service & Production Control

Weekly Build, Daily Ship Schedule

Weekly Schedule

Weekly Schedule

Plastics Supplier

3 Days

2 - 8 Hour Shifts X 5 Days 10 Operations 10 People/ Shift	
Assembly/Pack	
C/T 7 Seconds	
Setup = N/A	
5% Rework	
98% Uptime	
200 Hrs. OT/Wk	

5 Days

10 Days

2 - 8 Hour Shifts X 5 Days 5 Machines 5 People/ Shift	
Molding Dept.	
C/T 4.5 Seconds	
Setup = 3 Hours	
10% Scrap	
85% Uptime	
100 Hrs. OT/Wk	

5 Days

5 Days   4.5 Seconds   10 Days   7 Seconds   5 Days

11.5 Seconds Value Added Time   20 Days Non-Value Added Time   Value Added Time = 0.001%!

While there are several different ways to do Future State Maps, WCM Associates strongly recommends the Product and Process Future State Value Stream Map be the initial focus for the team. The steps for implementing this type of Value Stream Map are as follows:

A. Begin with the Current State Value Stream Map with "Lighting Bolts" of opportunity highlighted.

In all likelihood it will not be realistic to target all opportunities identified. The team should start with agreed-upon priorities that all concur can be supported and successfully completed in a reasonable time frame.

B. Validate and verify senior management support, gather suggestions for the team to consider in setting goals.

Top management will want to support making improvements but also needs to know what resources and support will be required. Input from top management is very important to the team, as top management usually has many insights into external factors (market conditions, new products, etc.) that the team needs to consider.

C. For each targeted area of improvement, the team must develop a goal for improvement within a realistic time frame.

Here again top management input and support is critical to the process as they help the teams prioritize and develop goals for improvement. For example, eliminating defects completely may require significant investment in tooling or equipment. Top management can help the team determine realistic paybacks for various efforts.

Finally, the team should recognize that many opportunities can be completed very quickly, in days or weeks, as opposed to over a year. The team should strive to identify as many short-term opportunities as possible. Many small "wins" will help everyone keep energy focused on the tougher, long-term improvements.

D. Draw the Future State Map.

The emphasis here should be on realistic expectations that the entire enterprise can and will support. The Future State Value Stream Map is the standard that all must strive to achieve within the implementation horizon.

STEP #4 - DEVELOP AN ACTION PLAN TO MAKE THE FUTURE STATE VSM THE CURRENT STATE VSM

Teams created to work on various improvements may or may not include members of the Value Stream Mapping Team. The emphasis should be on putting the right members on a team to complete various projects. Initially great care is needed to ensure teams are supported with a skilled facilitator and the resources to meet the goals.

A simple yet often overlooked task is to make sure there are regularly scheduled meetings for all participants. Teams need a structure to work on problem solving and complete tasks. Progress on goals and support for the process needs to be verified continuously. Information on progress needs to be collected and periodically reviewed with top management.

Since literally everyone will be affected in some way by the efforts to move to an improved future state, an initial "kick off" event involving all stakeholders is recommended. During this activity, everyone can be informed about what was learned in the process, and what we will be doing about it. Take care to present the information in a non-threatening manner. Understanding why changes are needed goes a long way toward getting buy-in!

Ongoing communication on progress needs to be continuously provided. Monthly "all hands" meetings along with posted information during each month can be an effective way to ensure good communications with all involved.

A simple approach for a top-level report-out for the entire company is to post three Value Stream Maps in a conspicuous place. One reflects the original current state, one shows the desired future state, and the last shows where the team stands now. Think about the third map as a "virtual current state map" – reflecting current performance. A simple comparison of the three value stream maps can speak volumes on progress, and highlight where more focus is needed!

Identifying and *Analyzing Problems*

There are two tools that may be used for both identifying and analyzing problems. These tools are the Pareto Chart and the Cause and Effect Diagram.

Pareto Chart

The pareto chart is named for its inventor Vilfredo Pareto, a turn-of-the-century economist. Pareto determined that 80% of all problems are caused by 20% of all factors. It was Joe Juran who first used the pareto principal in the manufacturing environment. Creating a pareto chart allows the team to see where most of the problems are coming from (problem identification). With this information, the team can decide where to focus its energy. A pareto chart can also be used to identify the major contributing factor(s) to a specific problem (problem analysis.)

A pareto chart is a bar graph that is created from information collected by the team. The chart measures dollars, time, occurrences, or any other unit that the team selects and compares the relative values for each problem or factor. Let's again refer to the team working on reducing downtime. The pareto principal tells us that 80% of the downtime is caused by 20% of the machines. In this situation, the team wants to know which machine is causing the most downtime.

For one week the team collects detailed information about downtime on each machine. The machine operators log every time the machine goes down. They also note why the machine went down and how long it was down. The log book could look something like this:

Unplanned Downtime Log

Date:	2-18-97	Shift:	3	Machine/Cell #:	5A	Operator:	Jackie

Time	Reason for Downtime	Number of Minutes Down
8:18 AM	Ran out of parts.	35

Figure 5.3

Collecting information this way gives the team lots of data. The team can determine not only the total amount of time each machine was down, but also have a detailed list of why each machine went down. The log also provides information that could signal an important pattern. Was most of the downtime on one day of the week? Did one shift have more trouble than another? Did one operator have more trouble than another? Was one part number more troublesome than another?

Make sure to inform the team that the purpose of collecting data is not to place blame on one person. Identifying problems in this way allows the team to provide help where it is needed—not to find fault with anyone.

At the end of the week, the team collects the log books from each machine and totals up the downtime minutes. The pareto chart looks like this:

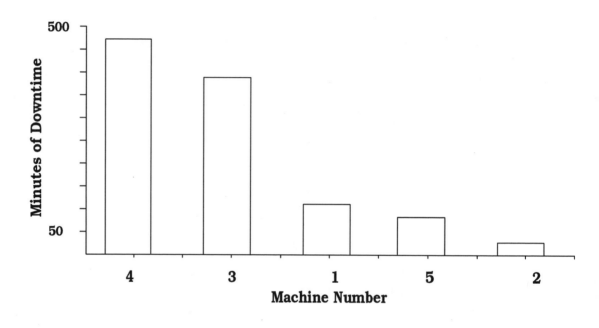

Figure 5.4

Note that the machines are not listed in numerical order but in the order of descending downtime values. That is, the machine number with the most downtime minutes is shown first, the machine with the next highest number of minutes is second, and so on. Figure 5.4 clearly indicates that machine number four should receive the team's attention.

Once the team has identified machine number four as its priority, it must now determine why the machine was down so much. The log book is used again to list all the reasons machine four experienced downtime. The number of minutes for each reason is totaled and the results are again shown in a pareto chart (Figure 5.5).

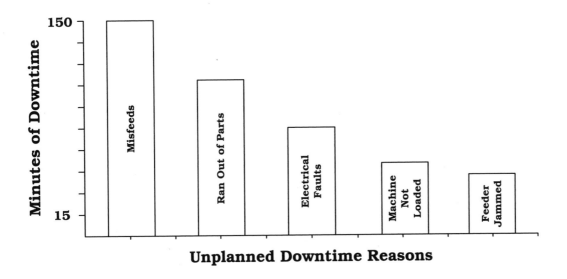

Figure 5.5

The team now has another clear picture of which reason for downtime should be addressed first. The pareto chart is one of the most useful tools for helping teams identify problems and prioritize projects.

Fishbone Diagram

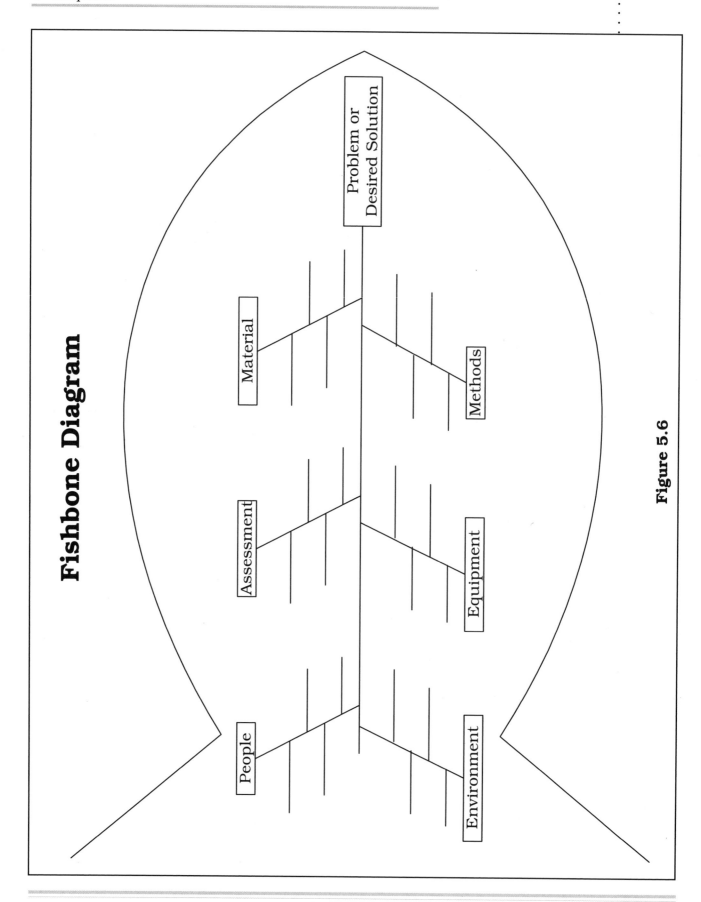

Figure 5.6

Cause and Effect Diagram

Another useful tool for both identifying and analyzing problems is the Cause and Effect Diagram. Also referred to as a Fishbone Diagram because of its appearance (Figure 5.6), or an Ishikawa diagram after its inventor, Kaoru Ishikawa. This tool is used when there is no clear comparison between the problem's contributing factors or when there are many factors to consider.

The primary benefit of the diagram is that it organizes all the data into six major categories—Material, Assessment, People, Method, Equipment, and Environment (problem identification). Each category is then reviewed for its potential impact on the problem or solution (problem analysis). To aid in remembering the categories, just think of MAPMEE, an invitation to map out the important factors influencing a problem.

To create the diagram, start with the problem, stated as a question, shown in a box on the right side of a white board or a large piece of paper clipped to a wall. Several pieces of flip chart paper taped together also work well. Draw a heavy main arrow pointing toward the box. Add six lighter arrows pointing to the main arrow. Label these six lines with the MAPMEE category titles as shown in Figure 5.6 on the previous page.

(The team working on the situation within the box may not include everyone who has useful information about the situation. Include all of these additional people for the next step.)

Position the entire group in full view of the paper or board. Be sure that the problem or solution is well defined and that everyone in the group has a good understanding of the process. Allow everyone several minutes to make a list of their own ideas about the factors contributing to the problem and into which of the six major categories each factor falls.

The team scribe combines everyone's lists onto the diagram, listing each factor only once. For example, the environment category could include factors such as inadequate lighting, too hot/cold, dirty, cramped, noise, etc. You are not limited to the number of contributing factors in any category so add lines as needed. In fact, it is not unusual to find that one category has many more factors than the others. Some categories could have no contributing factors, depending on the problem. (This process is a type of brainstorming, so follow the brainstorming rules.)

Do not allow discussion about actually solving the problem while the ideas are being added to the diagram. This will come later. Right now, the team should focus on identifying as many causes of the problem as possible.

When all ideas are written on the diagram, have the team discuss which ones are the most likely causes of the problem. Using this information, more data may be collected and the most likely factors studied more closely. The team works on eliminating the most likely causes one at a time.

Analyzing Problems

Several tools are available to analyze problems in depth using specific data. These tools are the Histogram, Scatter Diagram, Control Chart, and Process Capability Study. Each of these tools has specific uses as defined below. They are not, however, always needed by teams working on improvement projects. For this reason, detailed instructions for using these tools are not provided in this text. More information is available in an Advanced Techniques booklet available through the publisher.

Histogram

The histogram will be displayed as a bar graph, very similar to a pareto analysis. The difference between the two, however, is very distinct. A pareto chart deals only with comparing characteristics of the problem such as time, dollars, types of defects, etc. A histogram uses measurements such as size, weight, temperature, etc., and displays how the data is distributed. It is designed to show how much variation a process has. Histograms typically look like Figure 5.7.

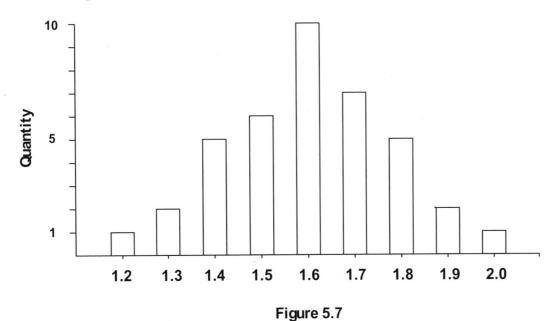

Figure 5.7

By studying how the data is distributed, the team can determine a lot about a process. Use this tool to determine how consistent and normal a process is.

Scatter Diagram

This type of diagram is used to determine if there is a relationship between two variables or conditions. For example, the curing time of paint may be affected by humidity. To test for this, the data collected must show the actual cure time and humidity level for a sufficient sample (usually 50 to 100 data points). The information is shown on the scatter diagram in Figure 5.8.

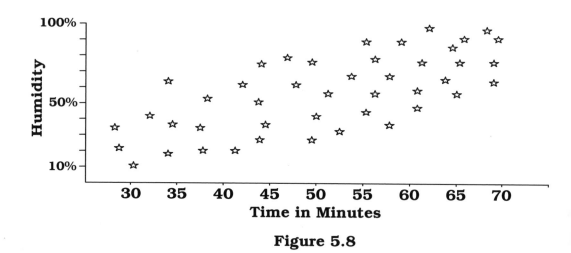

Figure 5.8

In this case, we see that the cure time takes longer when the humidity is higher, indicating that humidity does have an affect on cure time.

Had the chart looked like this:

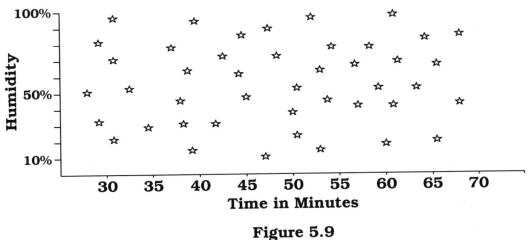

Figure 5.9

we would determine that cure time was not affected by humidity. Understanding if there is a relationship between two variables and what that relationship is can help a team determine the cause of a mysterious problem.

Control Chart

The most common tool for controlling a process is the control chart. All processes have a normal amount of variation. This variation is caused by differences in material from part to part, differences in how machines or operators position the part in the machine, size variations from part to part, or hundreds of other factors. The control chart is used to create a picture of how well a process is regularly producing a specific feature, such as the size of a hole or paint thickness, compared to the expected amount of variation. Once the team knows what features on a part are important for making quality products, the control chart is used to make sure the feature always meets specifications.

As in a scatter diagram, actual measurements of the characteristic are used. The measurements are taken at regular intervals and the information is then drawn on the control chart. Control charts usually look like this for a process that has the expected amount of variation (the process is in control):

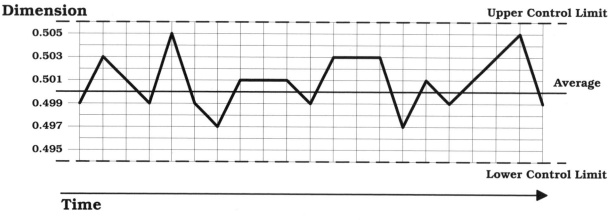

Figure 5.10

A control chart can provide important signals that a process is out of control or headed in that direction.

If the data points move so that seven in a row are either above or below the average line, the operator knows that something sudden happened to change the process average. This is called a *shift* and could be caused by a change in material or supplier, a change in operator, damage to the gauge, damage to the tool, etc.

If seven points in a row go up or down, it is called a *trend*. This can be caused by a slow drifting of a functional part of the machine or the tool, tool wear, poor maintenance, accumulation of dirt, operator fatigue, etc.

Shift Example

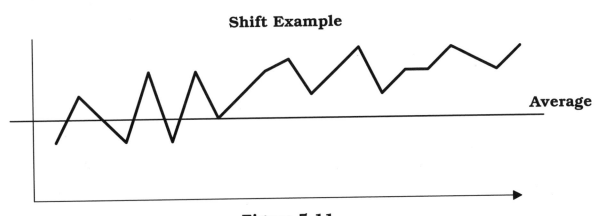

Figure 5.11

Trend Pattern Examples

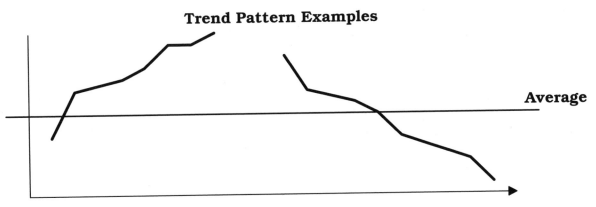

Figure 5.12

When data points show extreme variation by jumping from one control limit to the other it is call *instability*. The likely causes in this case are over adjusting the process, a loose tool or fixture, errors in plotting the points, a damaged gauge, etc.

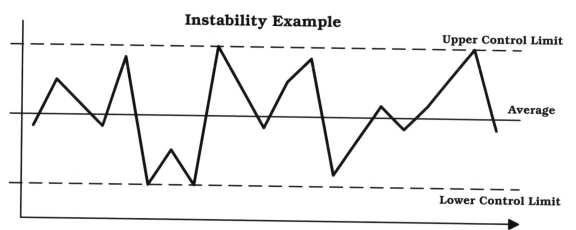

Figure 5.13

Sometimes, there will appear to be very little variation in the process. When this happens, all the data points are very close to the process average line on the chart. This is called *stratification*. The most frequent cause for this condition is incorrectly calculating the control limits. Math errors which result in the misplacement of the decimal point will also cause this condition.

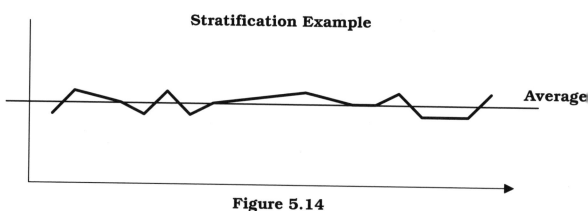

Figure 5.14

Shifts, trends, instability, and stratification all say that the process has more than the normal amount of variation. The excess variation comes from special causes. Some of these special causes have already been mentioned. Whenever an operator sees that the variation is being affected by special causes, he should ask, "What has changed in this process that can be causing this condition?" The process should not continue to run until the special cause has been identified and the situation corrected.

By watching the control chart carefully, the person performing the operation can see if the process is changing. If so, action can be taken to correct the problem before a defective part is made. Having a control chart does not actually control the process, however. Taking action based on what the control chart shows about the process is what really controls the process.

Process Capability Study

This study determines the process average and normal variation. (These dimensions are the average (solid line) and control limits (dashed lines) on the control chart.) The capability study is done on a measurable feature to determine if the process is capable of maintaining the dimension over time. It evaluates how close the process average is to the required dimension and determines if the normal process variation is within specification limits. With this information, the team can determine what action, if any, is required to insure the process will make good parts. The capability study identifies how a process needs to be corrected in order to make good parts.

For example, a capability study is performed on a machine's ability to maintain the location of a hole. The average hole location is exactly the target dimension shown on the engineering drawing. The variation of the hole location from part to part is actually twice the amount allowed on the drawing. This indicates that the team should evaluate why the machine has so much variation in the hole location. If the amount of process variation is less than the amount allowed on the drawing but the process average is outside of the drawing specification, the team knows they must retarget the machine to put the hole in the right location.

The capability study provides valuable information about what actions must be taken to ensure the process consistently produces a good part. This study must be completed before control charts are established.

Team Building Rule #9

Train the team in the principals of error-proofing and visual communication.

Error Proofing

Contrary to popular belief, there are ways to make sure that mistakes do not happen in a process. The Japanese call it Poka Yoke. We call it *Error Proofing*. Error proofing requires a complete understanding of the process and the problem. It also requires the desire to find the solution.

Our experience is that nearly everyone accepts that errors will occur. The belief is that no solution is completely error proof. This is not true. All processes can be developed to eliminate the possibility of errors. First, however, you must accept that error proofing is possible. With this thought in mind, the next step is to ask "What has to change in this process so this error cannot occur?" Adding more inspections or detailed job instructions will not error proof a process.

The Japanese Quality Evolution

	Japanese QA Method Used (% of Industry)			
	Inspection	SPC	Design of Experiments (Taguchi)	Error Proofing
1950	100	0	0	0
1960	55	45	0	0
1970	22	48	30	0
1980	15	23	62	0
1990	12	19	35	34

Figure 5.15

The Japanese are now using error proofing as part of their quality improvement strategy as shown in Figure 5.15. Inspection and SPC become unnecessary if the operator or the machine cannot produce a defective product.

Brainstorming is an excellent method for developing error proofed solutions to problems. A creative group can devise some inexpensive and simple solutions. We recommend *Poka-Yoke: Improving Product Quality by Preventing Defects* published by Productivity Press to help your team visualize some successful error proof solutions and to provide ideas for the team to create some of its own solutions. Here are some of the more memorable solutions that teams we know have developed.

THE CASE OF THE INCOMPLETE HOLE

The team was concerned with a defect reported by the customer for which a solution had supposedly been made. The defect affected the plunger in a hydraulic valve. The plunger needed a narrow hole through the entire length of the part. The hole did not have to be straight nor was size very critical. The hole just had to be completely through the length of the part. If the hole was incomplete, the plunger's up and down movement in the barrel would eventually create a vacuum causing the valve to stop working. Unfortunately, it would take some time for the plunger to build up enough vacuum pressure to prevent the valve from operating. This prevented the problem from being discovered during the valve-testing process.

The supplier of the plunger was consulted. He indicated that it was difficult to drill such a small hole for any distance without the drill breaking inside the part. Even though the process included frequent inspections of the drill and specific times when the drill had to be changed, he had also instructed his operators to hold every part up to the light and make sure the hole went all the way through the part. This process was difficult and time consuming for the operator. In addition, the drills broke so infrequently because of the operator's attention to them that the visual inspection became almost useless.

The team decided to provide special containers to the supplier. These containers were open racks with long pins welded to the cross bars at the bottom. Each completed part was placed over a pin in the rack. If the hole did not go completely through the part, the plunger would noticeably stick up out of the rack. Not only did this container eliminate the need to visually check for the hole but it also eliminated a packaging problem. Because the parts needed to be protected from handling damage, they had been packed upright in a box with dividers between each part. This packaging made it very difficult to remove the parts from the box for washing and grinding operations. The new racks were used all the way through the process, including the wash cycle. The racks eliminated unnecessary handling of the parts, reduced handling damage, and provided a surefire way to check for the critical hole. It also eliminated the cost of the cardboard packaging.

THE CASE OF THE MISPLACED HOLE

This case involved a small housing with several holes drilled through it. The problem involved the square shape of the housing and the location of the hole pattern. The housing arrived at the drilling operation with several holes already in it. The location of the drilled hole pattern to these existing holes was critical. Unfortunately, the square shape of the part made it possible to incorrectly load the part into the drilling fixture, causing the hole pattern to be off location by 90°. The operators had been informed of the problem several times and their process sheets clearly showed how to correctly load the part into the fixture. The defect continued to occur occasionally.

The team evaluated the drilling fixture and suggested the addition of a locating pin. This pin would use one of the existing holes in the housing to correctly locate the part in the fixture every time. This change eliminated the defect.

THE CASE OF THE MISSING BEND

This case involved a metal strap made from a stamping. Once the material was stamped, the part proceeded through a series of four small presses to receive five bends. Adding to the complexity of the part was the fact that there was a left hand and right hand version of the strap. The difference between the two parts was the location and bend direction of a small anti-rotation tab on one end of the strap.

In order to save tooling costs, the plant had made one fixture for the first press operation. This was the station that bent the small ear on the end of the strap. One side of the fixture was for the right hand part, while the other side of the fixture was for the left hand part. If a right hand part was placed on the left hand side of the fixture, the ear would not bend at all. If the part was placed on the correct side of the fixture but upside down, the bend would go the wrong way. The operators used the direction of bend to determine how the part was placed in the fixtures at each of the other three presses. The customer continuously received very small quantities of parts bent the wrong way and even fewer parts where the ear was not bent at all. Although the quantities were small, the continuous flow of defective parts was a serious concern.

The team was hesitant about changing the fixture at Press #1 to include any error proofing devices. The concern was that the missing bend defect could be caused by two conditions. First, the part could be placed on the wrong side of the fixture. Second, anyone walking by the operation could pick up a part that had not been through station one and accidentally place it in station one's complete box. The small size of the ear and the number of parts produced per hour made 100% inspection impractical. However, the team did decide to block off the unused side of the fixture and prevent the first possible error. This did not prove satisfactory since there was still another opportunity for defects to occur.

The team asked for help from the customer's engineering department. Together they decided to include a bend detecting device at station two. This device would prevent the part from loading into the press if the small ear was not bent. It could not, however, detect if the bend was the wrong way. It was during the evaluation at station two that the team recognized that a tooling hole in the part would resolve the problem. The tooling hole would be used to locate the part through all four presses and ensure that the bends were made correctly. The bend detecting device would ensure that parts that had not been through station one would be caught. All possible error conditions had been addressed.

Error Proofing Summary

The last case was very exciting because the team was so certain that this process could not be error proofed. They experienced periods of frustration as several possible solutions failed, but they did not give up. This determination was the key to the team's success.

Figure 5.16 Error Proofing Example

This hydraulic component test stand will not start unless the finger switch senses that the operator has removed an o-ring which is shipped with the component to the customer.

Visual Communication

As stated several times in this chapter, communication is the key to making teams effective and successful. Communication is important among team members, between management and the team, and between the team and other members of the organization. Speaking is one way to share information. However, we do not always have time to get everyone together and tell them what is going on. There are faster, more effective ways to get the message across.

Visual communication uses specific methods and techniques to provide fast, two-way communication between teams, shifts, coworkers, and management. Visuals provide information that can be used to compare the goals of the team and the company so that performance can be measured. Focus the visual communication on the performance of the group compared to its goals.

Visual communication can be used anywhere in the organization. For example, visuals can show the performance of the plant against its productivity goals, the performance of a work cell against its quality and productivity objectives, and how well a specific part of the process is performing. Visual communication may be used to identify missing tools or materials and is extremely effective in pull systems. The only limit to the effectiveness of visual communication is a team's creativity.

Visual Communication in the Organization

Every organization has specific goals to meet. In the past, the only people who knew about these goals were managers and supervisors. If the plant performed poorly against the goals, management would meet with supervisors to tell them the bad news and insist on better performance. Supervisors in turn would meet with their departments and insist on better performance without providing any specific information. The missing link was the awareness by individual operators of how their performance affected the company's goals. Visual communication ties all the goals together and keeps the company focused on measuring a few key standards.

Figure 5.17

Typical team break room and meeting room in a Japanese facility. Note the wide use of visual communication to keep the team aware of performance versus the goals.

Safety

Lost-time accidents are nightmares for organizations. Not only is the contribution of the injured employee lost, but the entire group the person worked with is also affected—they worry about their coworker and their own safety. Lost-time accidents force the organization to find and train replacement workers and cost the company a lot of money.

Visual communication brings safety awareness to every worker. The objective is to prevent accidents from happening in the first place. Every employee must be instructed to bring any unsafe conditions to the attention of the team. The team then includes elimination of the unsafe condition as an immediate project.

Many companies use a safety board to track their safety performance. The board measures the occurrence of any accidents during every day and month of the year. The World Class safety board looks like this:

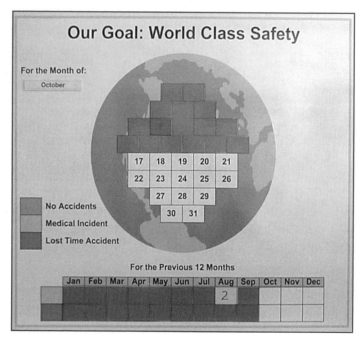

Figure 5.18

Each square on the safety board represents one day. Any day when there are no accidents in the plant, the corresponding square for that day is covered/filled in with green. When an accident occurs that does not result in lost time for the employee, the square is covered/filled in with yellow. If a lost-time accident occurs, the square for the day is covered/filled in with red. Below the world is an area which tracks the previous 12 months safety performance. The objective is to have a completely green board at the end of the year. Post the safety board in an area where every employee will see it every day. The company lunch room or each of the main exits to the building are popular choices. The safety board may also be used in individual departments.

Some companies take their safety goals so seriously that they provide a special lunch to all employees after every month without any accident. Three months of accident-free performance makes everyone eligible for a prize such as a radio, or gift certificate. After an entire accident-free year, the prize is more valuable. The prizes do not have to be gifts or money. Perhaps the lucky winner is awarded a premium parking spot or extra vacation days. Be imaginative and let the people who work in the organization determine what is appropriate. Stress the importance of a safe working environment every day and in all activities.

"You will achieve the level of safety that you demonstrate you want to achieve."

DUPONT

Quality

Quality is another category that has a major affect on a company's success. Customers can provide a great deal of input about an organization's performance in this area. So can the internal quality department. Quality can be measured as the cost of quality in dollars, or numbers of defects as a percent rejected, or the number of defective parts per million (PPM). The organization's total quality performance may be posted daily (if the information is available on a daily basis), weekly, or monthly. Most companies update their charts on a monthly basis and use PPM as a standard measure of quality performance. Whether you track cost of quality or PPM, the objective is to get this number as close to zero as possible. (The current world class standard for PPM is 25.) A quality chart could look like this:

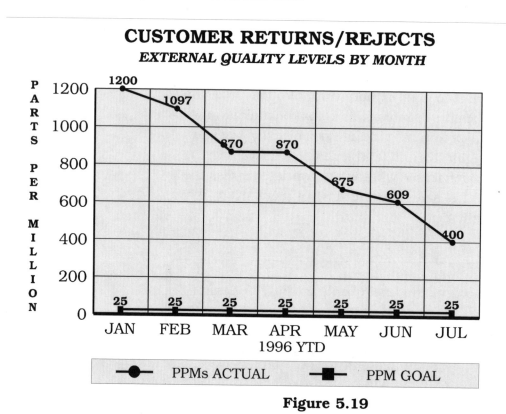

CUSTOMER RETURNS/REJECTS
EXTERNAL QUALITY LEVELS BY MONTH

Figure 5.19

Delivery

Many organizations track their on-time delivery perfor-mance. Most customers provide this information to their suppliers along with the quality data. Delivery is an im-portant measure of customer satisfaction since early ship-ments require the customer to store material as inventory and late shipments may cause delays in their production schedule. The number is usually shown as a percentage of deliveries received on-time by the customer compared to their delivery "window." The higher the percentage the better. Your organization must clarify with the customer how last-minute delivery changes will affect your delivery performance. A delivery chart could look like this:

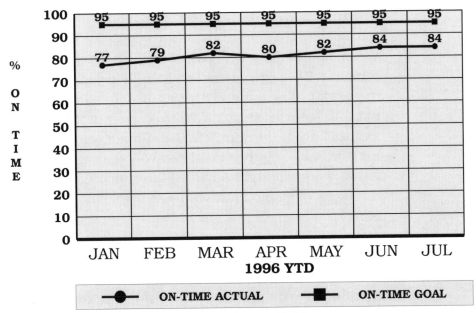

CUSTOMER ON-TIME DELIVERIES
AS MEASURED BY CUSTOMER REQUESTED DATE

Figure 5.20

While safety, quality, and delivery are three of the most common measures of an organization's performance, there are many others. Savings from improvement activities, suggestions per employee, and inventory information are some typical examples. Organizations must develop measurements to provide feedback about their performance to their goals. Once the measurements have been determined, everyone in the plant must be told which measurements were selected, why they were selected, the goal for each measurement, and how every employee and department affects the goals. Monthly meetings to review the plant's performance will reinforce management's commitment to meeting these goals. Post the performance charts where all members of the organization will see them everyday. Keep the charts current. An outdated visual communication chart does not reinforce commitment.

Visual Communication in the Self-Directed Work Team

Visual communication works very well in the SDWT environment. Team members can literally tell at a glance how the work cell is doing. With clearly defined goals for each measurement, the team is able to correct problems as soon as they become evident. The team must work on developing and selecting the visual controls that are appropriate for its work site. Our emphasis in this section will be on the types of visual controls most commonly used by the SDWT.

Safety

The team should keep track of its own safety performance. It is only when each team eliminates the opportunity for accidents to occur in its area that the organization can achieve an accident-free environment. The World Class safety board (page 188) is an excellent tool to measure safety. As noted previously, the board should be placed in a spot where everyone on the team, and everyone outside the team, will see it daily.

Quality

The team should use plant-wide measurements to keep track of its own quality performance. This provides a long-term, overall view of the group's quality performance and highlights quality problems that need to be addressed.

Not only should the team measure its overall department quality, but it should also track the quality of every job as it is running (short-term quality performance). This daily information shared among team members allows the group to react immediately to any conditions which cause defects to occur. Once a defect is noted and the cause of the defect corrected, no further defects are made. The fewer the number of parts to be sorted, the more likely it is that all defective parts will be found. Control charts are useful for identifying process changes which could result in product defects.

Other tools are also available for controlling part quality as the job is running. Some testing equipment has lights which indicate a part has passed or failed a test. Machines can have audible alarms which alert the operator if the process has not been completed properly. Electronic eyes can detect the presence of all the required features such as holes or assembled gaskets. Locating pins on fixtures guarantee a part is positioned properly. There are as many visual control devices as there are operations. Review the section on error proofing for more ideas. The objective here is to prevent the defect from occurring or, at the very least, make it immediately obvious to the operator that a problem has developed.

Posting information about defects alerts all team members to the problem so they may watch for a recurrence once they believe the problem is corrected. Sharing the information between shifts alerts others working in the area that the situation occurred and what was done to correct it. If the problem returns repeatedly, the team can make correcting the problem a team project.

Productivity

Each team needs to measure its productivity as compared to the customer's requirements. The easiest way to accomplish this is by using a production board to identify the part number running on a machine or in a work cell and note how many parts per hour are needed to meet the customer's needs. The board is also used to note the reasons the required production was not made during any given hour. Reasons that show up often on the production board will ultimately become team projects.

Teams must calculate the amount of parts needed every hour to meet the customer's delivery requirements. Most departments do not work the same number of minutes for each of the eight hours in the day. Breaks, lunch, and other down periods will vary the minutes per hour. The tool used to balance the number of parts needed per hour based on the number of available production minutes is "takt time."

The word takt is a musical term from the German language meaning beat. Takt time is a calculation that establishes exactly how often (the beat) a part must be completed if the team is to meet customer demand. It accounts for how many minutes of the day are actually available for production and uses the customer's delivery requirements to determine the amount of time each part should take. The team must know the takt time for each part they produce if they are to make the right number of parts per hour. The takt time formula is very simple:

$$\frac{\text{Total minutes available for production}}{\text{Number of parts needed by customer daily}} = \text{Takt Time}$$

A sample Takt time calculation is shown on the following page.

Production Boards. The *Production Board* is the single most useful visual communication device that self-directed work teams have at their disposal. It is also the most under used. A well designed production board placed in a strategic location provides feedback at a glance about how the work site is performing. It immediately alerts team members to problems that may prevent them from meeting their quality and productivity goals, and allows them to take corrective action before the situation gets out of hand. The supervisor does not have to question team members to know what is happening. Quality, maintenance, and management personnel can also see what is happening just by looking at the board. Second shift has a complete picture of what happened on first shift and what problems, if any, occurred. More importantly, first shift will be able to see how second shift performed, even though no one from second shift is there to tell them what happened.

It is important to remember that "what gets measured gets done." So any activity that requires improvement must be measured. Measuring and Production Boards apply to all office information processes and information products also!

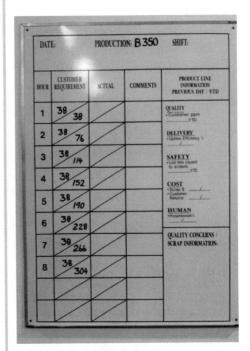

Typical Production Board

Here is an example of how to calculate takt time:

A customer needs 1500 fountain pens a day. The company that makes the pens operates that department on two shifts. First shift needs 5 minutes every morning to start up the equipment and gather its tools. Both shifts have a 5-minute team meeting at the start of the shift to review the previous shift's performance and note any quality or production problems they experienced. Both shifts have one 15-minute break during the first part of the shift and one 10-minute break during the last part of the shift plus a 20-minute paid lunch. There is a 5-minute 5S period at the end of each shift. In addition, second shift has an additional 5 minutes to shut down the equipment and put tools away. (NOTE: When the team works a full 8 hours with a 30-minute unpaid lunch, the lunch break does not reduce the total number of productive minutes in the shift. It will, however, reduce the number of minutes per hour available during the hour it occurs.)

Two 8-hour production shifts have a maximum of 960 minutes available for production (2 shifts X 8 hours per shift X 60 minutes per hour). We subtract from this number the total of all the nonproductive time. The total nonproductive time is:

5 minutes	First shift start up time
10 minutes	Team meeting at start of shift—both shifts—5 minutes each
30 minutes	First break—both shifts—15 minutes each
20 minutes	Second break—both shifts—10 minutes each
40 minutes	Paid lunch—both shifts—20 minutes each
10 minutes	5S time—both shifts—5 minutes each
<u>5 minutes</u>	Second shift shut down time
120 minutes	Total for both shifts

960 minutes	Maximum available time
<u>120 minutes</u>	Total nonproductive time
840 minutes	Total productive time

Plug the numbers into the formula:

$$\frac{840 \text{ minutes available for production}}{1500 \text{ parts required per day}} = 0.56 \text{ minutes per part}$$

We can determine how many seconds 0.56 of one minute is by multiplying by 60.

$$0.56 \text{ X } 60 = 33.6 \text{ seconds} \quad (\text{Round up to } 34 \text{ seconds.})$$

We now know that the team must produce one complete fountain pen every 34 seconds to produce 1500 fountain pens per day.

Now that the team knows they must have a completed pen every 34 seconds, they can determine how many pens they must produce every hour of the day. We already know that the first hour on first shift has only 50 productive minutes available. There is a 5-minute team meeting and a 5-minute start up period. We divide the amount of time available by the amount of time allowed to produce each part to determine how many parts must be produced in the first hour.

50 minutes X 60 seconds per minute = 3000 seconds in the first hour.

$$\frac{3000 \text{ seconds productive time}}{34 \text{ seconds per part}} = 88 \text{ parts}$$

The team should have made 88 parts at the end of the first hour. The second hour is a full 60 minutes long (3600 seconds).

$$\frac{3600 \text{ seconds productive time}}{34 \text{ seconds per part}} = 105 \text{ parts}$$

Complete this exercise for every hour of the shift. Once the hourly quantities are figured out for the shift, the numbers will not change unless the quantity required by the customer changes. (For more information on takt time see Chapter 7 on Manufacturing Cells.)

Workplace Organization—5S

The SDWT has many opportunities to use visual controls in their work area. Here are more ideas.

5S. Visual controls provide an easy way to maintain good 5S practices once they are established. Mark the floor to show where everything in the department belongs. This includes work benches, trash cans, cabinets, chairs, containers of parts, scrap bins, production boards, machines, and any other equipment that belongs in the work site. Permanently identifying the location of each item on the floor in the work area makes it immediately obvious if something is out of place, missing, or added. Label each floor location with the specific item that belongs in that spot so there is no confusion. It then becomes the duty of each team member to make sure all items are where they belong.

This technique works well for locating hand tools either at each work station or in their storage locations. See pages 79 through 81 in Chapter 4 for specific examples.

Inventory Control. Marking a floor location for incoming and outgoing material has two advantages. First, the location never varies so team members and truck drivers always know where to go for parts. Second, the identified incoming area prevents overstocking the work site with more material than is needed or can be handled.

Work Site Status. A very effective method for letting everyone know the status and needs of a work site is an Andon light system. This is nothing more that a column of different colored lights where each light has a specific meaning. A green light indicates the work site is running and meeting its production and quality goals. A red light indicates the work site is down and immediate assistance is needed. This light can be wired so an alarm rings when it is turned on. A blue light indicates the work site needs parts delivered or picked up. An amber or yellow light is the signal that a supervisor is needed in the area. The white light, as known as the "brag light," means the team has implemented an improvement which allows the work site to run quality parts at a rate that is higher than the "standard" rate.

The light columns may be mounted to every machine in a machining center or on a post next to a traffic aisle for a work cell. They must be visible to everyone who is expected to respond to the light signals (i.e., maintenance, truck drivers, supervisors, and team members). The lights from each machine or work cell can be wired to a duplicate set of lights in a central location in the plant. Here a manager, maintenance technician, or supervisor can see the status of all the machines or work cells at once. Label the light columns with their corresponding work site identification.

Figure 5.21 Example of Centralized Andon System
Andon lights are available from Patlite Corporation, (888) 214-2580

If you use the light columns, make sure everyone in the plant understands their purpose and what each color means. It is possible for a green, blue, and amber light to all be on at the same time. It is not possible for the green or red lights to be on together. Used correctly, the lights provide an easy way to stay informed about how the work site is doing and request any help that may be needed. (One creative team used neon colored bicycle flags until it could purchase lights.)

Visual Communication Summary

The opportunities for using visual controls are almost as limitless as the types on controls that can be used. Keep in mind that the purpose for having visual controls is to provide effective communication about how the team is performing to its goals. Your team will determine which controls work best in the work area. Here are some guidelines for developing visual controls.

- ♦ Define what you are trying to communicate
- ♦ Define who needs this information
- ♦ Get input from everyone who will be affected when selecting or developing the visual control that best suits the situation
- ♦ Be creative when developing visual controls
- ♦ Inform everyone who is affected by the communication device what the visual control method is, what it is meant to do, and how they must respond to it

More Examples of Visual Communication

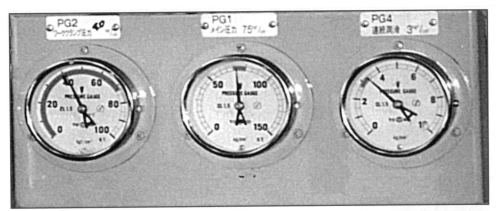

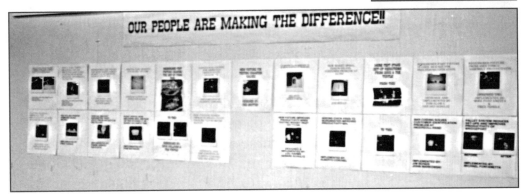

Figure 5.22

Clockwise from top: Gauges have normal operating range marked in green on face so conditions can be checked easily by operator. Right, electronic production board in an automotive supplier plant gives a running comparison of the goal versus actually produced. Bottom, part of a plant's suggestion recognition program. Left, highly visible scrap table (painted red) means scrap will get attention.

Developing a Continuous Improvement Plan

The Plan - Do - Check - Act Model (PDCA)

There is a model for helping teams make any kind of improvements and keeping the SDWT on track during improvement activities. (Refer to the PDCA chart, Figure 5.23. The cycle starts in the upper right corner. For SDWTs, the pilot area and team member selections are already complete.)

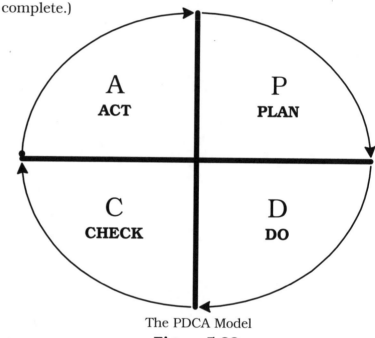

The PDCA Model

Figure 5.23

The PDCA cycle organizes the activity into 4 stages. The planning stage is the longest. Teams must determine their goals, communicate with everyone who will be affected by their activity, define the current situation and all the problems it has, collect data, generate ideas for improvement, and develop a new method for doing the process. Obviously, this will take time and effort. Do not shortcut the planning process. This will only result in a poorly developed new process with more problems than it had originally. Your team will know if it is trying to go too fast. On the other hand, do not plan the project to death.

The next step, after all the planning, is to make the change. This is the "Do" part of the cycle. Unfortunately, many teams get so wrapped up in the planning that they never actually do anything. Continuous improvement requires that action must be taken before improvement can be seen. A general rule to follow is that if you have a better than 50% chance of success, take action. Let everyone who will be affected by the change know when and how the change will be made. If possible, anyone who participated in the brainstorming and improvement development processes should help in making the change happen. This provides everyone with a sense of ownership in the change and increases the chances of the change being supported.

After a change has been made, the team should always watch the process very closely and "check" the results. It is rare that a change does not result in questions or other problems. If the team has found the root cause of the problem, collected good data, and considered all the facts, the new problems will mostly be minor. However, make sure the change is giving you the results you expected and watch for any unexpected problems.

Once the team has identified any problems with the change, they must "Act" quickly to eliminate them. Often the new procedure needs just a minor change or adjustment to solve the problem. However, if the change has resulted in some major new problems, the team must return to the original process and come up with a new solution. Continue this procedure until the improved process provides the required results and everyone is comfortable with it. Do not start another project until the new process is stable. Allow about thirty days for everyone to become comfortable with the new process.

Following the PDCA model for all your improvement projects will greatly increase your chance of success.

Team Building Rule #11

Implement 5S as the first work site project for the team. (Refer to Chapter 4.)

The Truth About Continuous Improvement

Chapter 10, Kaizen, talks at length about continuous improvement and specific things that teams can do to make their work sites world class. Continuous improvement is so important, however, that it needs special attention here.

Every team must understand that there is an unlimited number of ways to improve its area. It is the responsibility of every member of a SDWT to always look for these opportunities. The reason for this was mentioned at the beginning of this chapter: competition. Your competitors are actively trying to take your customers away from you. They are constantly looking for better manufacturing methods to produce a higher quality part for less money. If you and your company are not doing the same, you will lose the customer. If that were not enough, your customers are demanding higher quality products for less money. If your company cannot provide that, your customer will find a supplier who can.

Team Building Rule #12

Provide management feedback and support! Let the team know how it compares to expectations. Allow team members to invite members of management to attend meetings. Answer questions whenever necessary. Provide the people, help, and supplies the team needs to implement its suggested improvements.

The challenge companies face today is to continuously improve their processes. An acceptable quality level today will not be acceptable tomorrow. What customers are willing to pay for your product today will be considered too much to pay tomorrow. These changes occur because someone in the marketplace can meet the improved levels. The SDWT, indeed everyone in the company, must understand and accept this. Good enough is never good enough.

Fortunately, every company has a powerful weapon to use against the competition. This weapon is their workforce. Developing the workforce into self-directed work teams and empowering them to interact with the customer and make appropriate changes keeps the organization focused on continuous improvement. Providing a clear vision to the teams enables them to actively participate in the company's growth. Companies that fail to develop and empower the workforce and provide a clear vision, are unlikely to be participating in the global market in the next decade.

Team Building Rule #13

Use members of the first successful self-directed work teams as facilitators for new teams.

Team Building Summary

Our experience has been that team building creates emotional involvement in a process. No one just sits on the sidelines and watches what happens. Using a team facilitator during the early stages of team development helps the team members become comfortable with the team process and greatly increases a team's chance for developing into a strong, productive unit. Management's support of the team process further creates the awareness that team involvement is a fact of life at your company. The requirement for this support is shown in Figure 5.24, entitled SDWT Evolution.

If your company is new to team development or has had bad experiences in the past, start the team-building process slowly. Using 5S as the training ground in only two or three areas to start with (the "Islands of Excellence") will help the entire organization support the efforts of these groups. Forming too many teams at once will lead to mass confusion. The demand for available resources (money, people, facilitators) will be overwhelming. Encouraging the teams to make improvements but then refusing their requests for resources will destroy the team-building process.

Some people at all levels in the organization will have serious concerns about how successful the SDWT concept will be. For this reason we suggest that you intentionally design the process to succeed. Use an area where there are a majority of very positive employees. (Move people there if needed.) Select an important but relatively simple department. Perhaps one that has only a few different types of products or a clearly defined process. As the members of these teams become skilled in the team process, they become an excellent source of team facilitators for new teams.

Everyone on the team and supporting the team should expect some rough going at the beginning. Do not give up! Trust the process - it works. The rewards are enormous. As teams begin creating positive change in the organization, we guarantee that no one will want to go back to the "old way."

SDWT Evolution

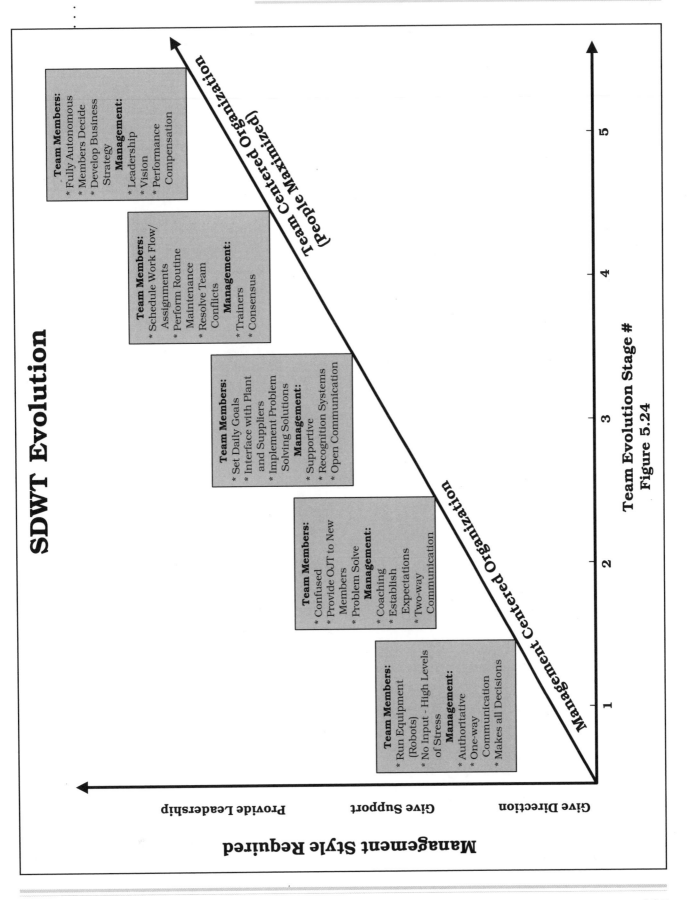

Team Evolution Stage #
Figure 5.24

Team Centered Organization
(People Centered Organization)

Management Centered Organization

Management Style Required

Provide Leadership | Give Support | Give Direction

1   2   3   4   5

Team Members:
* Run Equipment (Robots)
* No Input - High Levels of Stress
Management:
* Authoritative
* One-way Communication
* Makes all Decisions

Team Members:
* Confused
* Provide OJT to New Members
* Problem Solve
Management:
* Coaching
* Establish Expectations
* Two-way Communication

Team Members:
* Set Daily Goals
* Interface with Plant and Suppliers
* Implement Problem Solving Solutions
Management:
* Supportive
* Recognition Systems
* Open Communication

Team Members:
* Schedule Work Flow/ Assignments
* Perform Routine Maintenance
* Resolve Team Conflicts
Management:
* Trainers
* Consensus

Team Members:
* Fully Autonomous
* Members Decide
* Develop Business Strategy
Management:
* Leadership
* Vision
* Performance Compensation

TEAM BUILDING RULES

1. Identify the areas where the first self-directed work teams will be formed. Use the "Islands of Excellence" as the first teams.

2. Conduct plant-wide information meetings to explain the concept of self-directed work teams and identify the target areas.

3. Identify individuals in the organization with the skills to be strong team facilitators. Provide training in the skills, if necessary. Explain to the facilitators their role in the development of self-directed work teams. Clearly describe the expected development level (how self-directed the teams will be) and the expectations for the teams (how much quality, productivity, and cost improvement is expected).

4. Meet with the people who work in the target areas to review the self-directed work team concept, explain why their areas were chosen as "Islands of Excellence." Introduce the team facilitators and establish the first meeting dates and times.

5. Train the team members in the stages of team development.

6. Train the team in communication, effective meetings, conflict resolution, and group decisions skills.

7. Use the guidelines and goal-setting exercises to practice communication, effective meetings, conflict resolution, and group decisions.

8. Train the team to use specific problem-solving techniques only when they are needed.

9. Train the team in the principals of error-proofing and visual communication.

10. Maintain safe practices at all times.

11. Implement 5S as the first work site project for the team. (Refer to Chapter 4.)

12. Provide management feedback and support! Let the team know how it compares to expectations. Allow team members to invite members of management to attend meetings. Answer questions whenever necessary. Provide the people, help, and supplies the team needs to implement its suggested improvements.

13. Use members of the first successful self-directed work teams as facilitators for new teams.

Total Productive Maintenance (TPM)

Improving Quality, Productivity, and Delivery Through Equipment Reliability

• • • • • • • • • • •

What is TPM?

TPM is a method for continuously improving the effectiveness of production equipment or manufacturing processes through the involvement of all the people in the organization. The key difference between TPM and other maintenance improvement initiatives (such as Preventative Maintenance or PM) is that TPM requires the *involvement of all the people in the organization.*

How Does TPM Improve Customer Satisfaction?

In the same way that we maintain our automobiles so that they will always be 100% available to start and drive when we need them, the goal of TPM is to maintain our equipment so that it will be able to achieve a 100% on-demand availability for immediate use by the next process or customer.

TPM accomplishes this goal by working on the elimination of certain conditions. These conditions or losses are:

◆ Equipment breakdowns (unplanned downtime)

◆ Scrap/rework caused by poor equipment performance

◆ Reduced productivity due to equipment:

> running at reduced speeds
> receiving unnecessary adjustment
> idling or stoppages which require the
> operator's attention

◆ Equipment start-up losses which occur before the process stabilizes

Setup time is also one of these conditions or losses which prevent our equipment from always being available to satisfy our customers. Since Chapter 8 is devoted entirely to setup reduction, it is not mentioned again in this chapter.

The Origin of TPM

Like most of the other WCM elements, TPM has its origins in U.S. manufacturing. In the early 1950s many Japanese managers and engineers came to the U.S.A. to study the manufacturing plants and systems which had so successfully supplied the American war effort. During these visits, they noted that American companies were beginning to experiment with preventative maintenance as an alternative to breakdown or "fire-fighting" maintenance. By the late 1960s, Nippondenso, a Toyota parts supplier, had developed a maintenance initiative which involved all the people in the organization in maintenance activities. In 1971, Nippondenso was the first Japanese plant to receive the Distinguished Plant Award from the Japan Institute of Plant Maintenance for their successful development and implementation of TPM.

In the U.S., Kodak's Tennessee Eastman facility is acknowledged as the TPM pioneer for their 1987 implementation.

Maintenance—American Manufacturing's Neglected Asset

Of all the elements of WCM, TPM is the most time consuming and culturally difficult to implement. Why? Over the years, maintenance has been, and still is, the most neglected part of our manufacturing organization. In most manufacturing plants today, the maintenance department is considered more a necessary evil than the *foundation of our manufacturing processes* and an integral part of the customers' satisfaction team. We rarely get our maintenance people involved in process improvement or customer related activities. When was the last time you took one of your maintenance people to your customer's facility to help with a product problem?

As a result of our failure to lead and properly guide the maintenance function, and our corresponding low expectations for our maintenance people, we have, over the years, developed a group of people with the following characteristics:

- They want the maintenance area (department) to be located as far away from production and management as possible

- They have little regard for the production process and consider themselves "on-call" in the maintenance department

♦ Machine maintenance is handled using a fire-fighting strategy

♦ The reasons given for our inattention to maintenance improvements are:

>   not enough people
>   no parts in stock
>   the equipment is never scheduled to be
>   down for us to work on it

Additionally, we have promoted this separation and lack of plant-wide team work by allowing our machine operators (perhaps because of archaic "job classifications"), to tell our maintenance people that "we only run the equipment, we don't fix it!"

TPM Rule #1

There are many shop floor concerns which will develop as a result of implementing TPM, including maintenance job security, additional job responsibilities for operators, job classifications, and union support. These issues must be resolved and communicated by top management to everyone before the implementation can start.

Why is TPM the First WCM Support Module?

TPM is an extremely powerful improvement tool which is perceived as being difficult and time consuming to implement in the traditional factory. For these reasons, this WCM bridge support must be started first.

The good news is that we have never met a maintenance person (or anyone else in a plant) who liked working in the above conditions! Again, our maintenance people have adapted to our expectations. The "culturally difficult to implement" statement comes from the standpoint that much change must occur from our current maintenance, machine operator, and engineering environment to meet the basics of a WCM environment.

TPM Rule #2

The success of a TPM implementation depends on TPM becoming a daily part of everyone's activities. TPM must develop into part of the company's culture.

Fortunately, the even better news is that, if you are the traditional manufacturing facility, implementing TPM will have the single largest positive impact on your plant's performance. It is estimated that between 10% and 40% of a traditional plant's product costs are a result of current "breakdown only" maintenance practices. TPM will also improve product quality, productivity, and customer on-time deliveries. Inventory will be reduced as a result of these improvements.

If your current plant environment includes effective self directed work teams, an alliance between the machine owner/operators and the maintenance department, and a maintenance management system, congratulations! You are on your way to an accelerated implementation.

What are the Results of TPM Implementation?

♦ **Improved quality**. Equipment in top running condition produces parts which have less variation in them.

♦ **Improved productivity**. Eliminating equipment downtime, stoppages, or reduced line speed makes us more productive.

♦ **Improved delivery**. Customer satisfaction improves because customers can now rely on the scheduled delivery date.

♦ **Reduced inventory**. We no longer have to produce "just in case there's a breakdown" inventory.

♦ **Improved team member job satisfaction**. There is nothing more frustrating for your best operators than to lose control of "their machine" when it breaks down. Additional frustration may build as a result of missing a customer delivery, producing defective parts that must be scrapped or reworked, or finding "fill in" work as a result of the equipment failure.

TPM Rule #3

To implement TPM, a partnership must be developed between manufacturing, maintenance, and engineering which fosters an atmosphere of equipment ownership. Like the race car driver and pit crew, everyone must work together for the team to be successful.

How Does Implementing TPM Improve Productivity?

Figure 6.0 illustrates how TPM strives to increase operator value added time by eliminating the equipment conditions which reduce operator and equipment productivity and create waste.

IMPROVEMENT = CHANGE

TPM recognizes that the equipment owner-operator has the most expertise and knowledge in the facility about the normal operation of the equipment. When this equipment knowledge is combined with training to complete prestart-up preventative maintenance activities, the owner-operator becomes a powerful tool in preventing breakdowns. This type of operator maintenance activity is referred to as independent or *autonomous maintenance*. Putting the owner-operator in control of the machines helps eliminate breakdowns.

Some members of the team may think that TPM is nothing more than another disguised attempt by management to "get the operators to work harder." This is not the case. The productivity improvements that come from TPM are obtained by eliminating equipment conditions which reduce productivity and create waste. TPM recognizes that these wastes cannot be eliminated without the skill and participation of the owner-operators. TPM makes operators full partners with the Maintenance Department.

How Does Implementing TPM Improve Productivity?

Converting an operator's time wasted due to equipment conditions or losses

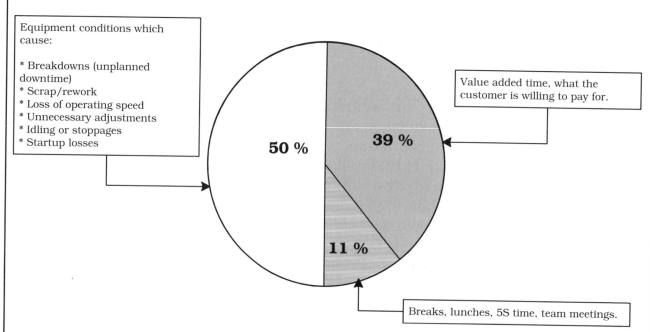

Equipment conditions which cause:

* Breakdowns (unplanned downtime)
* Scrap/rework
* Loss of operating speed
* Unnecessary adjustments
* Idling or stoppages
* Startup losses

50 %

39 %

11 %

Value added time, what the customer is willing to pay for.

Breaks, lunches, 5S time, team meetings.

To owner/operator preventative maintenance activities and value-added time

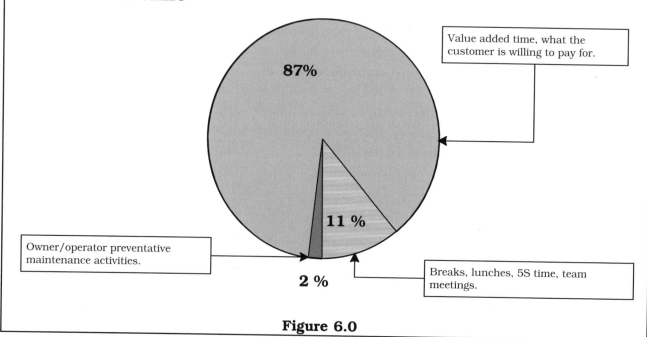

87%

11 %

2 %

Value added time, what the customer is willing to pay for.

Owner/operator preventative maintenance activities.

Breaks, lunches, 5S time, team meetings.

Figure 6.0

TPM Rule #4

The key to an effective preventative maintenance component within the TPM initiative is the machine operators. Up to 75% of breakdowns can be detected and prevented by well-trained operators.

Since most members of the team want to feel good about their contribution to the team's goals, the additional TPM skills training and responsibility for the owner-operators, when completely understood and implemented, is a welcome change. The frustration of equipment downtime or improper operation is more tiring to good operators than a productive double shift.

To complement the operator's efforts at eliminating waste and equipment losses, the TPM focused Maintenance Department spends its time on completing scheduled preventative maintenance equipment inspections, performing major equipment overhauls, and developing predictive maintenance strategies and procedures. The Maintenance Department also assumes responsibility for providing technical support for the maintenance performed by the operators.

The additional organizational role changes that must occur in the conversion from traditional manufacturing to the TPM element of WCM are shown in Figure 6.1.

TPM Implementation Prerequisites

 ◆ Top management commitment. While we have already stated this numerous times with regard to implementing WCM, it bears repeating again here. A world class level TPM implementation can take

The Required Plant-Wide Role Changes for a TPM Implementation

Traditional Role	Traditional Responsibilities	TPM Role	TPM Responsibilities
Operator	* Told what to do. * Ideas or opinions never asked for. * Use arms and legs but not brain. * Feels no connection to job, customer, or company.	Owner/ Operator	* Empowered to run their part of the business. * Visits and talks to customer. * Trained to conduct daily, routine preventative maintenance tasks. Does minor repairs. * Leads and contributes to problem solving.
Journeyman Maintenance	* Fix equipment as it breaks down, never given time to do it right. * Is physically and emotionally separated from company, production and customers. * Has developed fire-fighting mentality.	Maintenance Technician	* Trains all operators in daily, routine preventative maintenance tasks. * Thinks preventative maintenance. * Conducts scheduled downtime preventative maintenance inspections and tasks. * Helps to diagnose, develop, and implement predictive maintenance strategies.
Industrial/ Manufacturing Engineer	* Responsible for equipment design and supplier selection. * Works through floor supervisors when equipment problems exist.	Industrial/ Manufacturing Engineer	* Educates equipment suppliers on requirements for documentation and maintainability. * Works on the floor with owner-operators and supervisors to solve problems. * Trains technicians. * Corrects/improves current equipment.
Management	* Limited trust of employees. * Not close to production process (except supervisors). * Limited communication with operators. * Comfortable with breakdown maintenance.	Management	* Spends up to 20% of their time on the floor as a TPM cheerleader and a roadblock buster. * Encourages planned shutdowns for improvements. * Open, rapid communication via daily walk-throughs and at least monthly plant-wide meetings. * Requires people training and development.

Figure 6.1

between three and eight years. Top management commitment must be there to support and encourage the organizational role changes (as shown in Figure 6.1) that will be required during this transition. If top management does not have the vision and "gut wrenching" desire to make this improvement, it will not happen.

♦ Chapter 4, 5S implementation, and Chapter 5, Team Building training. A successful TPM implementation cannot be accomplished without these supporting structures in place.

♦ Dedicated people. We like the use of "Project Champions" to take the leadership position for initiatives which are plant-wide, generally have broad support throughout the plant, and can become self-sustaining in six to eighteen months. (Chapter 4 for example). Project Champions eventually return to their original home base (assignment) when their initiative becomes self-sustaining.

TPM does not fit this model for champions. TPM, because of its long implementation time, requires the dedicated resource of a full-time TPM facilitator. One half of a resource here only gets you from zero to one half of an implementation. Been there!

The TPM facilitator should report directly to the person responsible for the TPM implementation (Maintenance Manager?) with a dotted line reporting relationship to the top management person in the facility. The desired qualities and responsibilities of the TPM facilitator will be discussed in TPM Implementation Step #1.

♦ Flexible, cross-trainable workers. In a union environment, this requires the direct and full support of the local since the move away from the traditional separation between operators and maintenance will be perceived as a radical change. This agreement and support must be worked out in advance of any implementation effort. A united, unwavering partnership is required here. (See Chapter 2 for additional discussion on WCM implementations in unionized facilities).

A TPM Implementation Model is shown in Figure 6.2.

Definition of Available Maintenance Strategies

1. **BREAKDOWN:** This is the "wait until it breaks and then scramble" or "fire-fighting" strategy. This type of maintenance is also called reactive maintenance.

2. **PREVENTATIVE:** This is periodic or scheduled maintenance involving oiling, greasing, adjusting, repair or replacement of machine components in order to prevent premature wear and major problems. Preventative maintenance includes overhauls which prevent equipment performance deterioration. Preventative maintenance activities are classified under "planned downtime."

"This is the worst condition this equipment will ever be in!"

Japanese manager's comment after receiving a brand new piece of equipment from the manufacturer, a comment that reflected his approach to taking new equipment and constantly making improvements to it.

TPM Implementation Model

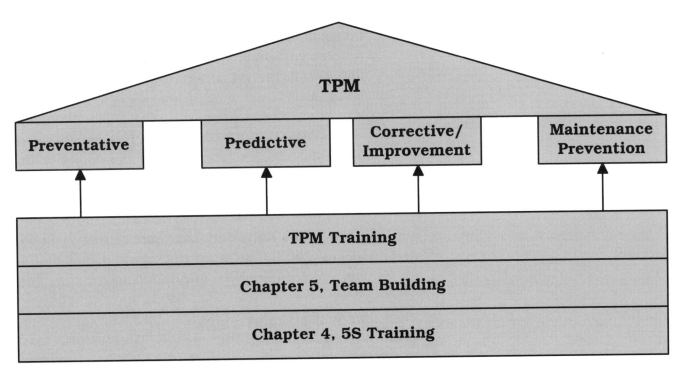

Figure 6.2

3. **PREDICTIVE:** This is the repair or replacement of machine components before failure based on monitoring equipment operation, historical data, or predicted life cycles. A life cycle can be predicted by:

- number of cycles
- operation time (hours)
- calendar time
- component wear data
- variations in the operating parameters of the component such as temperature or vibration

4. CORRECTIVE or IMPROVEMENT: This is the result of root cause analysis on component failure or wear out when it occurs, followed by the installation of equipment modifications or upgrades to prevent recurrence. An example might be to install a larger set of bearings to prevent future failures.

5. MAINTENANCE PREVENTION: This results when we design or specify equipment purchases in an attempt to eliminate all forms of maintenance. Examples are sealed "maintenance free" automotive batteries or "sealed bearings" used in an automotive chassis or electric motors. Part of this strategy includes designing or specifying equipment that is easy to clean, inspect, and lubricate.

TPM Cost Strategies

Cost strategies must be clearly understood and communicated to everyone so that it does not appear to be "double-talk."

We recognize that, in most cases, American Manufacturing has failed to properly guide and financially support the maintenance department. But is it possible to spend too much money on maintenance? Yes! We will use the automotive analogy again. Recent studies indicate that changing your engine oil and filter, under normal driving conditions, after roughly every 5,000–6,000 miles of normal use provides for maximum engine life. Understanding this, is it cost-effective to change the oil and filter every 1,000 miles? No! The cost of maintaining the engine to that level does not significantly improve engine life, and the cost of this level of service exceeds the cost of replacing the engine with a rebuilt one. Additionally, the automotive engine, serviced at the 6,000-mile intervals, would give months of warning (excessive oil usage) that rebuilding was required,

TPM Cost Analysis

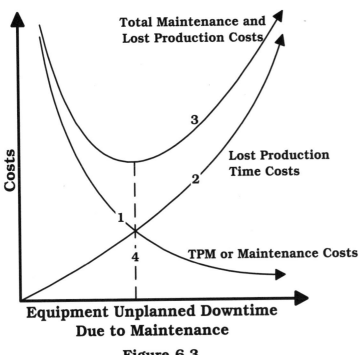

Figure 6.3

while still satisfactorily meeting requirements for transportation. There would be no catastrophic failure that would leave you stranded (assuming you paid attention to the warning signs).

This type of analysis can be applied to equipment maintenance. Figure 6.3 shows the general relationship in a manufacturing plant between maintenance costs (curve #1) and lost production time costs (curve #2) due to unplanned equipment downtime. Note that lost production time costs can rapidly increase when excessive unplanned machine downtime causes overtime, premium inbound and outbound freight shipments, and other customer penalties.

Curve #3 represents total cost of both the maintenance costs and the lost production time costs and is developed by adding the numerical values of curve #1 and curve #2. The lowest point on curve #3 represents the balance or optimum point between maintenance and lost production time costs, shown as line #4. The balance point cost usually is reached when between 5 and 20 percent of all maintenance activities are on unplanned downtime. The relationship between planned and unplanned maintenance activities is sometimes used as the baseline measurement for TPM improvement activities. Other TPM improvement measurements are discussed later in this chapter.

Over a period of time, the balance point cost can be reduced or the point lowered on the curve by using corrective maintenance, maintenance prevention, or both. These strategies reduce unplanned downtime without significantly adding to the daily cost of TPM. More information on balance point costs is available in Chapter 6 Bibliography references - Campbell and Wireman.

Figure 6.4A shows the "bath tub" life-cycle curve of typical manufacturing equipment. Breakdowns are highly probable when the equipment is undergoing debugging and tryout after being delivered from the equipment manufacturer. After this "infant mortality" period, failures drop substantially and the equipment enters its normal life-span. Breakdowns during this period are of a random nature and are generally a result of poor maintenance practices, operator errors, or poor equipment design. At the beginning of the end of its life-span, the "wear-out" period, the quality of the product the equipment produces degrades and the equipment is unable run at normal speed. The equipment is "worn out" when it no longer produces an acceptable product or can no longer keep up with production.

Equipment Rebuild Strategy

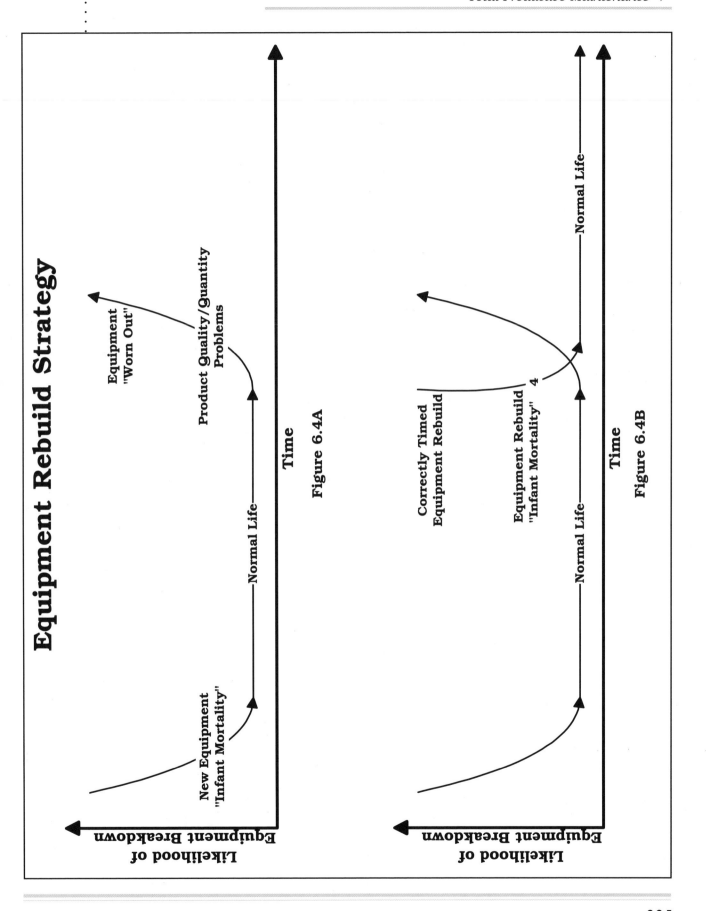

Figure 6.4A

Figure 6.4B

> ## All We Need is a Preventative Maintenance Computer Program!
>
> There is a tendency by people who suddenly recognize the value of getting out of the fire-fighting maintenance mode to immediately spend $100 to $200,000 on one of over 200 PC or mainframe based computer programs. They believe these programs are the solution to their maintenance problems or are at least the first step toward the solution. **Stop!**
>
> Computers can speed up a manual system, but they cannot create the system. The initial steps to an effective TPM program are training, mindset changes, and development, by the combined efforts of all of your people, of a manual system that fits your facility. This system, as a minimum, should include preventative maintenance, an equipment work order system, spare parts inventory/material usage, downtime and equipment histories. Like other elements of WCM, automation should be considered only when you are unable to make further improvements in the manual system.

Figure 6.4B shows a strategy for rebuilding equipment. As equipment approaches the end of its known normal life-span, it is pulled out of production and rebuilt. When the rebuild occurs with remanufactured parts that are correctly installed, the time-length of the "infant mortality" curve is reduced (curve #4). The equipment reenters the normal life-span period without ever going through the product quality/quantity problems associated with the "wear-out" part of the life cycle.

The Parts of the TPM Model Implemented in this Chapter

The TPM implementation model is shown in Figure 6.2. This chapter gives implementation guidance for Preventative Maintenance and Predictive Maintenance. While not the complete TPM implementation package, these first two elements comprise 75–90% of the improvements that can be made in most manufacturing companies. The implementation of Corrective/Improvement Maintenance and Maintenance Prevention were determined to be beyond the scope of this book. Both of these topics will be covered in volume 2.

TPM IMPROVEMENT MEASUREMENTS

The one TPM improvement measurement that has gained wide acceptance is overall equipment effectiveness or OEE. Overall equipment effectiveness measures how the plant is performing relative to reducing the equipment losses and conditions which prevent customer satisfaction. As developed earlier in this chapter, these conditions and losses are:

- Equipment breakdowns (unplanned downtime)

- Scrap/rework caused by poor equipment performance

- Reduced productivity due to equipment:
    running at reduced speed
    receiving unnecessary adjustment
    idling or stoppages which require the operator's attention

- Equipment start-up losses which occur before the process stabilizes

The OEE improvement measurement is the product of three different measurements. These three preliminary measurements and calculations are:

- Equipment Availability

- Equipment Efficiency Performance

- Equipment Quality Performance

Equipment Availability
Equipment Availability (EA) is the basic TPM performance measurement and is sometimes used as the sole TPM performance measurement. Some companies use EA as the starting measurement and then move to OEE as their TPM initiative grows in sophistication.

Equipment Availability measures how often equipment is not producing parts (unplanned downtime) due to breakdown or adjustment losses. It compares the actual time the equipment was producing parts (uptime) to the time it was scheduled to produce parts (scheduled production time). A breakdown here is defined as a condition which requires the skill of a specially trained maintenance technician/engineer. Equipment adjustments are normally performed by the operator.

Unplanned downtime does not include breaks, lunches, personal relief, team meetings, or scheduled maintenance.

Equipment Availability (EA) is calculated as follows:

$$\text{EA} = \frac{\textbf{Scheduled Production Time - Unplanned Downtime}}{\textbf{Scheduled Production Time}}$$

Since,   **Uptime = Scheduled Production Time - Unplanned Downtime**

Then, $$\text{EA} = \frac{\textbf{Uptime}}{\textbf{Scheduled Production Time}}$$

This answer is then converted to percent by multiplying it by 100. This percentage gives the actual time the machine is running versus what it should be running (100%).

Equipment Efficiency Performance.
Equipment Efficiency Performance (EEP) measures the actual machine cycle time versus the theoretical or "standard" cycle time. It compares the actual number of parts produced versus the "standard" number of parts the machine should have produced in a given length of time (uptime). Uptime is the same number that was previously defined in the EA calculation. The standard cycle time assumes there are no minor stoppage losses or reduced speed losses. Minor stoppages are defined as stoppages which can be corrected by the operator.

Equipment Efficiency Performance (EEP) is calculated as follows:

$$\text{EEP} = \frac{\textbf{(Standard Cycle Time) X (\# of Pieces Produced)}}{\textbf{Uptime}}$$

The number of pieces produced includes any defective parts that were produced during that period of uptime.

This answer is then converted to percent by multiplying it by 100. This percentage shows the percent of parts produced versus the "standard" quantity that should have been produced.

Equipment Quality Performance

Equipment Quality Performance (EQP) measures the performance of the machine from a quality standpoint. It compares the number of good pieces produced to the total number of pieces produced for a given period of time. Defective parts can be produced when the equipment does not perform properly or during machine start-up, before the process has stabilized. Parts which can be reworked are counted as defective.

Equipment Quality Performance (EQP) is measured as follows:

$$\textbf{EQP} = \frac{\textbf{Total \# Produced - Total \# Defective}}{\textbf{Total \# Produced}}$$

Since,   **# of Good Pieces = Total # Produced - Total # Defective**

Then, $$\textbf{EQP} = \frac{\textbf{\# of Good Pieces}}{\textbf{Total \# Produced}}$$

Overall Equipment Effectiveness

OEE can then be calculated as follows:

$$\textbf{OEE = (EA) X (EEP) X (EQP)}$$

Current World Class benchmarks for these measurements are:
EA = 90%, EEP = 95%, EQP = 99%
OEE = 85%

Implementing TPM

Introduction

Like the other WCM initiatives, a successful TPM launch is an important signal for the facility and for the future of the TPM implementation process. The success of this launch and the speed at which it occurs depend upon a properly trained and committed TPM facilitator and teams who have the total, enthusiastic, visible support of upper management.

TPM represents a drastic, but required, change in how your facility does business. The team will be skeptical, frightened, and perhaps even resistant to this change.

TPM Implementation Outline

STEP #1 - Select TPM facilitator

STEP #2 - Select first TPM pilot area and first TPM team

STEP #3 - Develop TPM pilot area improvement goals and set TPM event schedule

STEP #4 - Train the operators in autonomous maintenance activities

STEP #5 - Provide training in preventative maintenance procedures to the maintenance technicians

STEP #6 - Provide training in predictive maintenance procedures to the maintenance technicians

STEP #1 - SELECTION: TPM FACILITATOR

TPM Facilitator

As discussed previously, recruit a champion to help launch and lead the initiative. Select a person who is willing to meet the needs of launching this initiative. Remember that people do best what they like to do! Following is a brief outline of who makes a good TPM facilitator.

The TPM facilitator is responsible for:

♦ Developing a clear understanding of the company's overall vision for the future and how the TPM initiative helps make the vision a reality. The vision of the future must come from the top person in the facility.

♦ Having a thorough understanding of this chapter.

♦ Visiting other companies, competitors if possible, that are benchmarks for TPM activities. Developing contacts at these companies will exploit the possibilities of shared technology activities. The "shared technology" concept allows groups of non-competing plants to share their knowledge and experiences in TPM or other WCM activities.

♦ Giving the entire plant a brief prelaunch overview of the TPM implementation process (Steps #1 through Step #4), as well as the current status during the monthly plant meeting.

♦ Launching the first TPM pilot area and developing this pilot area into a TPM "Island of Excellence."

♦ Developing a rewards and recognition system for the TPM initiative.

TPM "Islands of Excellence"

The initial TPM pilot area should be developed and used as a TPM "Island of Excellence" similar to the "Islands" of Chapter 4. This TPM island will be used as a TPM model for the entire facility. Islands will calm the initial fears (and put a lot of rumors to rest!) of what TPM is all about, and will jump-start your people on the TPM learning curve. Since TPM can be a difficult implementation, we suggest that you start with only one area. After completion of the TPM "Island" model implementation, simultaneous, multiple-area implementations should be considered.

One more comment on islands: take many before and after pictures to remind everyone of where they started and what they achieved.

Who Makes a Good TPM Facilitator?

A facilitator is a resource for the TPM teams who teaches TPM fundamentals, helps the group overcome obstacles, and demonstrates team behavior. (The word *facilitate* means to make easier; move forward.) The facilitator helps the team, but does **not** take responsibility for, or contribute to, the team's task. This neutral, objective observer provides a source of feedback when the team experiences difficulty or becomes blocked.

Ideally, the facilitator is someone respected and trusted by almost everyone in the facility. This person should have a technical background and excellent people and training skills.

A facilitator helps the TPM team by adjusting appropriately to the team's need for a

♦ TPM trainer. Provide initial training and, later, review information that may have not been understood by everyone in the initial training. Update the teams with new techniques or technology developed by other plant teams or from outside of the company (shared technology).

♦ Team developer. Help the team overcome dispute and discipline problems both from within the team and from outside (such as lack of plant support or poor participation by a team member). Keep all lines of communication open.

♦ Coach, adviser. Help the team stay focused and on track. Make sure the team is measuring its own performance. Prepare the team for presentations at a plant meeting.

♦ Cheerleader. Alternately encourage or coax the team or individual members as the circumstances require.

♦ Liaison. Make sure that management and the rest of the plant know how the team is doing on an on-going basis.

Remember, complete TPM implementation will require at least three years; make sure you have a facilitator committed to a successful implementation.

STEP #2 - SELECT FIRST TPM PILOT AREA AND FIRST TPM TEAM.

We suggest that your first TPM pilot area meet these criteria:

♦ A manufacturing area or cell that currently runs no more than two shifts, five days a week. This is important because the manufacturing area will be shut down for 3–5 days during the TPM training and it will necessary to build a bank of product from this area to protect customer shipments during this period.

♦ A manufacturing area where equipment downtime, lost production costs, or product quality are a major problem which puts customer satisfaction in jeopardy. Ideally there is a plant measurement that defines how bad the problem is.

♦ A manufacturing area where all the equipment maintenance is currently the responsibility of the plant's maintenance department (versus some or all contract maintenance).

♦ The people working in the manufacturing area have 5S (Chapter 4) and Team Building Training (Chapter 5).

The important issue here is to launch the TPM initiative in an area where the people are receptive and there are no known implementation conflicts of any type (such as unresolved job responsibility issues). This first TPM team must understand and accept the responsibility for developing and being the "model" area.

Team Selection

Endeavor to have the following cross-section of 7–14 members on the TPM pilot team:

♦ All operators from all shifts that work in the pilot area. Neglecting the representation and input from any shift will drastically slow the implementation. While it may be difficult to schedule one training schedule for multiple shifts, it is absolutely essential.

♦ Maintenance technicians who are responsible for the maintenance activities for this area of the plant and who will remain so after the event. The operators and technicians will develop a new relationship as a result of this event and this relationship must be allowed to continue to grow after the event. Again, all shifts should be represented. There should be at least two technicians.

♦ The maintenance manager (this is important not only from a leadership/learning/knowledge standpoint but also to positively establish the level of the plant's commitment). The maintenance manager should be the team leader for the TPM pilot. Future TPM implementations can use team leaders developed and selected from this pilot team.

♦ A process/manufacturing engineering representative, someone who is responsible for specifying/purchasing equipment. It will be important for this individual to learn how the implementation of TPM affects future equipment specifications from a documentation, maintainability, and maintenance prevention standpoint.

♦ A shift supervisor.

Other people to consider: Equipment or MRO buyer, QA representative.

Also, consider inviting representatives from the manufacturers of the equipment that is in use in the pilot area. Often suppliers can give the team ideas and updates on documentation and maintainability improvements that have been made or are available for the equipment. These suppliers may also learn how to make improvements in their future equipment designs as a result of the activity.

It is possible to have larger or smaller teams after the pilot implementation.

STEP #3 - DEVELOP TPM PILOT AREA IMPROVEMENT GOALS AND SET TPM EVENT SCHEDULE.

The team should set the improvement goal for the pilot area based on one of the TPM performance measurements previously discussed. A team visit to a benchmark in TPM activities would be beneficial. Remember, the goal must be attainable, but at the same time the pilot area will be a model (and minimum goal) for future plant activities in other areas. The pilot team and plant management must be in agreement that if all plant areas were able to obtain the pilot area goal this would be an excellent first step for the plant TPM initiative.

Notes to the Team Leader

1. Team leaders are the center of the TPM event. Your job is to keep the team involved, communicating, and focused on the event's goals. Avoid getting bogged down in the detail work—your job is to lead. Discuss any questions you have about the team leader position with the TPM facilitator.

2. Since you and your team will spend most of the time on the shop floor, set up a working/meeting table and chairs in or near the event site. Include a flip chart, markers, pencils, paper, etc.

3. Additional information on team leadership is available in Chapter 5. Additional WCM "event" information is available in Chapter 10.

TPM Event Schedule.

Because TPM will probably require a radical change in your team's thinking, tasks, and responsibilities, it must be implemented using the WCM "event" format. Events are 3–5 day implementation activities where the team spends the entire day at the work site learning and implementing one of the WCM initiatives. A schedule must be developed where the team and the work site will be available full time for the length of the event.

After the initial 3–5 day event, the team should meet for at least one hour every week until all activities not completed during the event are finished. Use this format for all future events.

The Operator/Maintenance Technician Partnership

Preventative Maintenance	Predictive Maintenance

Operator Independent Activities Preventative Maintenance (Step #4)

1. Initial equipment cleanup.

2. Improve ability to clean, inspect, and prevent defects.

3. Develop cleaning, lubrication standards, and checklists.

4. Develop equipment operating skills, standards, and checklists.

5. Implement daily operator activities.

Maintenance Technician Activities Preventative Maintenance (Step #5)

1. Provide technical support to operators during and after the development of autonomous activities.

2. Develop critical spare parts management program.

3. Eliminate equipment deterioration through scheduled general inspections and equipment overhauls.

4. Identify chronic equipment problems and error proof.

Maintenance Technician Activities Predictive Maintenance (Step #6)

1. Develop and analyze equipment histories.

2. Determine equipment physical parameters that predict failure.

3. Develop equipment condition monitoring systems.

Figure 6.5

STEP #4 - TRAIN THE OPERATORS IN AUTONOMOUS (INDEPENDENT) MAINTE-NANCE ACTIVITIES.

Please note that the entire team should go through all the steps. So the "team" understands what each other's responsibilities are, maintenance technicians should learn this step and operators should learn Step #5. Working together on these steps helps establish common ground between these two groups. Like the special relationship that exists between a race car driver and the pit crew, operators and maintenance technicians must work together to eliminate the losses and conditions which prevent us from satisfying the customer.

Figure 6.5 shows this relationship/responsibilities between the maintenance department and the machine operators developed in TPM. It also provides a summary of Steps #4, 5, and 6.

TPM Rule #5

Safety training (lock out/tag out, confined space entry, etc.) must occur for everyone involved in the operation, inspection, cleanup, or maintenance of the equipment before a TPM implementation can start.

Step #4, Part 1 - Initial Equipment Cleanup

The initial cleanup has a twofold purpose: First, it improves the operator's and maintenance technician's ability to make their daily and scheduled inspections. The issue here is how does anyone perform an inspection on a piece of equipment when dirt and filth hide problems. Second, the act of thoroughly cleaning the machine (getting upfront and personal with it) allows the operator and technicians to discover problems and potential problems. The act of cleaning also promotes a better understanding of how the equipment functions, and helps develop pride and ownership.

Every problem and potential problem discovered during the cleanup step should be identified with a yellow TPM Action Tag as shown in Figure 6.6. It is not unusual to find more than 100 yellow tags on a piece of equipment during its first real cleanup. Experience indicates that finding less than 100 tagged items during a first-time cleanup may indicate that all problems have not been found.

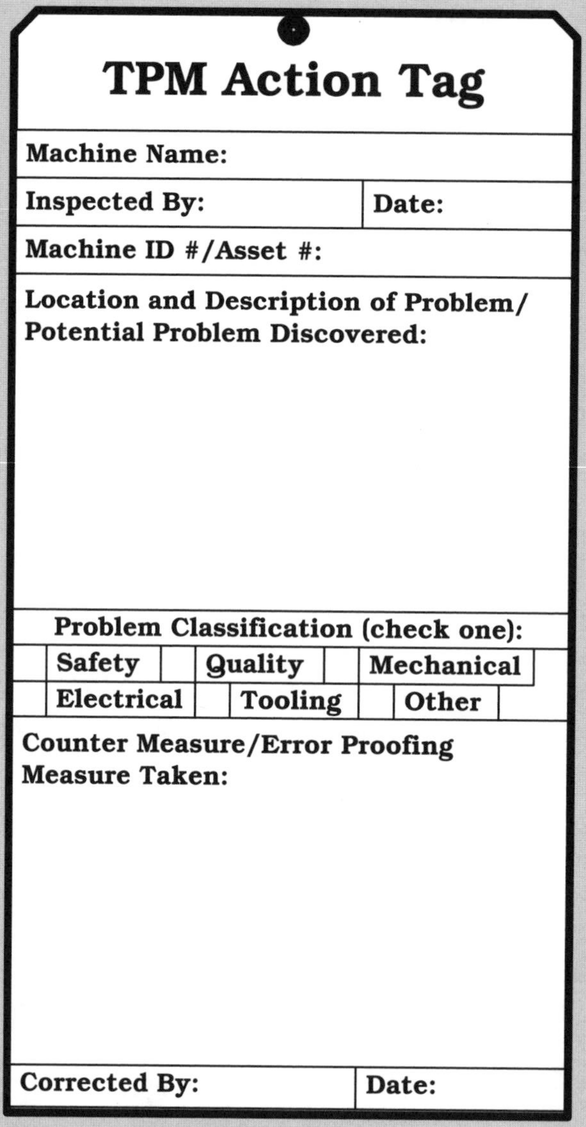

TPM Action Tag

Machine Name:	
Inspected By:	Date:
Machine ID #/Asset #:	

Location and Description of Problem/ Potential Problem Discovered:

Problem Classification (check one):

Safety		Quality		Mechanical	
Electrical		Tooling		Other	

Counter Measure/Error Proofing Measure Taken:

Corrected By:	Date:

Figure 6.6

The TPM Action Tag contains a section for problem classification. The classifications will be used in Step #5 to identify chronic equipment problems.

The initial top-to-bottom machine cleanup activities should also include:

♦ Marking all lubrication and adjustment points on the machine. Use or develop a plant-wide color coding scheme to identify the type of lubricant to be used at each lubrication point.

♦ Correcting all discovered problems. Save all completed yellow tags for Step #5.

♦ Tightening, lubricating, and generally restoring the equipment to "as new" operating condition.

♦ Painting equipment.

The TPM pilot team is responsible for developing equipment cleaning procedures for all future TPM teams to use. This procedure will be part of the "Islands of Excellence" model and will set the cleanliness baseline for all future TPM events. This procedure will give equipment cleaning directions (how to, with what, look for, and where to) as well as cleaning precautions (safety issues, potential equipment damage issues).

Step #4, Part 2 - Improve the Ability to Clean, Inspect, and Prevent Failures

The purpose of this part is also twofold. The first purpose is to reduce or eliminate the sources of contamination which cause the equipment to become dirty. The second is to modify equipment to facilitate easier cleaning, inspection, and lubrication. Both purposes support the goal of preventing equipment failure.

The root causes of dirt and contamination in a plant are generally one or any combination of these three sources:

♦ Equipment oil or process fluid leaks. On machine tools and presses, this is usually hydraulic oil or processing fluids such as cutting fluid or mold release sprays.

♦ Process material waste or scrap loss. Process material waste occurs in machine tool metal cutting operations in the form of metal chips. Also the cold and hot forming of materials in presses can causes waste from process dust, adhesive sprays, and trimming losses.

♦ Airborne or traffic borne dust and dirt from other worksites in the plant. This may include unfiltered make-up air which is brought in from outside the plant.

Dirt and contamination reduce the life of moving parts such as bearings, shaft seals, and sliding or telescoping covers, and limit the ability of the operator or maintenance technician to perform visual daily and scheduled equipment inspections.

Every effort must be made to eliminate the source of the dirt and contamination. It may be necessary to upgrade or replace the plumbing on some equipment hydraulic systems to make them leak proof. Eliminate the need for all oil drip pans.

Controlling process waste and losses can be accomplished also by developing custom guards which direct the metal chips and cutting fluid and other process waste into recycling containers. Use guards to eliminate contamination from reaching sensitive machine areas such as processing and safety sensors, limit switches, bearings, shaft seals, and the actual part-forming, cutting, or processing area. Ideas from the equipment supplier may be very helpful here.

Modifying equipment to facilitate proper cleaning, inspection, and lubrication includes replacing steel guards with plexiglass inspection windows, using quick release fasteners for other panels which must be removed, adding t-bars or handles to filter housings so they can be removed without wrenches, replumbing all grease fittings to a single, easy to access location, and adding inspection platforms.

TPM Rule #6

All TPM inspection items on the operator check sheet must be accessible for the operator. Operators should not be required to get down on their hands and knees or use ladders to read gauges or make checks.

"World class facilities develop beginning with the 5S's, and facilities that fail, fall apart beginning with the 5S's."

FROM THE WORDS OF HIROYUKI HIRANO
5 PILLARS OF THE VISUAL WORKPLACE

Activities for Step 4, Part 2 also include:

♦ Using the "5 why" analysis to determine the root cause of dirt and contamination

♦ Consideration of alternate machining or manufacturing methods which do not create metal chips and other process waste or contamination

♦ Revising oil level gauges and oil fill locations to improve cleanliness and reduce servicing time.

♦ Using TPM Action Tags to highlight any newly discovered problems

♦ Correcting any new problems. Again, save all yellow tags for Step #5.

Step #4, Part 3 - Develop Cleaning and Lubrication Standards and Checklists
The goal for Part 3 is for the team to use its experiences from parts 1 and 2 to develop cleaning and lubrication work standards for the machines in the worksite. These cleaning and lubrication work standards and checklists are usually combined so that the operator can efficiently perform both during one walk around the equipment. Checklists of this type are used by the operator on a daily basis and in general can be successfully accomplished in 10 minutes or less per shift.

It is important for all operators to understand that both cleaning and lubricating are forms of inspection (often automotive service technicians find steering or powertrain problems during chassis lubrications). Since many problems show up visually as deterioration before they affect the performance of the equipment, cleaning and lubricating are powerful tools in the operator's preventative maintenance toolbox.

TPM Rule #7

Component failure analysis studies indicate that from 60–75% of all equipment mechanical failures are a result of lubrication failure (contaminated, wrong type, inadequate, or excessive).

The criteria for developing the work standard is to keep the equipment in an "as new" condition. Having a representative of the equipment manufacturer on the team can really help. Otherwise, use the manufacturer's manuals, drawings, or any plant historical data that may be available on the equipment. Often, equipment suppliers assemble their machines using the electrical motors and controls, hydraulic power supplies, and other components from their suppliers. Contacting these suppliers may also provide some additional preventative maintenance information.

Since one of the goals of TPM implementation is to eliminate all recurring problems, a review of all the repairs made as a result of the TPM Action Tags is appropriate. This will ensure that any cleaning or lubrication problems are accounted for and added to these checklists.

As the work standards are developed, it is extremely important that all operators understand why each step of the standard is necessary and the consequences of not performing that step. The team should not proceed beyond this part until there is complete understanding and agreement.

Figure 6.7 illustrates the elements of a lubrication-only checklist. Figure 6.8 shows the reference numbers on the machine that correspond to those on the checklist which states the lubrication specifications and requirements.

Also, all operator checklists must include instructions on what to do if an item on the checklist cannot be completed.

TPM Rule #8

All gauges should have a colored band indicating the normal operating range. Air line filter/lubricator/regulator devices should also be marked with "drain," "refill," and "operating range" colored bands.

PREVENTATIVE MAINTENACE LOG

MACHINE: AUTOMATIC CUTTING OFF MACHINE (LARGE)
MANUFACTURER: MODERN MACHINE TOOL CO.
2005 LOSEY AVE. JACKSON, MI. 49203 (517) 788-9120
MODEL #: 8KD

MONTH:_____

DATE	CONSTANT CHECKS				DAILY CHECKS						COMMENTS
	*1	6	7	8	2	3	5	9	10	13	
	MOTOR BASE	SIGHT GLASS	SIGHT FEED OILERS	AIR LINE OILER							

AFTER SERVICE CHECK THE APPROPRIATE BOX.
* = CHECK AT EACH SPEED CHANGE
COMPLETE A SHEET FOR EACH MONTH.
TURN IN COMPLETED SHEETS TO YOUR SUPERVISOR.
TRANSFER ANY QUARTERLY INFORMATION TO A NEW SHEET.

MONTHLY / **QUARTERLY	
**4	NEXT SERVICE ___/___/__
CHECK BOX & ADD NEXT DATE TO SERVICE	
12	
SERVICE FIRST OF THE MONTH & CHECK BOX	

Figure 6.7

A–A

MACHINE:
MANUFACTURER
MODEL NUMBER:

AUTOMATIC CUTTING-OFF MACHINE (LARGE)
MODERN MACHINE TOOL CO.
2005 LOSEY AVE., JACKSON, MI. 49203 (517) 788-9120
6KD

P R E V E N T A T I V E   M A I N T E N A N C E

AREA	TYPE OF LUBRICANTS	FREQUENCY CHECKS
1 (1) MOTOR BASE	AW 32 HYD.OIL	AT EACH SPEED CHANGE
2 (4) FEED ROLL	TUBE GREASE	ONCE EACH DAY
3 (2) FRONT THRUST RING	TUBE GREASE	ONCE EACH DAY
4 (3) LINKAGE GREASE	TUBE GREASE	EVERY 3 MONTHS
5 (4) SLIDE GREASE	AW 32 HYD. OIL	ONCE EACH DAY
6 (1) SIGHT GLASS (CIRCULATING OIL)	AW 32 HYD. OIL	CONSTANT (REFILL TANK WHEN OIL REACHES MIDDLE OF SIGHT GLASS)
7 (4) SIGHT FEED OILERS	AW 32 HYD.OIL	CONSTANT (AT ANY TIME THE OIL CEASES TO DRIP THE MACHINE SHOULD BE SHUT OFF) REFILL THE TANK AND FIND THE SOURCE OF THE TROUBLE.)
8 (1) AIR LINE OILER	AW 32 HYD.OIL	KEEP BOWL FULL; ADJUST OIL FLOW FOR A DROP EVERY 3 TO 5 CYCLES OF THE MACHINE.
9 (1 WING NUT) HYDRAULIC SYSTEM	AW 32 HYD.OIL	ONCE DAILY (REMOVE NUT, EMPTY FULL OIL GUN INTO HOLE, REPLACE NUT, CYCLE MACHINE & BLEED.)
10 (1) STOCK STOP GREASE	TUBE GREASE	DAILY
11 SELF OILING	AW 32 HYD. OIL	
12 BAR FEED TABLE - ALL POINTS	TUBE GREASE COOLANT (COMPERIAL 1011)	MONTHLY (SEE SEPARATE DIAGRAM NOT SHOWN HERE)
13 RESEVOIR BASE		ONCE DAILY (KEEP FILLED BETWEEN THE LINES. MIX COOLANT WITH WATER @ 15:1 RATIO)

Figure 6.8

Activities for Step 4, Part 3 should also include or consider:

♦ Marking and specifying all lubrication points on the equipment with the lubrication color code scheme used by the plant

♦ Using pictures of the machine to clearly note each lubrication and cleaning point (Figure 6.8)

♦ Establishing lubrication levels or amounts for each point. Also include any necessary filter change information.

♦ Developing lubrication servicing carts or "one stop" lubrication centers

♦ Developing photographs and a written description of what the equipment should look like (the "as-new" condition) after the cleaning and lubricating is completed.

Step #4, Part 4 - Develop Equipment Operating Skills and General Inspection Standards and Checklists

While the majority of the operator's autonomous activities are covered in performing the cleaning and lubrication checks that were developed in Step #4, Part 3, additional training probably will be necessary to complete the operator's knowledge and understanding of how the equipment operates.

This additional equipment-specific training usually occurs in the areas of:

♦ Hydraulics/Pneumatics

♦ Electrical

♦ Mechanical drive systems

♦ Any remaining lubrication issues

♦ Safety

This additional knowledge gives the operator the opportunity to assess and determine the required response to equipment problems or abnormal conditions as they occur. The required response may range from immediately shutting the equipment down to scheduling downtime for equipment repair. This training is usually conducted by the maintenance technicians.

This step begins the long-term relationship and partnership between the operators and the maintenance technicians and corresponds to Step #5, Part 1 of the maintenance technician activities (Figure 6.5).

After this additional training for the operator, two general inspection checklists will be created. General inspections of the hydraulic, pneumatic, electrical, and mechanical drive systems of the equipment are required. One checklist is for the operators and the other checklist is for the maintenance technicians. The TPM implementation team must decide as a group what duties should go on each checklist based on the skill level required and how often these checklists will be used. Use a checklist format similar to the one that was developed for the lubrication and cleaning checklist (Figures 6.7 and 6.8).

General inspections include minor repair and replacement. The TPM implementation team must decide as a group what repairs the operator is responsible for and what repairs the technicians will accomplish. Consideration must be given to safety risks involved, length and difficulty of the task, and the need for special skills or equipment. Remember this division of responsibilities will be part of the "Islands of Excellence" model and will set the baseline for all future TPM events. The technicians are responsible for training the operators in any and all repair and replacement procedures.

Both the operator and technician general inspection checklists must include instructions for how to handle specification conditions. The operator's correct response may be to call the supervisor or maintenance technician. An out-of-specification condition on the technician's general checklist may require scheduling a repair or overhaul. Responses in either case are generally based on the equipment manufacturer's recommendations, the maintenance department's experience with the equipment, or a combination of both.

The creation of the general inspection standards and checklists should also include or consider:

♦ Contacting the equipment supplier if a representative of the equipment supplier is not on the team. Otherwise use the manufacturer's manuals, drawings, or any plant historical data that may be available on the equipment to determine what items should be accounted for on the checklists.

♦ Equipment adjustments and calibrations

♦ Equipment assembly bolt retorque values

♦ Visual checks of all gauges/readouts for the hydraulic, pneumatic, electrical, mechanical drive systems, and cooling water

♦ How often and when the checklists will be used

♦ Use of TPM Action Tags to highlight any newly discovered problems

♦ Correcting any new problems. Again, save all yellow tags for Step #5

TPM Rule #9

Equipment builders who do not support TPM efforts on their already purchased equipment should not be considered for future equipment purchases.

Examples of general inspection checklists for operators are shown in Figures 6.9 and 6.10.

Know-How Sheet
The "Know-How Sheet," or single point lesson, is a powerful training tool that can be used to visually instruct operators in new inspection or repair procedures, demonstrate basic skills, show boundary samples for visual product quality checks, or show process or equipment improvements. An example of a Know-How Sheet is shown in Figure 6.11. This sheet shows the improvement of "coloring in" the normal operating range of gauges

Daily Operator Checklist Press 43
Puntos De Revision Diaria Prenja 43

Operator		Document #	FMFC043
Shift		Rev. Lev.	A 5/6/97
Date		Approvals	

1		Green ☐ Verde	Red ☐ Rojo	Liquid in traps should be below "empty" line
				El liquido en las trampas debe de estar debajo de la linea de vacio
2		Green ☐ Verde	Red ☐ Rojo	Oil in lubricators should be between lines
				El aceite en los lubricadores debe de estar entre las lineas verdes
3		Clean ☐ Limpio	Dirty ☐ Sucio	Dial on oil filters should read clean
				El marcador en los filtros de aceite debe marcar clean
4		On ☐ Abierto	Off ☐ Cerrado	Tower water supply valves should be on
				Las valvulas suministradoras de la torre de agua deben de estar abiertas
5		Green ☐ Verde	Red/Yellow ☐ Rojo/Anarillo	Dial on oil filters should be in green range
				El marcador en los filtros de aceite debe de indicar verde
6		Green ☐ Verde	Red ☐ Rojo	Oil temperature should be in green marks (90-130 deg.)
				La temperatura debe de marcar entre las marcas verdes
7		Green ☐ Verde	Red ☐ Rojo	Feed throat temperature should be between green marks
				La temperatura de la garganta alimentadora debe de marcar entre las marcas verdes
8		Green ☐ Verde	Red ☐ Rojo	Extruder motor oil level should be in green
				El nivel del aceite del motor del extruder debe de marcar entre las lineas verdes
9	Please circle any oil or water leaks found on drawing below			
	Por favor marca si hay alguna fuga de aceite o de agua en el siguiente dibujo			

After completing checklist turn in with scrap sheets
Depuses de completar la lista entregarla gunto con su hoja de scrap

Figure 6.9

Preventative Maintenance Checklist
For Assembly Operators

Week Start Date: _____ Machine #: _____ Assembly Line: _____

*Refer to Number Column for Machine Visual Reference Numbers

Note: Place initials according to day/shift in box, if it applies to your machine. Top triangle=1st   Bottom Triangle=2nd

Steps	Number	P/V	Checklist Instructions For Assembly Operators	Time	M	T	W	TH	F	SA	SU
1	X	P	Before running, clean in and around machine and area.								
2		V	Check air pressure gauge for proper settings(Between Green)*								
3		V	Check condensate bowl for any fluids.*								
4		P	Clean light curtain and make sure it is in proper working order.*								
5	X	P	Date stamp should be legible and available at machine.*								
6		V	Check temperatures on glue pots.*								
7		V	Check Heat Stake, make sure pre-heat is on.(Blue Light on CP)*								
8		P	Clean glue guns and paint guns before and after use.								
9	X	P	Empty the slugs from bins under punch presses and punch hole.								
10		V	Check to see if all part hold downs and fasteners are in place.*								
11		P	Check Cycle Buttons, it takes two, to start cycle on machines.*								

Comments:

* If any of the tasks or checks can't be performed immediately call a supervisor and comment in box.

X=Steps that must be done
P=Physical Requirement
V=Visual Requirement

NOTE: Checklist should not leave machine until week's end!!!!!

Figure 6.10

Know-How/Lesson Sheet

Type of Information:		Information for:		Training Record		Date:		2/2/96
X	Inspection	X	Operator	Date		Issued By:		PF
	Repair		Technician	Date		Machine #		105
	Boundary Sample		QA	Date		Cell #/Equipment Location		19
X	Improvement		Other ___	Trained By				

Theme of Lesson:

Normal operating range of gauges on hydraulic power supply marked in green on face of gauge

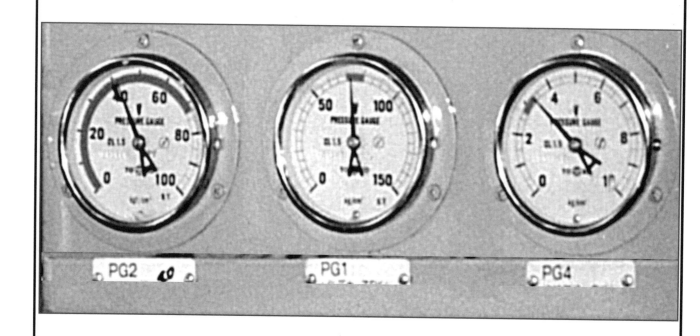

Figure 6.11

used in a hydraulic power supply. This coloring reduces the amount of time necessary to check for proper operation of the power supply. For use as a QA boundary sample Know-How Sheet, side-by-side pictures of good and bad products would be shown.

Know How Sheets are created when some condition changes or an improvement is made in the equipment and the implementer wishes to focus attention on that particular issue. The creator of the sheet can be a maintenance technician, supervisor, safety committee member, QA representative, or even an operator who wishes to instruct the other shift members in a common procedure. The training for these sheets is completed in a "five minute" lecture at the worksite by the author of the sheet.

Know-How Sheets can be hung in the information center of the worksite, or they can be laminated with plastic and displayed at the repair or inspection area referenced on the sheet. These sheets should be displayed until they are incorporated into the appropriate operating procedure, checklist, or manual.

Step #4, Part 5 - Implement Daily Operator Activities.
The purpose of this step is to verify that the two operator checklists (lubrication/cleaning and general inspection) are complete and accurate. With the team present, this step is literally a walk-through by an operator following and performing all of the instructions on the checklists.

Make changes and corrections to the checklists as required. The maintenance technicians can complete any additional operator training as needed. Evaluate whether the operator has the proper cleaning supplies, oils and lubricants, grease guns, funnels, tools, torque wrenches, and any other equipment they may need to complete the lists. Arrange for 5S (Chapter 4) storage of this material at the worksite. Develop how the operator will obtain any spare or replacement parts require. Consider using kanbans (Chapter 9) to automate the replacement part cycle between the machine and the parts stockroom.

When the checklist revisions are complete, finalize the operator time and day schedules for both the cleaning/lubrication checklist and the operator general inspection checklist.

STEP #5 - TRAIN THE MAINTENANCE TECHNICIANS IN PREVENTATIVE MAINTE-NANCE ACTIVITIES.

TPM represents a radical shift in thinking for the maintenance technicians. A review of those changes is appropriate here. Below is a summary of the role changes required for the technicians during a TPM implementation as shown earlier in this chapter in Figure 6.1. This figure provides a summary of Steps #5 and #6.

Traditional Role	Traditional Responsibilities	TPM Role	TPM Responsibilities
Journeyman Maintenance	* Fix equipment as it breaks down, never given time to do it right. * Is physically and emotionally separated from company, production and customers. * Has developed fire-fighting mentality.	Maintenance Technician	* Trains all operators in daily, routine preventative maintenance tasks. * Thinks preventative maintenance. * Conducts scheduled downtime preventative maintenance inspections and tasks. * Helps to develop and implement predictive maintenance strategies.

Also, note that, because implementing TPM creates a partnership between the operators and the maintenance technicians, some of the activities for Step #5 have already been completed in Step #4.

Step #5, Part 1 - Provide Technical Support to Operators

Technical support is day-to-day ongoing support after the event. Operators will need to ask questions so they can better understand how their equipment functions. The start of this relationship was developed in Step #4.

Allow the operators to contact the technician directly (instead of going through a supervisor) perhaps via an andon light system as is shown in Chapter 5, Figure 5.21.

To help educate all of the operators on some common issues and questions that will arise, it may be necessary for the technicians to develop internal training manuals. A plant-wide operator equipment lubrication manual is an example.

Step #5, Part 2 - Develop Critical Spares Management Program

The primary purpose of Step 5, Part 2 is to eliminate any machine downtime due to a lack of spare parts. It is not the intent of this step to eliminate downtime due to spares by increasing replacement parts inventories.

Spares management begins in the stockroom. Secure it and make one technician responsible. Use 5S methods to organize what is currently in stock. Use 5S visuals to show what is in stock and it's location. Develop kanbans (Chapter 9) to automate the replenishment cycle for replacement parts that are used regularly in the plant. Kanbans will reduce inventories while improving the "in-stock" percent. Faxable kanbans work well in this situation because they eliminate paperwork and paperwork delays. They also put the person in the stockroom in direct contact with the supplier.

Critical spares lists begin with the plant's historical data. This data should provide parts usage and part shortages information. Premium inbound freight charges and downtime logs may also provide an insight to critical spares information.

The equipment manufacturer can supply recommended spares information based on their knowledge and their experience with other equipment users. Until the spares program has eliminated spares downtime, ask parts suppliers for a 24-hour, 7-day contact/order line. Develop similar arrangements with shipping services.

Spares management includes being prepared for all scheduled equipment overhauls.

There are now companies in the marketplace that will come in and manage, supply an attendant, and run a plant's MRO (maintenance, repair, overhaul) stockroom. A discussion with one of these companies may give the facility some insight on how they are performing in spares management, and perhaps some ideas on how they could improve by using the MRO company's services.

Additional spares management information is available through the "shared technology" concept mentioned earlier in the chapter.

Step #5, Part 3 - Eliminate Equipment Deterioration Through Scheduled General Inspections and Equipment Overhauls

Like the operator checklist walk-throughs that were completed in Step 4, Step #5, Part 3 involves the maintenance technician, with the team present, performing all of the instructions on the general inspection checklist that was created for maintenance. Again the purpose is to verify the accuracy and completeness of the list.

The technician should verify what tools, parts, and equipment are needed to complete the checklist. These items then become a permanent part of that checklist. Consider keeping checklists and tools together in a TPM tool box or cart.

Establish the length of time needed to complete the list. Make checklist revisions as necessary. When the checklist revisions are complete, finalize the maintenance general inspection checklist schedule.

Step #5, Part 4 - Identify Chronic Equipment Problems and Error Proof

The purpose of Part 4 is to identify recurring equipment problems and eliminate them.

The recommended way to identify chronic equipment problems is with a Machine Breakdown History Board (BHB). An example of one is shown in Figure 6.12. A BHB is attached to the side of each machine. As yellow TPM Action Tags are written up and then completed, the completed tag is placed on the BHB under the machine system that created the breakdown. BHB are typically constructed of "peg board" with peg board hooks holding the TPM Action Tags. Over time, systems and problems which chronically cause breakdowns can be easily identified and addressed.

The team should create boards for the machines in the pilot worksite, and post the completed yellow tags that were created and completed as part of Step #4. While these tags were created over just a few days, indications of chronic problems may still exist. For example:

♦ Numerous hydraulic leaks may indicate that the hydraulic system is operating at a temperature above the maximum temperature for which the seals were designed. It is also possible that the hydraulic system was designed or assembled with the wrong type of fluid connectors for this type of application.

♦ Indications of wear on mechanical drive chain links may indicate sprocket misalignment.

Machine Breakdown History Board					
Safety	Quality	Hydraulic/ Pnuematic	Mechanical	Electrical	Tooling

Figure 6.12

♦ Mechanical drive belt cracking may be due to operating at too high a temperature.

♦ Bearing wear may not be normal, but may instead indicate a lubrication problem.

All problems must be examined using a 5 Why analysis to determine the root cause. The team should use the brainstorming and error proofing techniques of Chapter 5 to determine the proper solution to these problems once the root cause is uncovered.

Note to the Event Team

The event ends with the completion of Step #5. Step #6 should be worked on and completed during the weekly team meetings following this event.

STEP #6 - PREDICTIVE MAINTENANCE

Predictive maintenance techniques attempt to predict machine component failures by looking for and measuring changes in the machine or component operating conditions or for changes in the quality of the product that the machine produces.

Predictive technologies can measures changes in machine conditions and performance that are not yet detectable by the five senses of the operator or maintenance technician. Typical of the predictive techniques used to measure changes in equipment conditions over time are:

- Oil analysis
- Temperature

- Vibration analysis
- Shock-pulse

- Laser alignment
- Ultrasound

- High speed video
- Infrared heat analysis

- Resistance
- Motor current signature analysis

Changes in product quality are measured by using standard QA techniques like Statistical Process Control (SPC).

As a correlation is developed between changes in machine or product conditions with component wear and failure, effective component life can be established. Parts can then be replaced on a scheduled basis before they affect the machine's OEE rating.

The development of a predictive maintenance program from "scratch" can be a very long and arduous journey. Having equipment suppliers who support TPM, or belonging to a local shared technology group can give the team a jump start on a predictive implementation.

Step #6, Part 1 - Develop and Analyze Equipment Histories

The purpose of this part is to start analyzing data that the facility already has collected on equipment histories in an attempt to correlate component or machine wear and failures with machine hours, machine cycles, or calendar days.

This data will be plotted on a large horizontal chart or spreadsheet with time or cycles on the x-axis and all repair/replacement categories and the machine's quality performance plotted separately on the y-axis. If good maintenance records were kept over a long enough time, some correlations will develop.

Verification of these failure correlations can be made by the removal and inspection of these parts before their predicted failure. Correct correlations can be enhanced by developing a component wear versus time or cycles chart. An upper control limit of wear can be established and this inspection and limit can be added to the technician's general inspection checklist. The repair/replacement of this component is automatically scheduled when the limit is reached.

Step #6, Part 2 - Determine Equipment Physical Parameters that Predict Failure
Here again is where a knowledgeable equipment manufacturer can be helpful.

Presented here are some guidelines, based on the type of equipment in the worksite, that will get the team headed in the right direction.

Oil analysis - extremely important in hydraulic and lubrication systems where the contamination generated from normal and abnormal wear can cause other components to fail. It is estimated that 70% of all hydraulic component failures are due to contaminated oil. An analysis of wear particles as part of the oil analysis may determine the exact component source.

Vibration analysis - monitors the frequency of vibrations of rotating equipment such as shafts and bearings. It is flexible and can accurately determine items such as worn bearings, defective bearings, rotating shaft imbalances, resonance, or misalignment, or any unusual rotating component wear. If this data is combined with a computer analysis, the remaining life of the component can be estimated.

Temperature/Infrared analysis - infrared is particularly effective in detecting "hot spots" in electrical panels, transformers, and electrical power transmission equipment. These hot spots are indicators of potential problems. Hot spots detected on bearings, motors, and mechanical power transmission equipment are compared to the "as-new" infrared analysis.

Temperature analysis is also necessary for hydraulic systems where rising oil temperatures usually indicate a worn component or a plugged heat exchanger.

Liquid penetrants/Ultrasound - Liquid penetrants are used for external crack detection in metal and ultrasound is used for internal crack detection in metal.

Use the equipment histories that were developed in Part 1 to determine which of the predictive strategies will work for the recorded equipment failures.

Step #6, Part 3 - Develop Equipment Condition Monitoring Systems

The maintenance technicians are responsible for setting up meetings with predictive equipment suppliers. Do not buy any equipment until the supplier proves it works on the facility's equipment. Ask for 30-day free trials on all equipment. Visit other plants that are using the predictive equipment.

Outsource services such as oil and infrared analysis in the beginning to avoid purchasing the equipment before the cost benefits are established.

Start the predictive maintenance strategy in the TPM pilot area only. Do not attempt to expand it until it is fully operational in that area. Make sure top plant management is aware of predictive equipment costs.

Summary

TPM is a tremendously powerful advanced manufacturing technique which can significantly improve a plant's quality, productivity, and product delivery.

TPM can generate culture changes in a plant that will begin to mold separate departments (engineering, manufacturing, maintenance) into a team focused on customer satisfaction.

> Ultimately, the only long-term competitive advantage any company can have is its people.

A TPM implementation will pave the way and speed the implementation of the remaining advanced manufacturing techniques.

Volume 2 of this book will include detailed coverage of corrective maintenance and maintenance prevention.

TPM Rules

1. Many shop floor concerns which may develop as a result of implementing TPM include maintenance job security, additional job responsibilities for operators, job classifications, and union support. These issues must be resolved and communicated by top management to everyone before the implementation can start.

2. The success of a TPM implementation depends on TPM becoming a daily part of everyone's activities. TPM must develop into part of the company's culture.

3. To implement TPM, a partnership must be developed between manufacturing, maintenance, and engineering which fosters an atmosphere of equipment ownership. Like the race car driver and pit crew, everyone must work together for the team to be successful.

4. The key to an effective preventative maintenance component of the TPM initiative is the machine operators. Up to 75% of breakdown maintenance occurrences can be detected and prevented by well-trained operators.

5. Safety training (lock out/tag out, confined space entry, etc.) must occur for everyone involved in the operation, inspection, cleanup, or maintenance of the equipment before a TPM implementation can start.

6. All TPM inspection items on the operator check sheet must be readily available to the operator. Operators should not be required to get down on their hands and knees or use ladders to read gauges or make checks.

7. Component failure analysis studies indicate that between 60 and 75% of all machine tool mechanical failures are a result of lubrication failure (contaminated, wrong type, inadequate, or excessive).

8. All gauges should be marked with a colored band indicating the normal operating range. Air line filter/lubricator/regulator devices should also be marked with "drain," "refill," and "operating range" colored bands.

9. Equipment builders who do not support TPM efforts on their equipment should not be considered for future equipment purchases.

Manufacturing/Office Cells

One Piece Flow and the Key to Employee Empowerment and Ownership

What is a Manufacturing/Office Cell?

A manufacturing/office cell comprises a group of equipment or desks, usually laid out in the shape of a "U", that is dedicated to the complete production of a family of similar products or parts. These manufacturing/office cells produce products, one at a time, by linking together a sequence of office, equipment, or assembly processes in a smooth production flow known as *One Piece Flow Production*. Cells generally start with raw material at the first operation and end with a finished product that is ready to be sent to their customer.

What's Wrong with Our Current Process-Oriented (Department Specialization) Company Layouts?

Figure 7.0 shows the actual equipment layout and material flow (spaghetti diagram) of a facility that manufactured and assembled fluid pumps in a process-oriented environment. The spaghetti diagram clearly shows that this layout is a material handling nightmare (or a dream come true for the material handling equipment supplier). This layout produced the following problems:

♦ Defects were not detected until the part went to inspection (some defects were not manufacturing defects but were actually created by excessive or sloppy material handling).

♦ It could take several months for a part to traverse the length of the department (the customer's expectation for delivery was 5-10 days).

♦ Raw and work-in-process (WIP) inventory on the floor, including rework and storage areas, occupied 25% of the available manufacturing space. The building had been added onto several times and these additions would not have been necessary had the plant adopted manufacturing cells.

These problems then created other problems:

♦ Identifying the root cause of defects was difficult due to the amount of time that passed between creation of the defect and its discovery and the number of people who had handled the part.

♦ Scheduling the Assembly Department was impossible. Customer satisfaction was dependent on the personal follow-up and expediting of the required parts through manufacturing by committed customer service champions.

♦ While the plant produced a superbly engineered product, customers were often forced to buy from the plant's competitors because of long lead times

Material Flow in a Traditional Factory with a Process Orientation

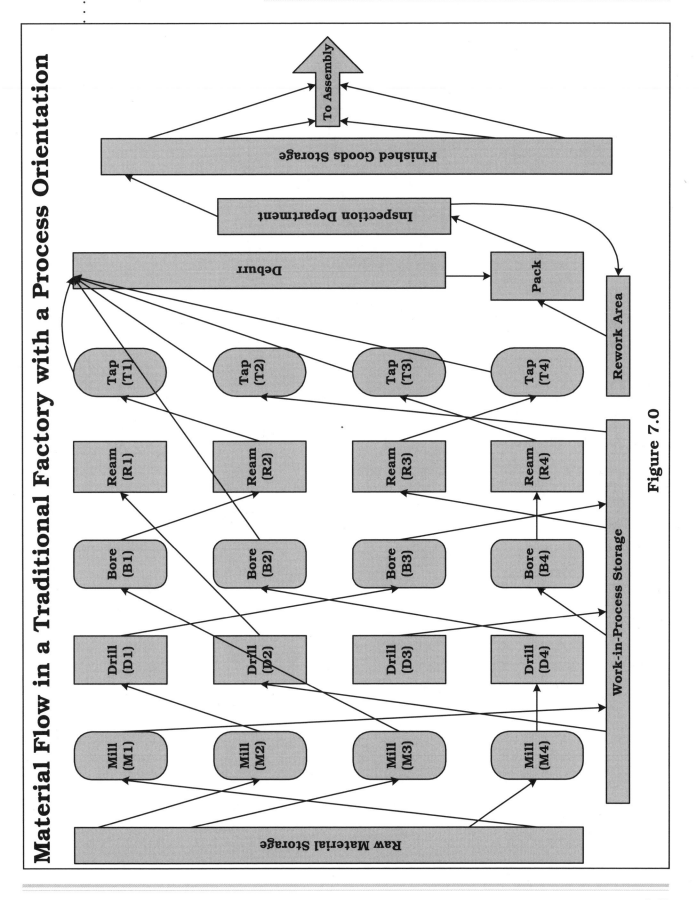

Figure 7.0

Flow of the "Knowledge" or "Information" Product in a Typical Office

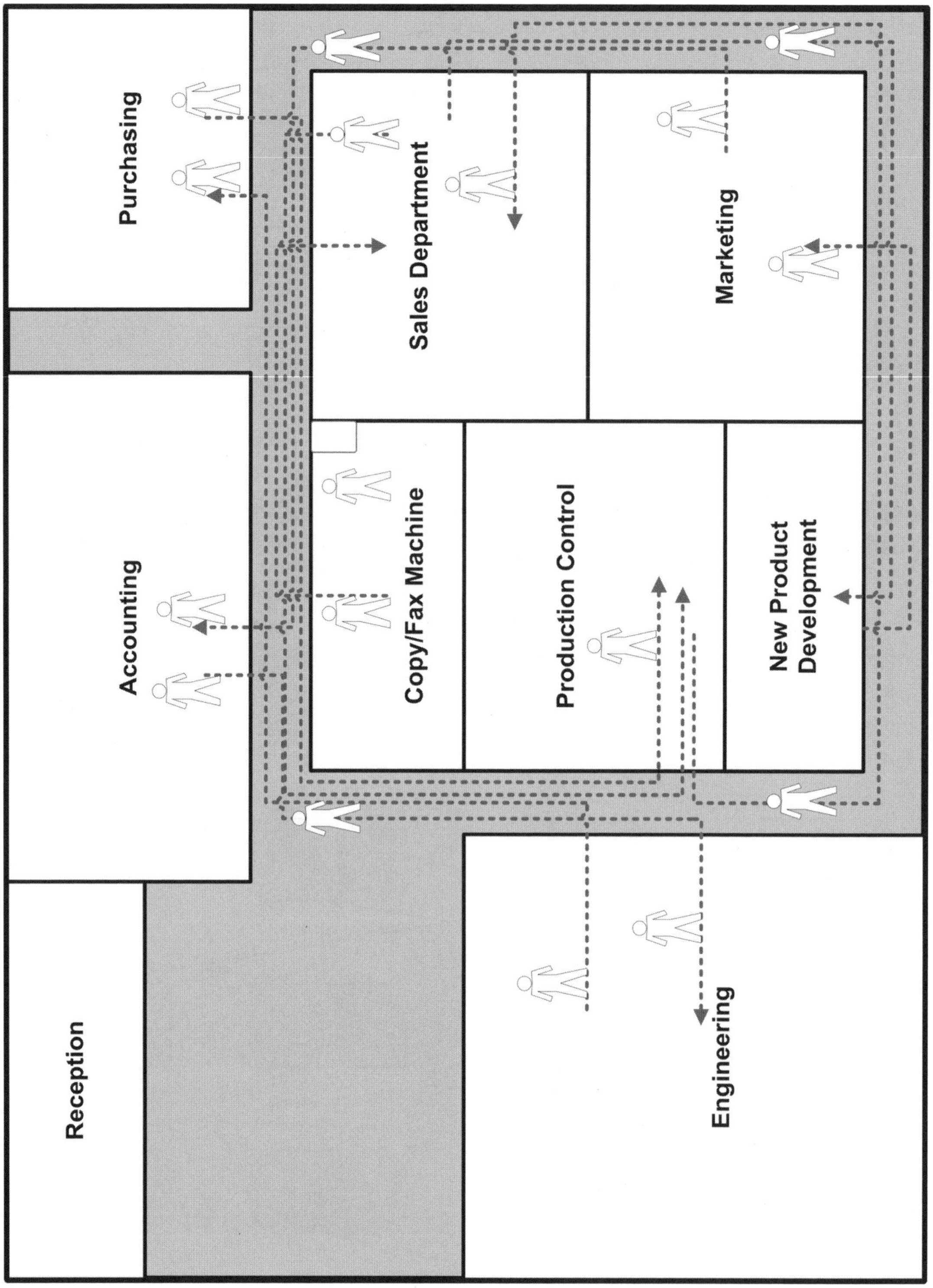

Figure 7.0A

or missed delivery schedules. Some competitors were actually spawned as a result of the plant's inability to serve its customers. The plant never reached its full sales potential because of its poor manufacturing performance.

Office Departmentalization

Figure 7.0A shows a typical office with a departmental layout. The creation of the office information product often requires movement (motion waste) and the transfer (transportation waste) of products between departments. Often, motion and transportation waste are expanded by multi-story buildings or by departments which are not in the same building.

The same benefits that accrue from manufacturing cells also occur in office cells.

The Benefits of Manufacturing/Office Cells

Manufacturing/Office cells and One Piece Flow Production provide the benefits of dramatically reducing:

- ♦ Product defects
- ♦ Lead times
- ♦ Work-in-process and finished goods inventory (Figure 7.1 shows the effect on the average inventory levels when a customer's requirement of 4,000 pieces per month are produced all at one time, in 5-day increments [1000 pieces], or in daily increments [200 pieces].)
- ♦ Required business space
- ♦ Information/material handling

while improving:

Manufacturing Cells Can Reduce Inventory

Customer Requirements for the Month Produced at One Time

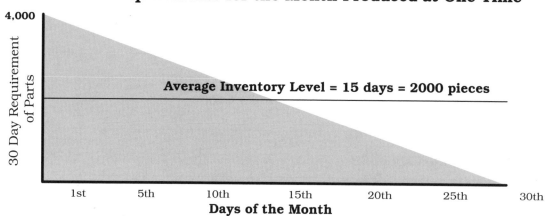

Customer Requirements for the Week Produced at One Time

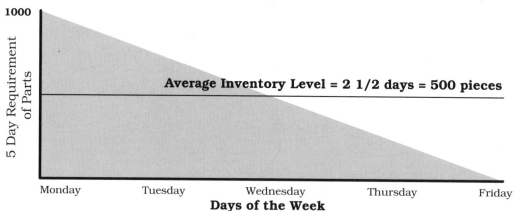

Customer Requirements for the Day Produced at One Time

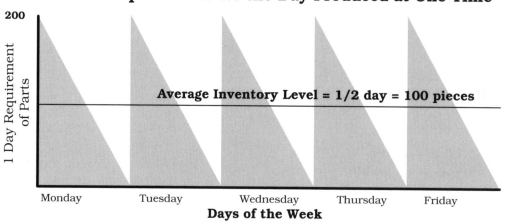

Figure 7.1

♦ Company-wide productivity
♦ Company-wide teamwork
♦ Company capacity
♦ Company flexibility

It is interesting to note that while companies have always measured the production performance of their shop floor associates (efficiency against the standard for example), there has been almost no measuring of office production performance.

The material flow in a typical manufacturing cell using the same machine routings as the Traditional Factory of Figure 7.0 is illustrated in Figure 7.2. Figure 7.2 also references inventory "Kanbans" which are introduced in Chapter 9. Kanbans enhance the performance of manufacturing cells but are not a prerequisite to implementing cells. Remember that each component of WCM will provide some improvement in your facility, but their real power occurs when all components are working together.

Where Do The Extra People Go?

Manufacturing/Office cells will improve your productivity and reduce your labor requirements by at least twenty percent. We would highly discourage anyone from thinking that any labor savings from implementing WCM can be immediately translated into workforce reductions. Improvement ideas that flow from the teams will stop immediately if they think their ideas may cost them their jobs. Only if the entire plant is about to go under will members of the team understand. As members of the team are made available as a result of the plant's improvement programs, they can be moved into Kaizen (Chapter 10) activities. In-sourcing, bringing work back into the company that is currently being done by an outside supplier, is another option. The long-term effect of implementing World Class Enterprise is for business growth through customer satisfaction, and that is when you will need those "extra" team members. In the short term, only normal or voluntary attrition should be used to reduce the workforce.

Manufacturing/Office Cell—One Piece Product Flow

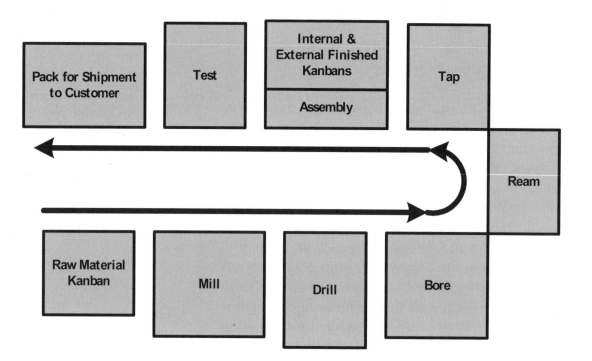

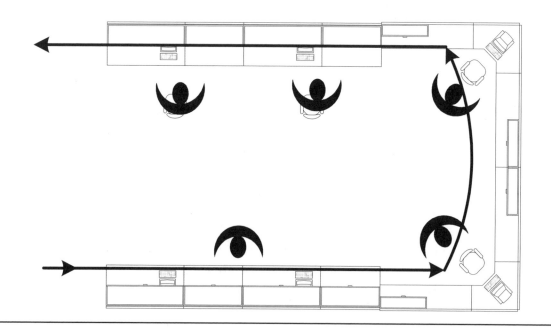

Figures 7.2 & 7.2A

Typical layouts for a manufacturing cell (above) and office cell (below)

While the noted improvements are more than enough justification to support moving from a process/department orientation into cells, they pale in comparison to the other improvements that work cells facilitate. Cells give management the opportunity to empower and give ownership to the team, and for the team to take that ownership.

With manufacturing/office cells, the team will experience and develop (reference Figures 7.2A & 7.3):

♦ Improved communication and teamwork – associates are close enough to talk and help each other if necessary

♦ An understanding of the entire process from raw material to the finished product

♦ An opportunity to meet and discuss issues with customers if any customer concerns develop

♦ An environment where the cell associates have a greater sense of control in how their business (cell) is run

♦ Higher job satisfaction through increased job responsibility, ownership, and variety

How Do Manufacturing/Office Cells Improve Productivity?

Some members of the team may immediately think that work cells are nothing more than another disguised attempt by management to "get us to work harder." This is not the case. The productivity improvements that come from work cells are obtained by eliminating *waste*, the part of each person's job that the customer will not pay for, and substituting *value added* operations. This substitution is illustrated in Figure 7.4. This figure is similar to

> "Make every job a business."
>
> TOM PETERS

Manufacturing/Office Cells Rule #1

Cells will make your company more productive. Prepare a plan NOW for redeploying the members of the team who become available as a result of this initiative. If you are converting from the traditional business of Figure 7.0 or 7.0A, work cells will reduce your labor requirements by a minimum of 20 percent. Tell your team in advance what will happen to the extra people.

Manufacturing Cell - Owner/Operators in Motion

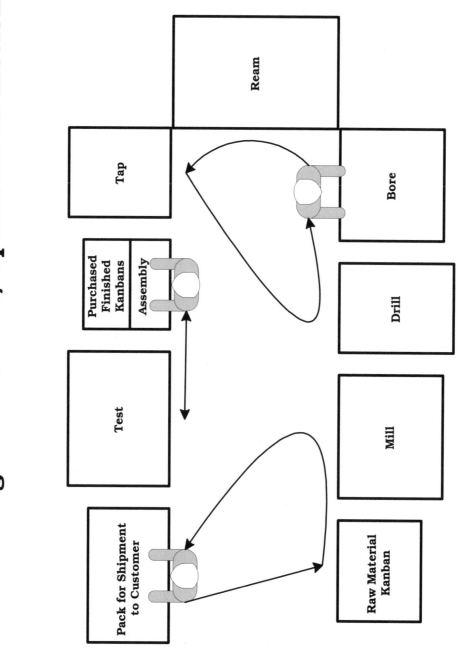

Figure 7.3

The cell operators, as a team, decide how often they will rotate jobs. Also, the cell design allows manning to be increased or decreased to match changes in customer requirements.

the productivity improvement goals of Chapter 6 shown in Figure 6.0. The difference is in the type of waste or losses being eliminated.

Since most members of the team want to feel good about their contribution to the team's goals, this substitution, when completely understood and implemented, is a welcome change. No one feels good about spending half the day creating waste.

Manufacturing/Office Cell Prerequisites

♦ **Product Families.** Product families are parts which share or could share the same manufacturing processes and equipment. Sufficient volume must exist for a single part or entire product family before dedicating manufacturing/office resources to creating a cell. If sufficient volume does not exist, combine with product families that have many of the same routings and processes.

♦ **Repetitive manufacturing/office processes.** Cells take time, energy, and money to design and develop. Therefore it is essential that the cell will produce a part or series of parts which customers repetitively require. As the team gains experience designing cells and making manufacturing/office equipment mobile, the payback time is reduced.

♦ **Small, dedicated, moveable equipment.** By definition, movable equipment has common termination for equipment utilities, and wheels (retractable base casters) or, as a minimum, forklift slots. The common termination of utilities means that all air, water, and electrical machine connections are common between all machines and are "quick disconnect" types of devices. Retractable base caster wheels allow the equipment to be moved easily by

---

Manufacturing/Office Cells Rule #2

A thorough inspection process must be designed into each work cell. Each part will be manufactured and inspected, one piece at a time, by the cell operators.

How Do Manufacturing/Office Cells Improve Productivity?

Converting time spent on waste:

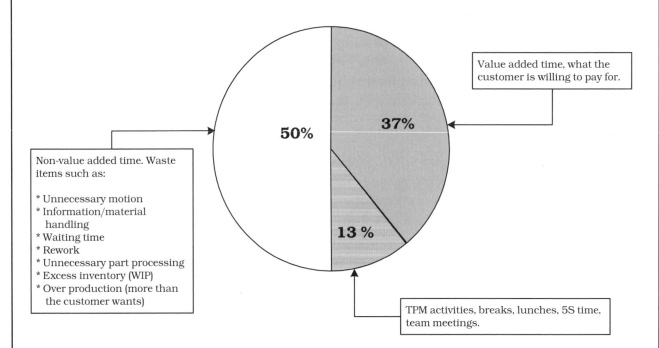

Value added time, what the customer is willing to pay for.

Non-value added time. Waste items such as:

* Unnecessary motion
* Information/material handling
* Waiting time
* Rework
* Unnecessary part processing
* Excess inventory (WIP)
* Over production (more than the customer wants)

TPM activities, breaks, lunches, 5S time, team meetings.

To value-added time:

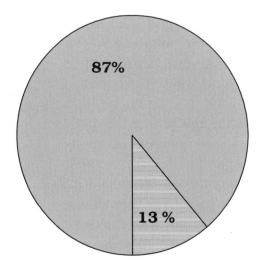

Figure 7.4

the on-site maintenance department versus the time and cost of hiring expensive machine moving fork trucks and other moving equipment.

The only goods news in our example of a traditional business (Figure 7.0 or 7.0A) is that all the equipment met the small and dedicated requirement. (This point will be made again in Chapter 8, Setup Reduction. Long setups cause large batches versus short setups which allow production of daily customer requirements.) Equipment that is difficult to move may prevent us from accepting business that does not seem repetitive enough. Additionally, once a cell is in place, difficult-to-move equipment prevents the cell team from easily optimizing the cell design and layout.

If some equipment in the facility is built into pits or has large below-ground bases, movement may be difficult. However, it is possible to build one or more cells around the immovable objects.

♦ **Flexible, cross-trainable associates.** Figure 7.3 shows what cell manning might look like in a work cell created from the traditional business of Figure 7.0. Cells typically require a reduction in job classifications while adding at least one new classification, "Cell Operator or Cell Associate." In a union environment, this change requires the direct and full support of the local union, because the move from a traditional process factory to manufacturing cells may be perceived as radical. This agreement and support must be worked out in advance of any implementation effort. A united, unwavering partnership is required.

♦ **Additional manufacturing/equipment/machine capacity.** If your facility is a one-shift operation, the conversion to manufacturing cells will probably cause some cells to work two shifts. This results from some loss of equipment capacity when the equipment is arranged into work cells. When machines/offices are aligned in a process orientation, Figure 7.0 & 7.0A, they have the flexibility of running many different products or parts from many different product families. Equipment rearranged into cells will be dedicated to run only the product family the cell is designed to produce.

If your facility is a three-shift operation, the cells will probably require the facility to obtain additional equipment to account for product family dedication.

For office cells, this will mean purchasing additional fax machines, copiers, and other office equipment that will now be dedicated to a particular office cell.

If obtaining additional equipment will not fit in the current budget, then a hybrid arrangement of some manufacturing cells and some process orientation should be used. The point is that each cell will provide incremental improvement in your facility. The great news is that manufacturing cells reduce inventory and manufacturing areas, freeing 25–40% of your facility's floor space.

Manufacturing/Office Cell Implementation

The remainder of this chapter is dedicated to the implementation of cells. While the examples given are for manufacturing cells, the same techniques, calculations, and criteria are used for office cells.

IMPLEMENTING MANUFACTURING CELLS—TWO PATHS

Which plant is yours?

A.

Factory with a Process Orientation

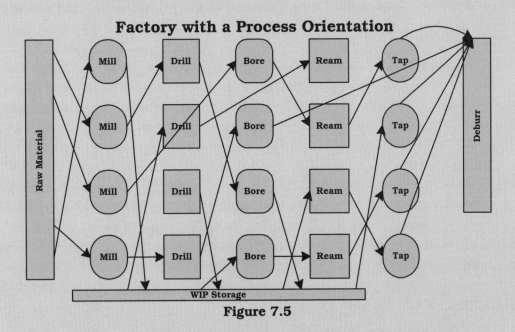

Figure 7.5

B.

Factory with a Line or Assembly Orientation

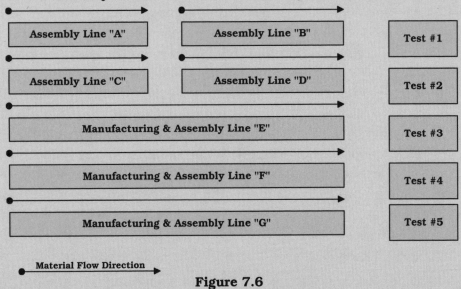

Figure 7.6

Plant A, follow implementation Steps #1 through 7

Plant B, follow implementation Steps #1, 6 & 7. Read for understanding Steps #2 through 5

IMPLEMENTING MANUFACTURING CELLS

STEP #1 – SELECTION: LAUNCH CHAMPION, FIRST WORK CELL, CELL TEAM

As with the other WCM initiatives, a successful launch is an important signal for the facility and for the future of the manufacturing cell process. The success of this launch, and the speed at which it occurs, depend upon properly trained and committed project champions and teams who have the total, enthusiastic support of upper management. Manufacturing cells represent a drastic, but required change in how your facility does business. The team will be skeptical, frightened, and perhaps even resistant to this change.

Launch Champion Selection

As discussed in Chapters 2, 4 and 6, recruit a champion to help launch and lead the initiative. The work cell champion should be someone who has a basic understanding of equipment and production scheduling, who is an outstanding leader, and someone who is trusted and respected, or can earn this trust and respect, throughout the organization. This person will make work cells an occupational hobby.

Responsibilities of the Launch Champion:

- ◆ Develop a clear understanding of the company's overall vision for the future and how the manufacturing cell initiative helps make this vision a reality. The vision of the future must come from the top person in the facility.

- ◆ Have a thorough understanding of this chapter.

- ◆ Visit other companies, competitors if possible, that are benchmarks for work cell activities.

- ◆ Give the entire plant a brief overview of the manufacturing cell implementation process, Steps #1 through #7, as well as the current status during the monthly plant meeting.

- ◆ Launch the first work cell.

First Work Cell Selection

Your first work cell project should meet this criteria:

♦ A medium-volume part or product family that currently runs no more than two shifts, five days a week

♦ A manufacturing area where the equipment is relatively easy to move

♦ The people working in the manufacturing area have Team Building Training (Chapter 5)

Team Selection

You should endeavor to have the following cross-section of members (5-14 people total) on each work cell project team:

♦ At least two operators from each production shift who will operate the proposed cell (Neglecting representation and input of a shift will drastically slow the implementation. While it may be difficult to schedule one meeting for multiple shifts, it is absolutely essential.)

♦ A maintenance journeyman

♦ A process/manufacturing engineering representative

♦ A production control/scheduling representative

♦ Other people to consider: QA representative, shift supervisor, accounting representative

When this cell is at a point where its success is relatively assured, and a list of "lessons learned" has been developed, a time line for the plant conversion to work cells should be completed.

Manufacturing Cells Rule #3

All shop floor issues affected by manufacturing cells – including job classifications, extra people, and union support – must be resolved and communicated to everyone by plant management before implementation begins.

STEP #2 – PRODUCT ROUTING ANALYSIS

The purpose of step #2 is to determine what product families, by part number, are manufactured on which piece of manufacturing equipment. A Part Routing is the official and standard engineering document which defines the exact machines and processes used to manufacture the part. An example of a Part Routing Analysis using a part number and machine number matrix for the traditional process oriented factory, Figure 7.0, is shown in Figure 7.7. An "X" was placed in the box under the machine numbers used to produce each part. Figure 7.7 will then be used to group machines into cells by product family as explained in Step #3, Product Grouping Analysis. (Note that all machines do not show usage in Figure 7.7 because the part numbers shown in this figure and used in this example represent only a small cross-section of all the product families manufactured by the facility.)

It is extremely important to remember the following during the part routing analysis:

- This list must include all active part numbers which are run in production. If service parts or other low volume part numbers are not included on this list, sufficient manufacturing equipment must be set aside for their production.

- Engineering releases for upcoming new part numbers should be included.

- Unless there is assurance that the computer file or master list of part number machine routings are 100% accurate, have them double checked by the team members who actually run the parts.

- If there are alternate methods for producing the part, these alternate part routings should be included. These part numbers should have a suffix or prefix added to the normal part number so that it can be distinguished as an alternate for this analysis.

Blank forms for all Implementation Steps are included at the end of this chapter.

Process Routing Analysis

(Reference Figure 7.0)

Part Number	Description	M1	M2	M3	M4	D1	D2	D3	D4	B1	B2	B3	B4	R1	R2	R3	R4	T1	T2	T3	T4	OTHER
																						Machine Number
6060	gear plate				X	X						X				X						
6061	cover plate	X							X				X	X				X				MC2
6065	body		X				X						X		X					X		
6066	flange	X							X				X	X								L4
6068	body		X				X						X		X					X		
6069	body		X				X						X		X					X		
6070	flange	X							X				X	X								L4
6071	flange	X							X				X	X								L4
6072	flange	X							X				X	X								L4
6077	gear plate				X	X						X				X						
6078	body		X				X						X		X					X		
6079	body		X				X						X		X					X		
6081	cover plate	X							X				X	X				X				MC2
6082	cover plate	X							X				X	X				X				
6087	flange	X							X				X	X								L4
6088	gear plate				X	X						X				X						
6089	gear plate				X	X						X				X						
6090	gear plate				X	X						X				X						
6091	cover plate	X							X				X	X				X				MC2

Figure 7.7

STEP #3 - PRODUCT GROUPING ANALYSIS

The purpose of step #3 is to group part numbers by their common manufacturing equipment and routing. Using the Process Routing Analysis that was completed in Step #2, a Product Grouping Analysis is completed as shown in Figure 7.8. These five gear plate part numbers now become our proposed "Gear Plate" cell.

Product Grouping Analysis

(Reference Figure 7.0)

Part Number	Description	M1	M2	M3	M4	D1	D2	D3	D4	B1	B2	B3	B4	R1	R2	R3	R4	T1	T2	T3	T4	OTHER
6060	gear plate				X	X						X				X						
6088	gear plate				X	X						X				X						
6089	gear plate				X	X						X				X						
6090	gear plate				X	X						X				X						
6077	gear plate				X	X						X				X						

Figure 7.8 Gear Plate Cell

The Product Grouping Analysis can be done either manually or by using a computer program. Which you use will depend on whether you are grouping 100 part numbers or 1000 part numbers and the number of different routings possible.

To determine whether the proposed cell will have enough production capacity to meet the customer's requirements, Implementation Step #4 will look at the production capacity of each machine that will be placed in the Gear Plate cell.

STEP #4 - PRODUCTION CAPACITY BY PROCESS

The purpose of step #4 is to determine the production capacity, including setup time, for each of the part numbers assigned to the proposed Gear Plate cell.

Using the Product Grouping Analysis that was developed in Step #3, a Production Capacity By Process analysis is completed for each of the five part numbers in the proposed cell. A completed Production Capacity By Process analysis for part number 6060 (all five part numbers must be completed) is shown in Figure 7.9. A detailed explanation of the Production Capacity By Process sheet is given in Figure 7.10. The information used for the Production Capacity By Process can come from the current routing sheets or from new time studies.

All obvious waste should be noted and written down if new time studies are performed (see Chapter 10 for time observation instruction and forms). This waste must be eliminated before or when the equipment is rearranged into cells.

Production Capacity By Process		Part Number:	6060				Max. Output Per Shift (pieces):			383		Dept. or Cell #:	Body Shop
		Part Name:	gear plate				Available Operator Time Per shift (minutes):			435		Date prepared or revised: 04/05/92	
				Base Time						Processing Capability Per Shift (pieces)			
Operation #	Operation Description	Machine Number	Manual Time (seconds)	Machine Time (seconds)	Time to Complete (seconds)	Setup Time (hours)						Remarks	
1	Mill face	M4	19	7	26	0.25				1003			
2	Drill thru holes	D1	32	18	50	0.25				522			
3	Bore gear housing, dowels	B3	53	15	68	1				383			
4	Ream dowels	R3	9	15	24	2				1087			
	Total		113										

Figure 7.9

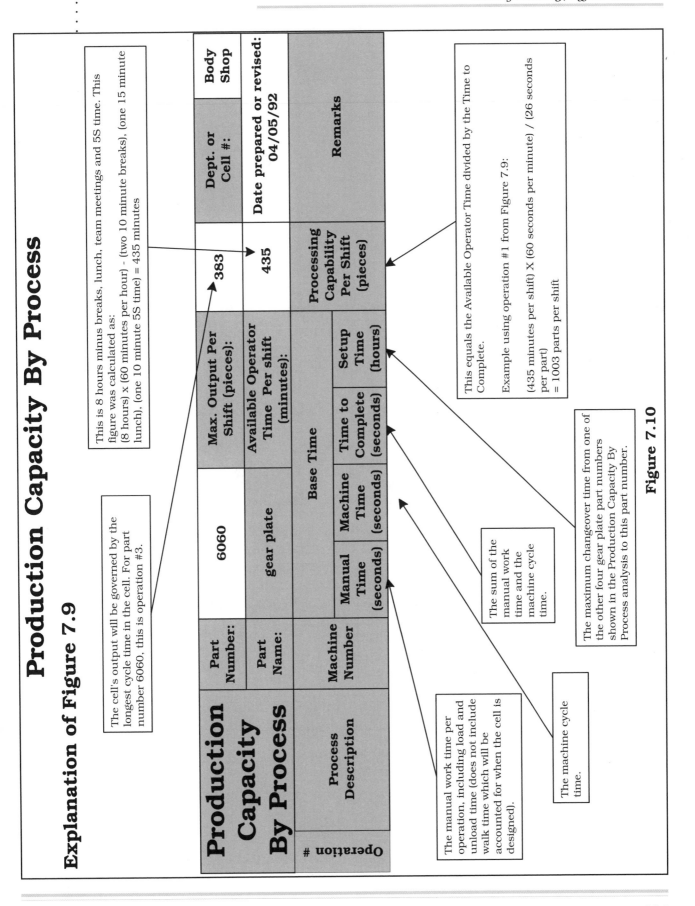

Figure 7.10

STEP #5 - CUSTOMER REQUIREMENTS AND CELL LOADING

The purpose of step #5 is to compare the cell Production Capacity information developed in Step #4 with the customer requirements for the gear plates produced in the cell. We will also look at the number of hours the cell is required to run to meet these requirements versus the number of hours the equipment is running in the current process oriented environment. We must attempt to "balance the load" between cells. The point is to design the cells so that each piece of equipment in the cell is assigned to run at least as many hours (or more) as that same equipment is running in the process-oriented environment. Step #6 will also discuss a method of cell load balancing, called secondary part routing.

Using the Production Capacity By Process analysis that was developed in Step #4, Figure 7.9, a Customer Requirements/Cell Loading Analysis is completed (see Figure 7.11). A detailed explanation of this chart is given in Figures 7.12 and 7.13.

Customer Requirements/Cell Loading Analysis

Part Number	Description	Customer Requirements in Pieces Per Week	M 4	D 1	B 3	R 3	Maximum Output Per Shift (pieces)	Setup Time, Hours	Total Time Required Per Week, Hours	Cumulative Cell Time Required, Hours
6060	gear plate	1550	X	X	X	X	383	2	31.34	31.34
6088	gear plate	210	X	X	X	X	362	2	6.2	37.54
6089	gear plate	50	X	X	X	X	248	2	3.06	40.60
6090	gear plate	2379	X	X	X	X	300	2	59.57	100.17
6077	gear plate	161	X	X	X	X	219	2	6.19	106.36

Figure 7.11

Gear Plate Cell

Customer Requirements/Cell Loading Analysis

Explanation of Figure 7.11

This is the sum of the required run time plus the setup time for each part. The required run time is calculated as follows:
(customer requirements per week) / (maximum output per shift) X (production hours per shift)

Production hours per shift = 435 minutes (from figure 7.9) / (60 minutes/hour) = 7.25 hours

The longest setup time of any operation to produce this part as recorded on the Production Capacity Sheet in Step #4. If setup time varies based on the previous part that was run on the equipment, a sequence of setup changes (or a part number run sequence) by part number must be established.

This number should be the average customer requirement. If this number increases, the cell may be required to work overtime, if it decreases, the cell team may be available to move to another cell.

Part Number	Description	Customer Requirements in Pieces Per Week	Routing				Maximum Output Per Shift (pieces)	Setup Time, Hours	Total Time Required Per Week, Hours	Cumulative Cell Time Required, Hours
			M 4	D 1	B 3	R 3				

The actual part routing sequence shown as equipment identification numbers (as previously shown and shown here as a reference).

The maximum output in pieces per shift as calculated on the Production Capacity By Process sheet (Figure 7.9).

This is the time required to run each individual part added together. Normally this cumulative time is limited to the time available from 3 shifts, 5 days a week.

For this example:

Hours Available = (120 hours minus breaks, lunches, 5S time and team meeting time).
= 120 hours - 11.25 hours
= 108.75 hours per week

Figure 7.12

Customer Requirements/Cell Loading Analysis

Continued Explanation of Figure 7.11

Part Number	Description	Customer Requirements in Pieces Per Week	Routing				Maximum Output Per Shift (pieces)	Setup Time, Hours	Total Time Required Per Week, Hours	Cumulative Cell Time Required, Hours
			M 4	D 1	B 3	R 3				
6060	gear plate	1550	X	X	X	X	383	2	31.34	31.34
6088	gear plate	210	X	X	X	X	362	2	6.2	37.54
6089	gear plate	50	X	X	X	X	248	2	3.06	40.60
6090	gear plate	2379	X	X	X	X	300	2	59.57	100.17
6077	gear plate	161	X	X	X	X	219	2	6.19	106.36

To determine how many hours of production time must be allocated to part number 6060 each week, perform the following calculation:

(customer requirements per week) / (maximum output per shift) X (production hours per shift)

Production hours per shift = 8 hours - (breaks, lunches, 5S time) = 7.25 hours per shift

(1550 parts per week) / (383 pieces per shift) X (7.25 hours per shift) = 29.34 hours per week

To calculate the total time devoted to part number 6060 per week we must include setup time.

Total Time = 29.34 hours production + 2 hours setup
       = 31.34 hours

This setup time is the longest setup time of any step as recorded on Production Capacity By Process. Note the impact of setup times on lot sizes. At two hours per setup, 8.3% of the available production hours are used for setup. If setup times were longer, for example 6 hours (25%), we would be forced to produce to the customer's monthly requirements. This occurs when long setup times eliminate enough production hours to prevent a cell from quickly switching over to run many part numbers in the same week. Conversely, if setup times were eliminated, this cell could easily produce the customer's daily requirements.

The cumulative cell time must be compared to the available production time. For a three shift operation, the available time was calculated to be:

(8 hours per shift) X (3 shifts) X (5 days per week) = 120 hours per week

120 hours - (breaks, lunches, 5S time) = 108.75 hours per week

If this amount of hours is exceeded, overtime must be used.

Figure 7.13

STEP #6 - MANUFACTURING CELL DESIGN AND LAYOUT

The key elements of work cells are "designed in" waste elimination and cell layout:

Waste Elimination

Care must be taken to prevent any of the following forms of manufacturing waste from being designed into the new work cells:

- WIP Inventory. Cells should be designed to run with the minimum amount of WIP at each operation; however, this cannot be less than one piece per machine.

- Finished Goods Inventory. Once the cell is operational, customer kanbans (Chapter 9) should be developed to prevent over production.

- Motion. All operator motion should perform value added work.

- Waiting. Use balancing (part of Implementation Step #7) to eliminate operator waiting time.

- Material Handling. Have suppliers deliver raw material directly to the point of use. Move material twice: First time to the cell—second time to the customer.

- Processing. Would the customer be willing to pay for all the operations performed on the part? Do all the processes add value?

- Rework. Have error-proofing devices been included in each operation to prevent defects from occurring?

Manufacturing Cells Rule #4

The design of work cells must consider:

- **the flow of the team working in the cell**
- **the flow of material and parts**
- **the flow of information**
- **5S**

Layout

♦ Layout the cell in a "U" shaped design to maximize operator flexibility and communication and minimize the cell footprint and operator movement.

♦ Right-handed people feel most comfortable with counter clockwise material flow.

♦ The layout must consider the ease of which 5S housekeeping and organization measures (Chapter 4) can be applied to the cell.

♦ Use secondary part routings to improve cell loading if necessary. Secondary part routings are parts which run across the same equipment that is already in the cell plus one or two additional operations (see Figure 7.14). In this example, two different product families (flange and cover plates) with similar routings are combined into one cell. Adding the cover plate parts requirement and the additional equipment required to manufacture it (T1 & MC2) to this cell loads the cell for one full shift. This layout can be used also when outside (the cell or plant) operations, such as heat treating or plating, are steps in the routing. For this situation and referencing Figure 7.14, the position shown as MC2 becomes the location for the parts going to the outside supplier, and the position shown as T1 becomes the location for parts coming back from the supplier.

♦ It is not necessary to use secondary routings to improve cell loading if it is acceptable for the team to shut down the cell and move to another cell when the customer's requirements have been produced. Generally this is a question of cell and machine availability and utilization.

Layout - Stage One

Stage one is the development of a two-dimensional scale model of the cell using the measurement, length and width, of all items that are necessary for the cell to operate. This layout and scale model could be designed by using a CAD program and a personal computer but we discourage this approach. The entire team, especially the cell operators, must be involved in the design of the cell. Remember, people and teams always find it easier to make their own marginal ideas work well, rather than to make an outsider's good ideas work at all. Since most people are not CAD operators, a layout that is easily "played and tinkered with" is the best choice. We recommend using the magnetic cell layout board shown in Figure 7.15. When the layout is completed, this board becomes a permanent part of the cell's information center.

Secondary Routing/Cell Loading Analysis

Part Number	Description	Customer Requirements in Pieces Per Week	Routing					Maximum Output Per Shift (pieces)	Setup Time, Hours	Total Time Required Per Week, Hours	Cumulative Cell Time Required, Hours
			M1	D4	B4	R1	OTHER				
6070	flange	27	X	X	X	X	L4	428	4	4.46	4.46
6071	flange	55	X	X	X	X	L4	383	4	5.04	9.50
6072	flange	55	X	X	X	X	L4	331	4	5.20	14.7
6066	flange	440	X	X	X	X	L4	428	4	11.44	26.12
6087	flange	222	X	X	X	X	L4	553	4	6.91	33.04
6081	cover plate	110	X	X	X	X	T1, MC2	609	0	1.3	34.35
6082	cover plate	27	X	X	X	X	T1, MC2	473	0	0.41	34.76
6091	cover plate	73	X	X	X	X	T1, MC2	428	0	1.24	36.00

Combined Flange/Cover Plate Cell

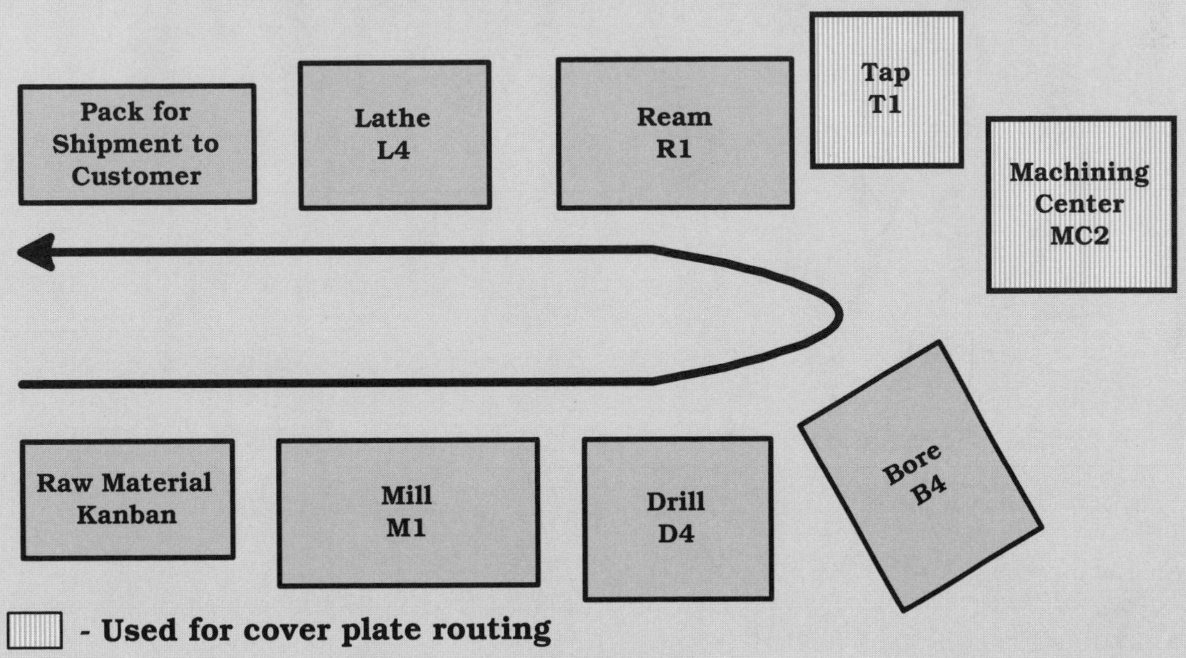

▨ - Used for cover plate routing

Figure 7.14

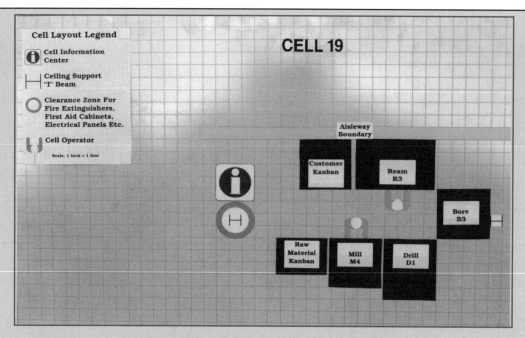

Figure 7.15 Cell Layout - Stage One

Two-dimensional scale magnetic models are made of all the people, equipment, and space that must be accounted for in the cell. These models are used to design the proposed cell which is then laid out on a magnetic, gridded, scale model of the location in the plant where the cell will be located. Cell layout materials available from Magnetic Concepts Corp., (800) 334-4245.

Figure 7.16 Cell Layout - Stage Two

In a "measure twice - cut once" strategy, the final cell design from the gridded magnetic board is laid out, using tape, in the actual cell location.

Manufacturing Cells Rule #5

Do not confuse motion or movement with value added work. Minimize movement.

For manufacturing cells, improvement means movement control; and therefore, it is very common to re-layout and move equipment several times after the initial setup. Knowing this, the team shouldn't agonize over whether it has designed the perfect cell. The concerns should be that all future cell design teams learn from the experiences of the initial team, and that equipment mobility becomes a priority. Once the team has developed consensus on a layout, proceed to stage two.

Manufacturing Cells Rule #6

In a cell material is kept in process until it is a finished product. It is never put it in a basket or on a pallet. Start a part—finish a part.

Layout - Stage Two

Stage two is a confirmation of the magnetic board layout. The outlines (corners) of all items required in the cell are marked with tape in their actual floor locations (see Figure 7.16). Be sure to check for:

♦ Adequate ceiling clearance and floor support for all items
♦ Availability of electrical power, cooling water, shop air, etc.
♦ Access in and out of the cell for raw material and finished products
♦ Adequate space for people to move, walk, and perform operations

Update any cell layout revisions to both the magnetic board and the taped floor markings. Leave the tape on the floor in place. It will be used by the equipment movers to spot the equipment locations.

The final cell layout is shown in Figure 7.17.

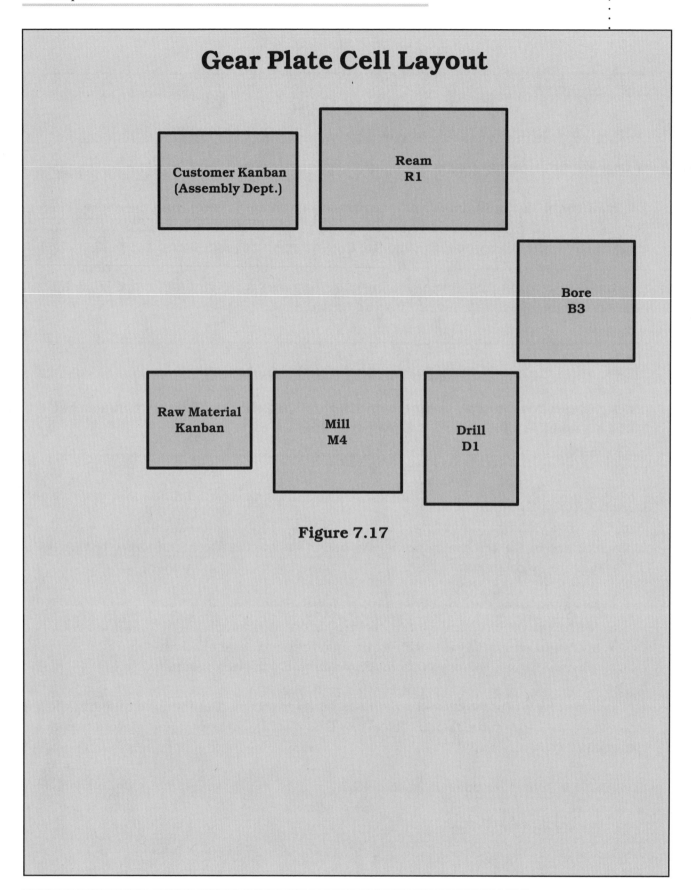

Gear Plate Cell Layout

Customer Kanban
(Assembly Dept.)

Ream
R1

Bore
B3

Raw Material
Kanban

Mill
M4

Drill
D1

Figure 7.17

STEP #7 - STANDARD OPERATIONS

Standard operations are the documented procedures used by people and machines combined to produce a part in a work cell while minimizing all forms of waste. Standard operations establish patterns for the work to be performed in producing the part. Additionally, standard operations are used for:

♦ Determining the number of work cell operators and their work sequence

♦ Instructing cell operator

♦ Training new cell operator

The three elements of standard operations are:

♦ Takt time

♦ Cell work distribution and sequence

♦ Standard cell WIP

Takt Time

Takt is a German word that means "time beat" or rhythm. In standard operations, it represents the amount of time given by the customers to produce the parts which are sold to them. In other words, takt time is the "beat" at which we must produce parts to meet the customer's requirements. Takt time is important because producing at too slow a beat may shut down the customer's assembly line, while producing at too fast a beat produces excess inventory which is waste.

Takt time is calculated as follows:

$$\text{Takt Time} = \frac{\text{Total Weekly Operating Time}}{\text{Total Weekly Customer Requirements}}$$

Manufacturing Cells Rule #7

Standard operations describe the normal operations or sequences in a cell. There can be no improvement when standards do not exist.

For manufacturing cells which only produce one part number, or for cells with "0" setup time between part numbers, use the daily operating time and daily customer requirements in the formula. If setup time is required, subtract it from the operating time.

Ultimately the takt time analysis is used to match the cell manning to the "beat" of the customer. As customer requirements change, takt time is recalculated to adjust the cell manning up or down to stay in rhythm with the customer.

Takt Time Analysis of the Gear Plate Cell

Because we are converting an existing process oriented business to work cells, the total daily operating time for each gear plate part number was determined in the Customer Requirements/Cell Loading Analysis (Implementation Step #5 for Plant "A").

For new business which will have its own cell, or for changing an existing manufacturing or assembly line (Plant "B") into cells, the initial operating time should be considered as one shift, 5 days per week. If this operating time reduces the takt time to less than the total cycle time of the bottleneck operation, then additional operating time (overtime or a second shift), or an additional cell must be added.

Example for a dedicated cell (Plant "B," no setups):

Customer Requirements = 8,000 pieces per week or 1600 pieces per day

Operating Time = 8 hours per shift (less breaks, lunch, team meetings, 5S)

= 7.25 hours per shift

$$\text{Takt Time} = \frac{(7.25 \text{ hours}) \times (3600 \text{ seconds per hour})}{1600 \text{ pieces}}$$

= 16.31 seconds per piece

If the total cycle time of the bottleneck operation actually equals 31 seconds:

$$\textbf{Capacity Required} = \frac{\textbf{Bottleneck Total Cycle Time}}{\textbf{Takt Time}}$$

$$= \frac{\textbf{31 seconds}}{\textbf{16.31 seconds}}$$

$$= \textbf{1.90 or 2}$$

Since our initial takt time calculation was for one 8-hour shift, the result of the calculation (2) indicates we need twice our initial capacity. This difference can be resolved by adding another shift to the same cell, adding another identical cell to run one shift, reducing the bottleneck operation cycle time, or running two bottleneck machines at one time in one cell.

Takt Time Calculation for the Gear Plate Cell (Reference Figure 7.13)

The takt time for part number 6060 is calculated by dividing the total operating time required per week (converted to seconds) by the customer requirements in pieces per week:

$$\textbf{Takt Time} = \frac{\textbf{(29.34 hours) X (3600 seconds per hour)}}{\textbf{1550 pieces}}$$

$$= \textbf{68 seconds per part}$$

Manufacturing Cells Rule #8

If the takt time becomes too short (less than 30 seconds), operators may not have time to walk between machines. Consider adding an additional shift or an extra cell to extend takt times.

Gear Plate Cell Takt Time Analysis

Part Number	Description	Customer Requirements in Pieces Per Week	Setup Time, Hours	Total Time Required Per Week, Hours	Takt Time Seconds
6060	gear plate	1550	2	31.34	68
6088	gear plate	210	2	6.2	72
6089	gear plate	50	2	3.46	76
6090	gear plate	2379	2	59.57	87
6077	gear plate	161	2	5.33	94

Figure 7.18

We subtracted the setup time from the total time required per week (31.34 hours) to arrive at the total operating time (machine run time) required per week. Figure 7.18 shows the summary of all the takt time calculations for the gear plate cell. Next we will determine the optimum number of operators for the gear plate cell.

Calculation of the Number of Gear Plate Cell Operators Required

The optimum number of Gear Plate cell operators is calculated by dividing the total amount of manual work required (all operations) to produce one piece (from Figure 7.9, Production Capability By Process) by the takt time (from Figure 7.18). For part number 6060, this calculation is as follows:

$$\text{Cell Operators} = \frac{\text{Total Manual Time}}{\text{Tact Time}}$$

$$= \frac{113 \text{ seconds}}{68 \text{ seconds}}$$

$$= 1.66 \text{ or } 2 \text{ operators}$$

Machine time is not included in this calculation because the operators can complete other work while the machines cycle. Walk time, however, must be included. Since we laid out the cell design earlier in this step, we will ultimately be able to walk the work sequence assigned to each operator as a double check. At this point though, we have not assigned machines and work sequences to each operator (this is the next step) so we do not know what machine walking route to measure. The normal assumption is to allow

Gear Plate Cell Operator Analysis

Part Number	Description	Total Manual Time, Seconds (From Production Capacity Sheet)	Takt Time Seconds	Number of Cell Operators (Takt Time/Manual Time)
6060	gear plate	113	68	1.66
6088	gear plate	113	72	1.57
6089	gear plate	113	76	1.49
6090	gear plate	113	87	1.3
6077	gear plate	113	94	1.2

Figure 7.19

between two and five seconds for walking time in a "U" shaped work cell. What does all this mean? When we assign work to each operator, the manual work time required must be less than the takt time to account for walking time. (If, in the above calculation, the answer would have been 2.00 operators, we would have had to "round up" to 3 operators because our answer included no allowance for walk time.) Ideally, the sum of the operator's manual time and walk time should equal the takt time. With at least one operator's time equal to the takt time, the cell will be in exact rhythm with the customer's requirements.

We will assume three seconds walking time for our cell work sequence calculations.

Figure 7.19 is a summary of the required operator calculations for all part numbers in the gear plate cell.

Manufacturing Cells Rule #9

Cells operate most successfully with an informal organizational structure. Cell size should therefore be limited to no more than eight people.

Gear Plate Cell Work Sequence

The purpose here is to develop a work sequence that does not exceed the takt time for each of our two operators. This is accomplished for Operator #1 using the Standard Work Sequence (or combination) Sheet shown in Figure 7.20. The development of these combinations and sequences is a trial-and-error task. The sheet is constructed as follows:

♦ A thick, (or red) line is drawn from the top to the bottom of the chart at the takt time. For part number 6060, this is 68 seconds. No combination of operator tasks can extend beyond this line.

♦ For each machine in the proposed sequence, fill in the manual operating time, the machine operating time, and the estimated walk time. Then draw in these times (manual time, solid line; machine time, dotted line) on the chart.

♦ A walk line (wavy line) is used to connect each subsequent operation, and is also used to return the operator back to the first operation or the starting point. If no walking is required to do the next operation, draw a straight line down to that operation.

♦ A double-ended arrow line indicates waiting time. This waiting time can occur in the process or it could mean that an operator's cycle time is less than the takt time, as shown in this figure.

The standard work sequence for Operator #2, while not charted here, would show that Operator #2 has a cycle time equal to the takt time.

Other Things to Consider!

♦ If an operator completes the cycle and returns to the first operation before the takt time, this operator becomes available for additional operations if additional work is available (Figure 7.21 shows that operator #1 has 11 seconds of wait time).

♦ Try to add assembly operations or part inspection to any walking time (walk and assemble at the same time).

♦ If machine run time exceeds the takt time, rearrange tasks so that the machine can be started at the "0" time point.

♦ Do not allow manual task times and machine operating times to run into each other (this causes wait time).

♦ Remember, the goal is to achieve the takt time and to have operators performing at 100% value added time.

Standard Work Sequence Sheet	Part Number:	6060	Output Per Shift: (pieces)	383	Date Prepared or Revised : 4/5/92		Cell #:
	Part Name:	Gear Plate	Takt Time: (seconds)	68	Operator #:	1	19

Operation #	Operation Description	Time (seconds)			Operation Time (seconds)
		Man Time	Auto Time	Walk Time	Manual ——— Machine – – – – Walking 〰〰
1	Mill face	19	7	3	
2	Drill thru holes	32	18	3	
Total		51	25	6	

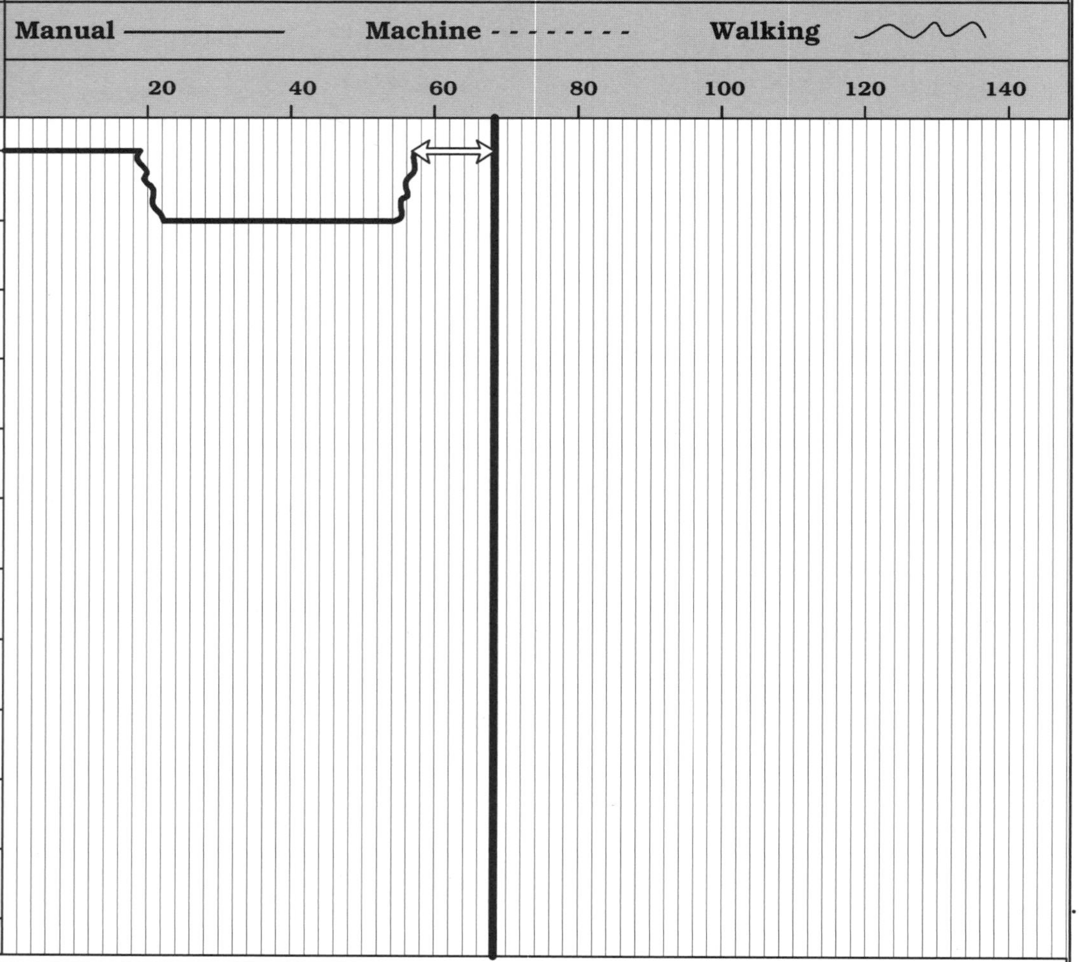

Figure 7.20

Standard Work Sheet

The purpose of a Standard Work Sheet is to provide a "standard" that shows:

♦ A fixed layout of the machines in the cell.

♦ The work sequence for each operator in the cell. This is not the sequence of processes to make the part, but rather the order of work sequences the operator follows.

♦ The minimum amount of WIP inventory necessary to complete the operation steps in sequence with one piece flow. This is known as the standard WIP, and it remains the same as long as the work sequence remains the same.

♦ Any quality assurance checks that must be made while the part is in the cell.

♦ Any safety issues in the cell that everyone should be aware of.

Figure 7.21 shows a Standard Work Sheet that was developed from the Standard Work Sequence Sheet for Operator #1 (Figure 7.20) of the Gear Plate Cell. The Standard Work Sheets for each operator, along with the Magnetic Cell Layout Board used to design the cell, should be displayed in the cell in appropriate locations.

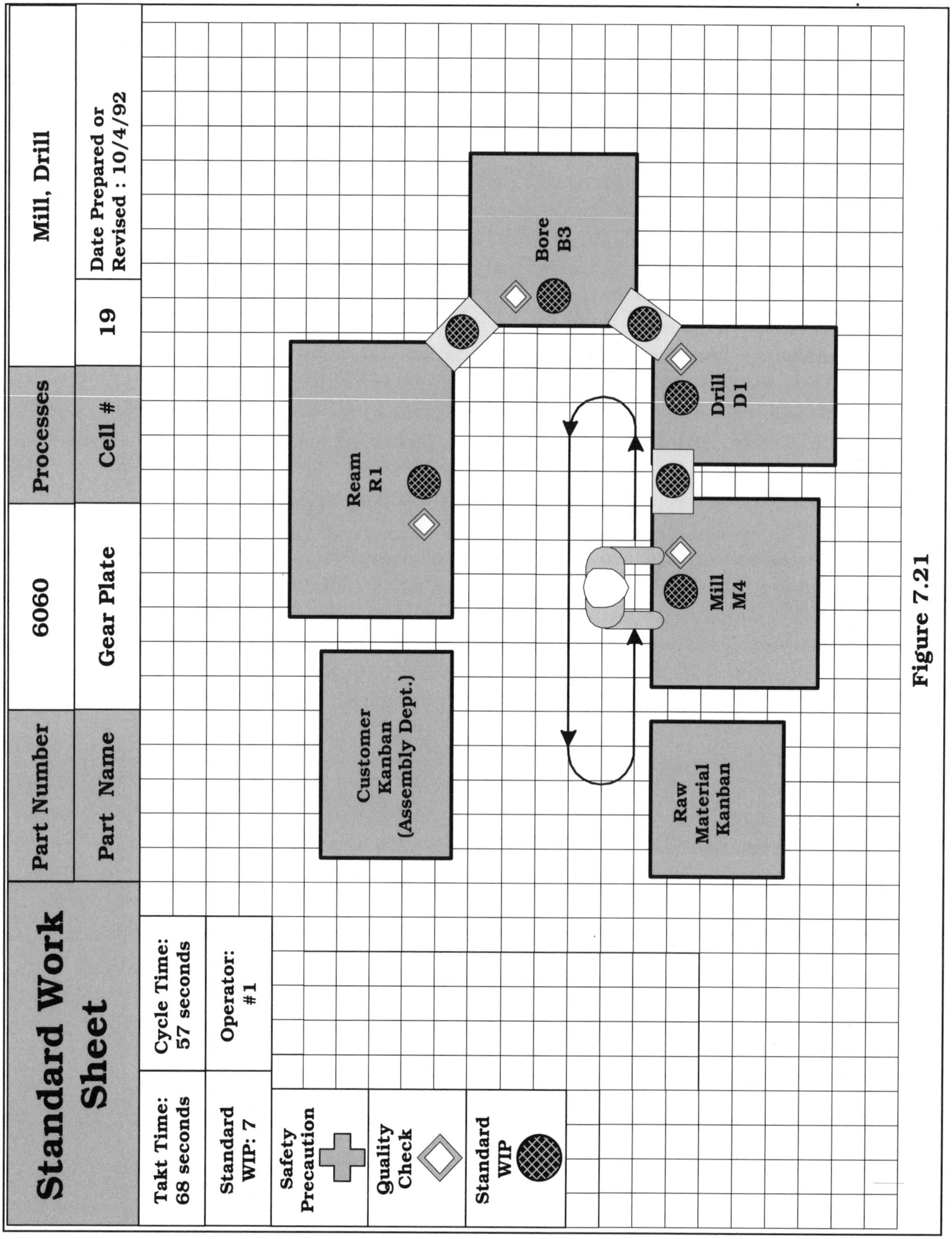
Standard Work Sheet
Part Number
6060
Processes
Mill, Drill
Part Name
Gear Plate
Cell #
19
Date Prepared or Revised : 10/4/92
Takt Time: 68 seconds
Cycle Time: 57 seconds
Standard WIP: 7
Operator: #1
Safety Precaution
Quality Check
Standard WIP
Customer Kanban (Assembly Dept.)
Ream R1
Bore B3
Drill D1
Mill M4
Raw Material Kanban

Figure 7.21

Summary

Manufacturing cells are powerful tools in improving:

- Productivity
- Team empowerment and business ownership
- Customer deliveries and product leadtimes
- Product quality
- Available manufacturing space

The performance of manufacturing cells is enhanced by Setup Reduction (Chapter 8) and Inventory Kanbans (Chapter 9).

Chapter 7 and this summary are only the beginning of the manufacturing cell journey. Chapter 10 will discuss how Kaizen and continuous improvement techniques apply to the cells that were designed in this chapter. What should your manufacturing cells look like in 3-5 years? The following page shows the vision of a World Class Manufacturing cell.

The Vision of a World Class Work Cell

	TRADITIONAL FACTORY WITH DEPARTMENTAL SPECIALIZATION (WORK CENTERS)	WORLD CLASS WORK CELL GOALS
PEOPLE	* Sitting and operating one machine. * Single skill.	* Walk from machine to machine. * Able to setup and run every machine (multi-skilled). * Stop and fix problems as they occur. * No part to next operation in cell unless perfect. * Help always available via andon system.
INFORMATION	* Daily schedule handed off by supervisor, who was handed it by production control.	* Hourly schedule on computer monitor in cell. * EH&S, educational information, training, pay and other programs on computer monitor in cell. * Current performance of cell against cell goals visible to everyone. * Operators moved after lunch if a cell is behind or customer requirements change.
MAINTENANCE	* Maintenance performed when cell has equipment or machine breakdown (fire fighting maintenance).	* Preventative and predictive maintenance provide for "0" unplanned downtime. * Every tool in its place.
MACHINES	* Very large equipment, shared by many parts. * Mounted in pits, anchored to floor, very difficult to move. * Setups take from hours to days.	* Small, dedicated. * On wheels, common termination of utilities. * Cell design is synchronized to customer requirements (Takt time). * All setups are less than 10 minutes. * 5S program visibly in place.
MATERIALS	* Large lot production, scrap/rework very visible. * Operations run at different cycle times, large quantities of work-in-process at various operations. * Material is moved and handled numerous times before it is shipped to the customer.	* One piece flow, no WIP, no scrap/rework in cell. * Operations are balanced, no bottlenecks (all bottlenecks). * All raw materials on pull system from suppliers using kanbans. * All certified suppliers, no receiving inspection. * All containers are reusable (no dunnage).

MANUFACTURING/OFFICE CELL RULES

1. Cells will make your plant more productive. Prepare a plan NOW for redeploying the members of the team who become available as a result of this initiative. If you are converting from the traditional factory of Figure 7.0 or 7.0A, work cells will reduce your labor requirements by a minimum of 20 percent. Tell your team in advance what will happen to the extra people.

2. A thorough inspection process must be designed into each work cell. Each part will be manufactured and inspected, one piece at a time, by the cell operators.

3. All shop floor issues affected by manufacturing cells—including job classifications, extra people, and union support—must be resolved and communicated to everyone before the implementation can start.

4. The design of work cells must consider:

    ♦ the flow of the team working in the cell
    ♦ the flow of material and parts
    ♦ the flow of information
    ♦ 5S

5. Do not confuse motion or movement with value added work. Minimize movement.

6. In a cell material is kept in process until it is a finished product. It is never put in a basket or on a pallet. Start a part—finish a part.

7. Standard operations describe the normal operations or sequences in a cell. There can be no improvement when standards do not exist.

8. If the takt time becomes too short (less than 30 seconds), operators may not have time to walk between machines. Consider adding an additional shift or an extra cell to extend takt times.

9. Cells operate most successfully with an informal organizational structure. Cell size should therefore be limited to no more than eight people.

Process Routing/Product Grouping Analysis

Equipment Designations

Part Number	Description																				OTHER

Production Capacity By Process

Part Number:		
Part Name:		
Max. Output Per Shift (pieces):		
Available Operator Time Per shift (minutes):		
Dept. or Cell #:		
Date prepared or revised:		

Operation #	Operation Description	Machine Number	Base Time				Processing Capability Per Shift (pieces)	Remarks
			Manual Time (seconds)	Machine Time (seconds)	Time to Complete (seconds)	Setup Time (hours)		
Total								

Customer Requirements/Cell Loading Analysis

Part Number	Description	Customer Requirements in Pieces Per Week	Routing (Reference)							Maximum Output Per Shift (pieces)	Setup Time, Hours	Total Time Required Per Week, Hours	Cumulative Cell Time Required, Hours

Standard Work Sequence Sheet

		Part Number:			Output Per Shift: (pieces)			Date Prepared or Revised :			Cell #
		Part Name:			Takt Time: (seconds)			Operator #:			

Operation Time (seconds)

Manual ——— Machine - - - - - Walking 〜〜〜

20 · 40 · 60 · 80 · 100 · 120 · 140

Operation #	Operation Description	Time (seconds)				
		Man Time	Auto Time	Walk Time		
Total						

Standard Work Sheet

Part Number:	Process:		Date Prepared or Revised :
Part Name:	Cell #:		

| Takt Time: | Cycle Time: | | |
| Standard WIP: | Operator: | | |

Safety Precaution	✚		
Quality Check	◇		
Standard WIP	⬤		

Setup Reduction

Reducing Product Delivery Lead Times and Improving Your Manufacturing Capacity

Why Setup Reduction?

The goal of setup reduction is to drastically reduce the time it takes from when a customer places an order to when it is delivered to the customer's receiving dock.

Setup reduction makes it feasible for a factory to fully utilize its assets by producing a wide variety of colors and sizes of parts using the same manufacturing equipment (Figure 8.0).

Setup reduction reduces inventory because it supports building products only *after* a customer's order is received. It eliminates the need to build products to a market demand forecast. Market demand forecasts are notorious inventory builders because it is impossible to accurately forecast a customer's purchases or requirements.

Lead Times are Reduced and Customer Satisfaction Increased with Setup Reduction

Setup Time	Machine Run Time	Lot Size	Number of Different Part Numbers Produced
2 HOURS	6 HOURS	512	1
1 HOUR	6 HOURS	256	2
30 MINUTES	6 HOURS	128	4
15 MINUTES	6 HOURS	64	8
7.5 MINUTES	6 HOURS	32	16
3.75 MINUTES	6 HOURS	16	32
113 SECONDS	6 HOURS	8	64
56 SECONDS	6 HOURS	4	128
28 SECONDS	6 HOURS	2	256
14 SECONDS	6 HOURS	1	512

Figure 8.0

This chart dramatically illustrates the increased flexibility of one machine as the setup time is reduced from two hours to 14 seconds per changeover. Note that the machine runs 6 hours in each case and that the total count of parts is always 512. However, the possibility exists to produce 512 different parts when the setup time is only 14 seconds. Last minute schedule changes from the customer become almost incidental.

Like the other WCM advanced methods, setup reduction is amazingly simple and usually can be carried out for little or no cost. Much as a race car pit crew prepares in advance for the car that will arrive in the pit area, double digit percent reductions in setup times can be accomplished by preparing to setup for part "B" while the machine is running part "A." With 5S Workplace Organizational Techniques of Chapter 4 in place, many requirements for setup reduction already exist or will be easily accomplished. Once preparation for a setup is complete, additional techniques can be used to complete the reduction. It is not unusual to reduce the total setup times from many hours to less than ten minutes.

The great news about setup reduction is that you will find your team extremely receptive to reducing setup time. While there are many craftsmen who take great pride in designing, building, or repairing equipment, we have not found anyone who looks forward to an eight-hour setup. Be prepared for this initiative to quickly "take root" in your facility.

Our "team best" setup reduction was from 21 hours to 81 seconds at a cost of $194.00.

The Origin of Setup Reduction

The origin of setup reduction supports the contention that excessive management breeds waste, and that *lean* manufacturing is the mother of invention and creativity.

Japan again. After World War II, the decimated Japanese economy and companies like Toyota were starving for capital. The Japanese government reduced the availability of capital by prohibiting foreign investment in the fledgling Japanese Automotive Industry, and high tariffs were placed on all cars imported into Japan. The government reasoned that it should protect the Japanese car market and the native producers in an attempt to allow these companies to gain a foothold in the car making business.

For Taiichi Ohno, Toyota's chief production engineer, this lack of capital presented several major problems. As he studied American car companies, he noted that each company had hundreds of stamping presses, each stamping out different sheet metal parts of a car (hoods, fenders, doors, floor pans, etc.). One reason each company had so many stamping presses was that each press was difficult to setup for a new part number. Setup times were typically 24 hours or more. Consequently, stamping presses were often left setup for several months at a time. Occasionally, presses were left permanently setup on one part number.

While Ohno was required to make the same number of each component as the Americans, he could afford to buy only a few stamping presses. Ohno concentrated his efforts on the one thing he thought he could control—setup times. If he could reduce press setup times, Ohno would be able to run many different car parts on the same press – and in the same day! To assist Ohno and Toyota in this endeavor, Shigeo Shingo from the Japan Management Association was called as a consultant. Shingo was in the process of developing a revolutionary setup concept—separating external setup elements from internal elements. By 1970, Shingo and Toyota were able to reduce the setup time for a 1,000 ton press from four hours to an amazing three minutes. In 1983, Shingo wrote the book that is the foundation of all setup reduction efforts, "A Revolution in Manufacturing: The SMED System." (SMED – Single Minute Exchange of Dies).

It was not until setup reduction and small lot production were carried out that Ohno discovered the favorable effects that these techniques had on *inventory* and *quality*.

How Does Setup Reduction Reduce Inventory?

Figure 8.1 shows an example of how setup reduction reduces inventory. In this example we show the average inventory level that must be stored, depending on whether you run a lot size of one month (top chart), one week (middle chart), or one day (bottom chart) of customer requirements.

Remember that storage space in your facility must be supplied for the maximum inventory conditions. Switching from a one-month lot size to a one-day lot size reduces the required inventory space by 97 percent.

Setup Reduction Rule #1

Do not attempt to go to one-day customer requirement lot production on any machine unless your TPM initiative is in place and equipment uptime is assured.

Setup Reduction Reduces Inventory

Customer Requirements for the *Month* Produced in One Lot

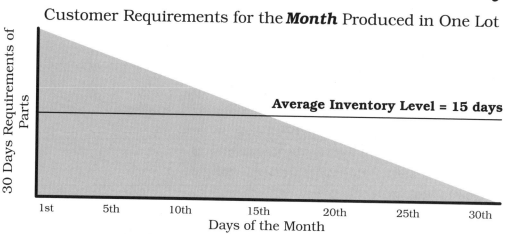

Average Inventory Level = 15 days

30 Days Requirements of Parts

1st   5th   10th   15th   20th   25th   30th

Days of the Month

Customer Requirements for the *Week* Produced in One Lot

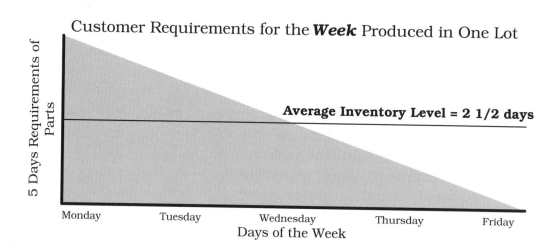

Average Inventory Level = 2 1/2 days

5 Days Requirements of Parts

Monday   Tuesday   Wednesday   Thursday   Friday

Days of the Week

Customer Requirements for the *Day* Produced in One Lot

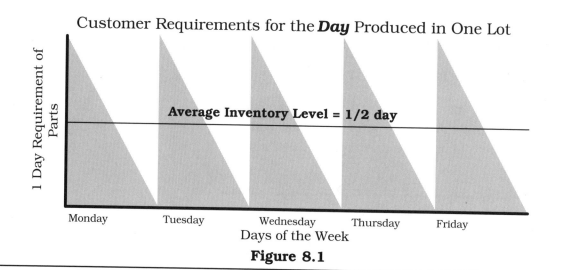

Average Inventory Level = 1/2 day

1 Day Requirement of Parts

Monday   Tuesday   Wednesday   Thursday   Friday

Days of the Week

Figure 8.1

You will probably not reduce a twenty hour setup to less than 10 minutes on the first pass. Be prepared to perform two or more setup reduction reviews for each machine. Once you have successfully reduced setup times to less than 10 minutes, you will be able to start reducing inventory levels. However, other problems, such as unplanned downtime or poor quality, can surface and require attention; therefore, approach inventory reductions cautiously, always taking care to protect delivery to your customer.

How Does Setup Reduction Improve Quality?

Quality problems and defects related to the setup process are reduced because setup errors are decreased and trial runs of the new part are eliminated (Figure 8.2). If defective parts are not produced, defective parts cannot be shipped to the customer. In addition, since parts are produced in smaller lots and assembled within a short time of their production, quality problems show up rapidly. This allows the root cause of quality problems to be found quickly while the manufacturing processing trail is still warm. If these defective parts must be reworked or scrapped, the smaller production lots limit your facility's loss.

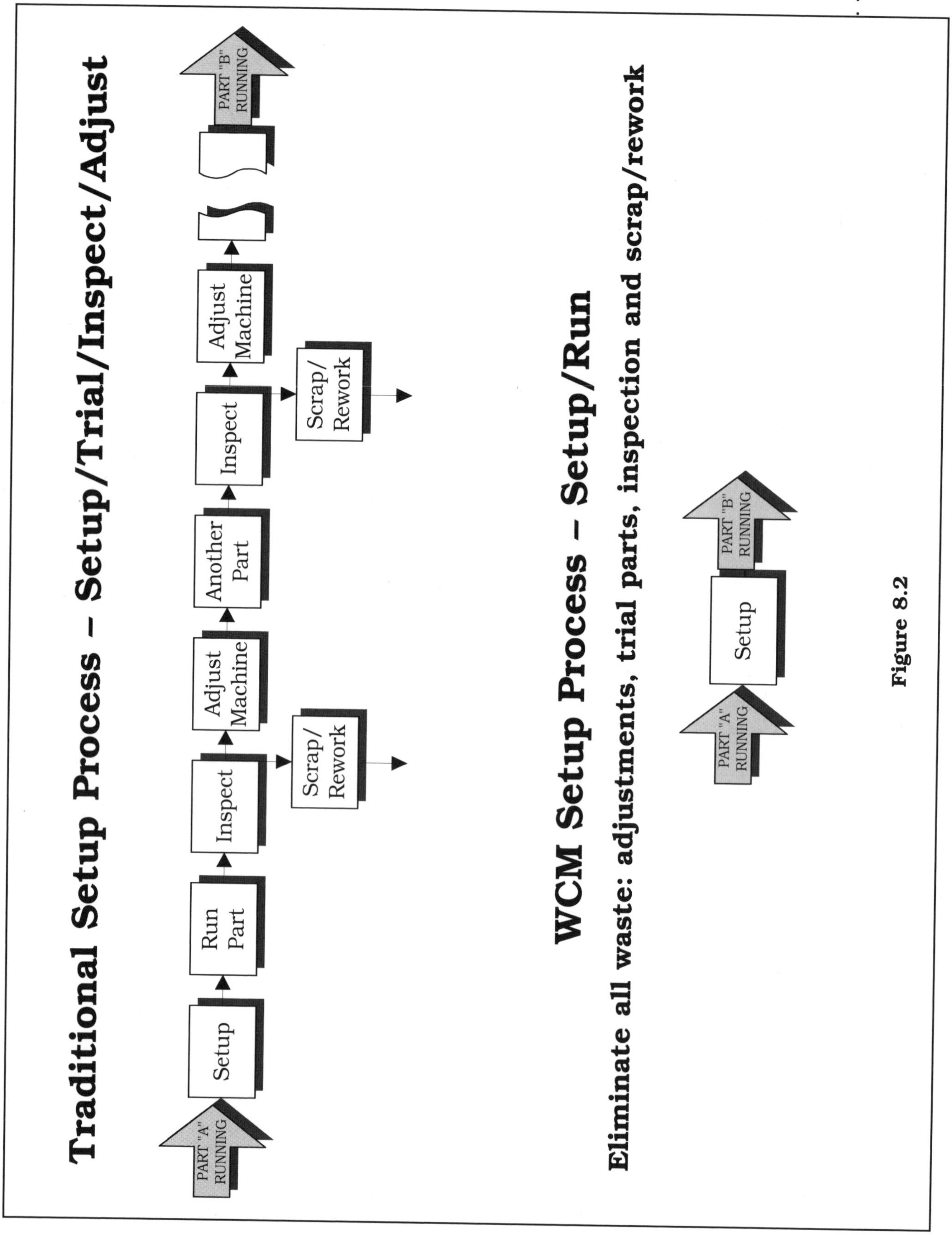
Traditional Setup Process – Setup/Trial/Inspect/Adjust
PART "A" RUNNING
Setup
Run Part
Inspect
Scrap/ Rework
Adjust Machine
Another Part
Inspect
Scrap/ Rework
Adjust Machine
PART "B" RUNNING
WCM Setup Process – Setup/Run
Eliminate all waste: adjustments, trial parts, inspection and scrap/rework
PART "A" RUNNING
Setup
PART "B" RUNNING

Figure 8.2

Setup Definitions

Setup time. The elapsed downtime between the last production piece of part "A" and the first good production piece of part "B."

Internal setup. That part of the setup which must be done while the machine is shut down, for example, removing or attaching dies.

External setup. That part of the setup which can be done while the machine is still running, for example, preheating a "hot" tool before the actual setup begins and while the press is still producing part "A."

Reviewing the Traditional Setup Procedure

Figure 8.2 shows the traditional setup process as it exists in most manufacturing plants today and the steps of the process that will be eliminated using the advanced techniques of WCM.

Does Setup Reduction Produce Lower Labor and Overhead Costs?

Setup reduction will improve your manufacturing capacity, reduce your inventory carrying costs, and reduce your scrap/rework variances. But what about labor and overhead costs? When you reduce a setup by eight hours, isn't there an eight-hour labor savings? No. The reality is that unless overtime is eliminated or the workforce reduced, labor and overhead costs remain intact. We highly discourage anyone from thinking that any labor savings from implementing WCM can be immediately translated into workforce reductions. The improvement ideas that flow from your teams will stop immediately if they think their ideas may cost them their jobs. Only when the immediate viability of the company is at stake can this strategy be used. As members of the team are made available as a result of the plant's improvement programs, they should be moved into Kaizen (Chapter 10) activities. The long-term effect of implementing WCM is for business growth through customer satisfaction. That is when you will need those extra team members. In the short term, only normal or voluntary attrition should be used to reduce the workforce.

What are the Goals of the Setup Initiative?

1. Elimination of all waste categories associated with the setup process:

♦ **Setup waste, external** - Activities such as searching, locating, or moving tools, jigs, bolts, clamps, fasteners, gauges, or instructions to the setup area

♦ **Setup waste, internal** - Alignment activities required to remove and install tools, for example, the time associated with using a fork truck to maneuver the old tool out and the new tool in while setting up a press

♦ **Replacement waste** - Activities related to removing items from the "A" tool to be installed in the "B" tool, for example, bolts, fasteners, clamps, gauges, and wiring harnesses

♦ **Adjustment waste** - Any activity that would cause the machine to cycle in a sample or trial mode which could create a part that must be inspected and then possibly scraped or reworked, for example, stroke or stop adjustments

2. Reduction of setups to the following one-step process:

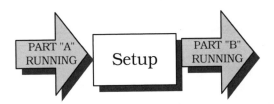

3. Reduction of setup times to "0," or to the point that the needs of the customer are the only consideration in the production scheduling of equipment.

Setup Reduction Rule #2

5S Workplace Organization must be in place to receive the fifty percent or more reduction in setup times which can occur just from being organized and ready (and generally at no cost). Make sure: Travel distances are minimized. Number of movements are reduced. Tools, tool carts, jigs, fixtures, gauges, and instructions are nearby and ready.

5S Helps Eliminate Internal Setup Waste

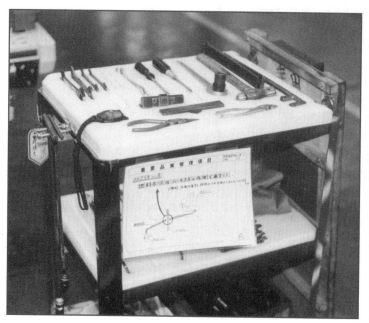

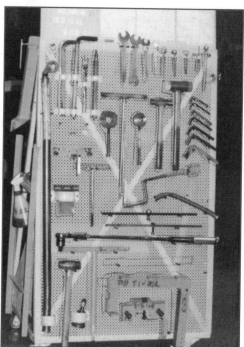

Figure 8.3

5S workplace organization is required to eliminate some forms of internal setup waste. These photographs show tool boards and setup parts storage which allow the setup people to be "ready" for the setup.

IMPLEMENTING SETUP REDUCTION

STEP #1 - TEAM AND EQUIPMENT SELECTION

As with the other WCM initiatives, a successful launch is an important signal for the facility and the setup reduction culture change process. The success of setup reduction, and the speed at which this success occurs, depends upon properly trained, committed project teams who have the total, enthusiastic support of upper management.

As discussed in earlier chapters, recruit a champion to launch and lead the initiative. Your team will be receptive to setup reduction, so recruiting a champion should be easy. Since this person will also do the training, the champion should be someone who has a basic understanding of equipment and production scheduling. If your plant has up to 500 people, find one champion to launch this initiative. Remember that people do best at what they like to do!

Responsibilities of the Launch Champion

The Launch Champion is responsible for the following:

- ◆ Developing a clear understanding of the company's overall vision for the future and what part the setup initiative has in making the vision a reality

- ◆ Having a thorough understanding of this chapter

- ◆ Visiting other companies (competitors if possible) that are benchmarks for setup activities

- ◆ Participating in the design, development, and implementation of rewards and recognition for excellence in setup (a recognition example is shown in Figure 8.13)

- ◆ Giving the entire plant a brief overview of the setup reduction process (Steps #2 through Step #6) as part of the monthly plant meeting

- ◆ Launching the first project teams

- ◆ Training additional trainers for additional project team training and launches

Team Selection

Endeavor to have the following cross-section of membership on each project team (5-8 people total):

♦ A representative(s) of the team actually responsible for this machine setup

♦ One operator of this machine from each production shift

♦ A maintenance or toolroom journeyman

♦ A process/manufacturing engineering representative

♦ A production control/scheduling representative (if the champion does not represent these areas)

Some members of the team should be new or have "fresh eyes" to the setup process. Since these team members do not have old setup habits, they can be counted on to question parts of the process that lack purpose or function.

We suggest that your first setup reduction project meet this criteria:

♦ Long setup time

♦ A part that runs regularly in your facility

If your plant has not worked on setup reduction before, these projects should yield 60-80% improvement quickly. This level of improvement will get the rest of your plant team excited about the possibilities.

Regardless of plant size, start two projects and two teams.

STEP #2 - ESTABLISH THE BASELINE

The purpose of establishing a baseline is to thoroughly understand both internal and external setup elements and the time involved in your current setup practices (Figure 8.4). This can be accomplished by video taping the current setup process. The advantages of video taping are as follows:

◆ It is impossible to write down everything that occurs in a setup as it happens

◆ Video taping preserves objectivity

◆ The setup may be reviewed as many times as desired

Video Taping Guidelines:

◆ Make sure the entire plant knows the intent of the video taping

◆ Use a tripod

◆ Video test the area in advance to make sure there is enough lighting and that the camera location gives a full view of the area

◆ Know the approximate length of the setup so that you are prepared with enough video tape and batteries

◆ Remind everyone involved in the setup that you want to video the *normal* setup process

◆ Video from the last part of "A" to the first good part of "B"

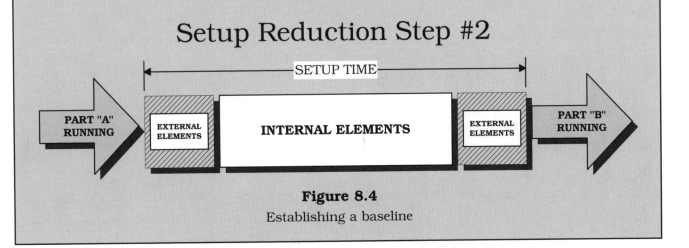

Setup Reduction Step #2

Figure 8.4

Establishing a baseline

STEP #3 – DOCUMENTING THE SETUP VIDEO, ISOLATING EXTERNAL ELEMENTS FROM INTERNAL ELEMENTS

The purpose of this step is to identify all the elements of the setup and to separate, move, and prevent obvious external elements from causing setup downtime.

The setup reduction goal for Step #3 is a minimum of 25%.

Reviewing the Definitions:

Internal setup - that part of the setup which must be done while the machine is not running.

External setup - that part of the setup which can be done while the machine is still running.

Use the video tape to study and breakdown the setup into elements or steps. Manually record these elements on the Setup Reduction Worksheet that is included at the end of this chapter. Code each element for the setup category— internal, external, or waste— and the length of time it took to accomplish that element. All waste will be categorized as internal, external, replacement, or adjustment.

Everyone doing the actual setup as well as the rest of the project team should participate in this step. The people involved in the setup should narrate the video while the rest of the team participates and shares their thoughts. Again, the goal here is to prevent the obvious external elements from causing downtime.

Use these guidelines for filling in the worksheet:

- ♦ Write down all items as they are on the video; avoid the temptation to document how it could be (make improvements) or how it should have been

- ♦ Be honest and fair

- ♦ Skip lines if the team detects a missing step

- ♦ Identify and classify waste

- ♦ Assign total and net times

- ♦ Listen to the experts (setup people/operators)

Look for these types of external activities which might be disguised as internal elements:

obtaining tools or tooling	changing chip hopper
obtaining raw material	cleaning tool/machine
obtaining drawings/process sheets	repairing tool/machine
returning tools or tooling	recording information/data
returning raw material	returning information
walking to, or moving	standing and waiting, or watching
cleaning up work area	taking breaks or lunch

Setup Reduction Rule #3

No guess work—video tape all setups that you want to improve. Use the time and date function on the camera.

Steps #2 and #3 are accomplished when the team's setup flow chart looks like Figure 8.5. This flow chart becomes the new setup baseline for this part.

Setup Reduction Step #3

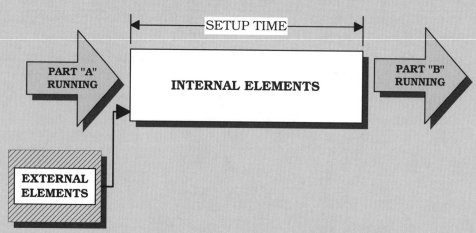

Figure 8.5
Eliminating downtime due to external elements.

STEP #4 – MOVE INTERNAL SETUP ELEMENTS TO EXTERNAL ELEMENTS

The purpose of this step is to attempt to convert all the internal elements of the setup to external elements. This will be accomplished by:

♦ Moving items which have always been assumed to be internal by assessing them against the definitions of internal and external elements

♦ Analyzing the true function or purpose of the remaining internal elements

Setup Reduction Rule #4

The greatest reductions in setup time occur from the elements that take the longest time. Concentrate on the longest time elements first.

The setup reduction goal for this step is a minimum of 25%.

As a starting point, look for these types of internal activities which can be converted to external elements:

♦ Taking tooling apart

♦ Writing program or loading program into machine

♦ Performing tool measurements

Internal Element Analysis Using the Five Whys

All problems are solvable once the root cause of the problem is discovered. The "Five Whys" are a powerful tool for use in root cause analysis. As Taiichi Ohno of Toyota discovered, if we ask why five times, we should be able to discover the root cause of the problem. In setup reduction, a five why analysis is used to determine whether an internal element can be eliminated, combined, or converted to an external element.

Analyze each internal element using this technique. Always begin analysis with the following question:

♦ What is the purpose or function of the element?

Depending on the element, asking the following additional questions, followed by the Five Whys, maybe helpful in determining how elements can be combined, changed, resequenced, or simplified:

♦ How, where, or when is this element being done? (followed by 5 Whys)

♦ Who is doing this element? (followed by 5 Whys)

Figure 8.6 shows a five why analysis on the "Taking Tooling Apart" internal activity from above.

Five Why Analysis on Internal Element: Taking Tooling Apart

Question: What is the function or purpose of taking the tool apart?

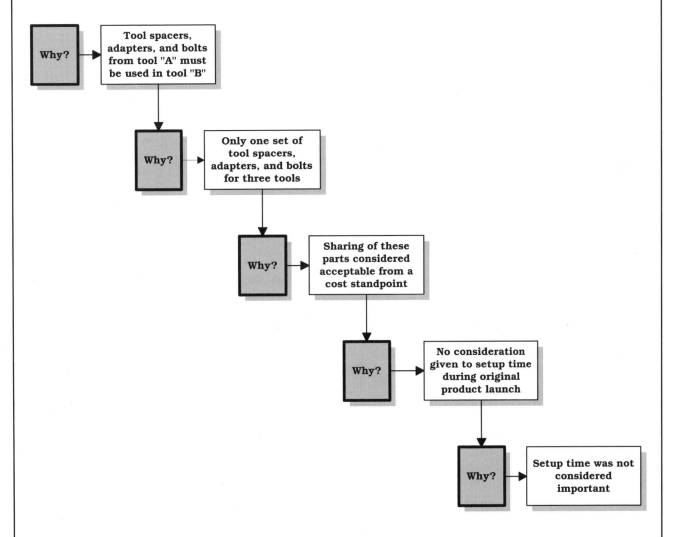

Why? → Tool spacers, adapters, and bolts from tool "A" must be used in tool "B"

Why? → Only one set of tool spacers, adapters, and bolts for three tools

Why? → Sharing of these parts considered acceptable from a cost standpoint

Why? → No consideration given to setup time during original product launch

Why? → Setup time was not considered important

How to make this external or eliminate:
Make or buy additional spacers, adapters, and bolts.

Figure 8.6

STEP #5 - WASTE ELIMINATION

The purpose of this step is to reduce the setup process to three elements. These three elements are: remove tool "A", install tool "B", run part "B"

The setup reduction goal for this step is a minimum of 35%.

Reviewing the Definitions of Setup Waste:

Setup waste, internal - Activities required to remove and install tools, for example, the time associated with using a fork truck to maneuver the old tool out and the new tool in.

Replacement waste - Activities related to removing items from the "A" tool to be installed in the "B" tool, for examples, bolts, fasteners, clamps, gauges, and wiring harnesses.

Adjustment waste - Any activity that would cause the machine to cycle in a sample or trial mode to create a part that must be inspected and then possibly scraped or reworked. Examples are stroke or stop adjustments.

Internal Setup Waste

Several different areas to consider with regard to internal setup waste are:

♦ Eliminating unnecessary movement (walking) of the setup person

♦ Reducing manual effort required by the setup people

♦ Reducing or eliminating tool/die transportation

Unnecessary Movement of the Setup Person

This area can be studied by using the setup video to develop a process map (sometimes called a spaghetti chart) of the setup person's movements. Analyze the process map to see if adding an additional person to the setup reduces or eliminates unnecessary movement. Two people, working together in parallel, can significantly reduce the movement and time required for this part of the setup. Figure 8.7 shows an example of process mapping and the parallel operation method. Note that the number of process mapping movements of the setup people should match the steps on the setup process sheet.

Reducing Movement and Travel Time
Using Parallel Operations

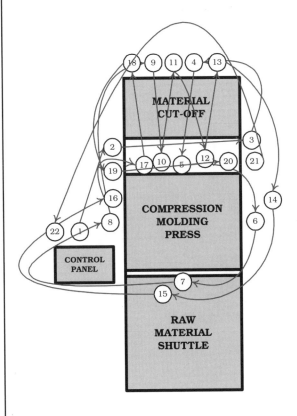

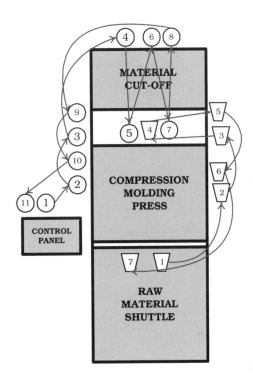

①- Single Setup Person

①- Lead Setup Person

⛶- Setup Helper

Figure 8.7

Reduction of Manual Effort

This refers to the tools required by the setup people to perform the tool change. Avoid hand tools. Power tools should be supplied to all setup people. If special power tools are required for particular setups, they should be included in a special setup tool kit.

Tool/Die Transportation

Figure 8.8 lists the current methods used to exchange tools. Use this list as a guide to reducing internal tool exchange time.

Setup Reduction Rule #5

Do not confuse motion or movement with work.

Comparison of Tool/Die Transportation Methods

Method	Potential Safety Hazards	Potential for Tool/Die or Press Damage	Required Labor Support	Speed of Tool/Die Change	Best Application	Other Considerations
Fork Truck/ Platform Truck	High	High	High	Slow (depends on driver)	Small tools, infrequent changes	* Truck size * Necessary space to press and around press
Overhead Crane	High	High	High	Slow	Large tools, infrequent changes	* Difficult to unload and load tools in horizontal opening presses
Rolling Bolsters	High (during prestaging)	Medium	Medium	Fast	All, when prestaging is not a problem	* Safety and damage issues exist when prestaging is completed using fork truck or overhead crane
Permanent Tables	High (during prestaging)	Medium	Medium	Fast (powered systems)	All, when prestaging is not a problem	* Dedicated system which obstructs press openings * Same safety and damage issues as Rolling Bolsters
Tool/Die Carts	Low	Low	Low	Fast	All, except multi-level tool/die storage	
Tool/Die Storage & Retrieval Systems	Low	Low	Low	Fast	Many tools/ dies per press with multi-level storage	

Figure 8.8

Replacement Waste

The goal of this section is to eliminate all replacement activities during a tool change as shown in Five Why example Figure 8.7. In this example, replacement waste, an internal setup element, can be eliminated by making or purchasing an extra set of spacers, adapters, and bolts.

Replacement waste generally occurs in the acts of removing and replacing fasteners, but it can also mean other waste, such as loading new programs into computer controlled equipment.

While bolts are the most common clamping device, bolts are an enemy of quick changeovers. Remember this for bolts: the first turn loosens, the last turn tightens, and everything in between is waste! Consider the following to eliminate replacement waste:

- ♦ Eliminate the use of bolts, nuts, and screws anywhere in the setup

- ♦ Use one-motion boltless clamping methods throughout the setup as shown in Figure 8.9

If this is not possible:

- ♦ Redesign tooling and the setup so nothing gets removed (bolts, nuts, or anything else) during changeover. It should only be necessary to loosen fasteners, not remove them

- ♦ Use one-turn clamping devices as shown in Figure 8.10

- ♦ Always use power tools

Power Clamping

Examples of power clamping methods are shown in Figure 8.11. Power clamping is not necessarily a better or faster solution to reducing setup times, but it is definitely more expensive. Give your setup team the opportunity to develop its own solutions to replacement waste. You will be amazed at how creative your team can be! Use power clamping solutions only as a last resort.

One Motion "Boltless" Clamping Methods

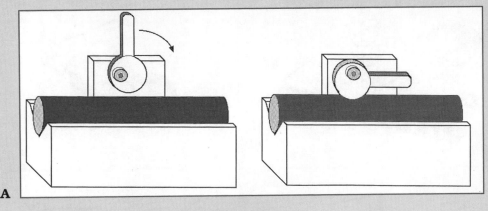

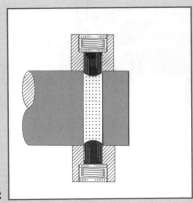

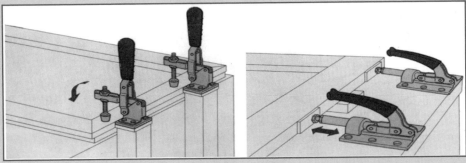

D, E

Figure 8.9

A. One hand motion cam action clamp design.

B. Latch action hand clamp holding cassette tool in place. Clamps of this design have holding capabilities up to 7,500 lbs. Carr Lane, (314) 647-6200

C. Shaft, with circular groove cut into it, is held in place by spring loaded pins (or balls) which fall into the groove when the shaft is slid through the retainer.

D., E. Vertical hold-down and straight-line (E) hand action clamps have holding capabilities up to 6,000 pounds (D) and 16,000 pounds (E). De-Sta-Co, (313) 589-2008

One Turn Clamping Methods

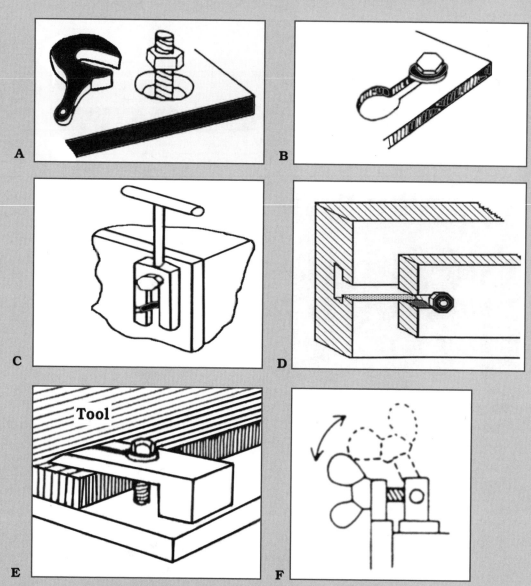

Figure 8.10

A. C-shaped washer used as spacer, washer is swivel mounted to tool.

B. Pear shaped slot in tool, bolt and washer stay in press bed.

C. T-handle used as spacer like C shaped washer shown in "A." Pin below bolt is in tool and prevents T-handle rotation. Bolt and washer stay with press bed.

D. Milled slot in tool aligns with T-slot in press bed, uses standard press bed T-bolts.

E. Clamp method, clamp and bolt stay with bed.

F. Swivelling wing nut which is mounted to the press bed. Tool is slotted to receive wing nut shaft.

Power Clamping Methods

A

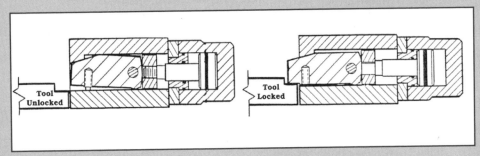

B

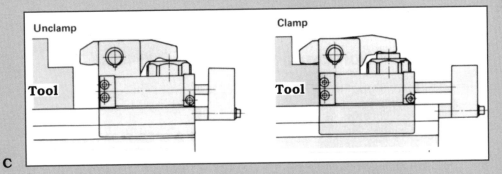

C

Figure 8.11

A. Hollow piston hydraulic clamping cylinder uses standard "T" slot in press bed and bolt. Hilma Div. Carr Lane Roemheld Mfg. Co. (314) 349-1133.

B. Hydraulic mold clamp uses a wedge design to lock tool in place.

C. Hydraulic clamp has capability of retracting away from tool or work piece for clearance.

Eliminating Replacement Waste
Tool Cassette
Figure 8.12 shows a final trim tool cassette for an automotive part which is cut with a series of individually actuated blade cutters. This is one of the more sophisticated examples of the cassette system since this type of cassette must carry its own air or hydraulic actuators. In this example, the press frame only supplies power (air, hydraulic, electrical), safety devices, and the raw material feed mechanism to the cassette.

In their simplest form, tool cassettes separate the mechanical opening and closing action of the press from the tool's ability to form the raw material to the correct specifications. Like the difference between a reel to reel audio tape recorder (the tape must be manually threaded through the mechanism) and a cassette tape recorder, cassette tool designs provides for quicker tool changeovers by eliminating replacement and adjustment waste.

Tool Setup Standardization
Standardize on function, not shape. While standardizing on shape would be of benefit to quick setups, all dies would need to conform to the largest die and that would generally be cost prohibitive. Standardizing on function requires uniformity in the parts used for setup, for example:

♦ Adding plates or blocks to the edge of tools so that the same clamping devices can be used on different presses

♦ Tools and fasteners (color code?)

♦ Gauges and measurement devices

♦ Tool lifting and transportation devices

Tool setup standardization also requires having documented procedures.

Tool Cassette Replacement Method

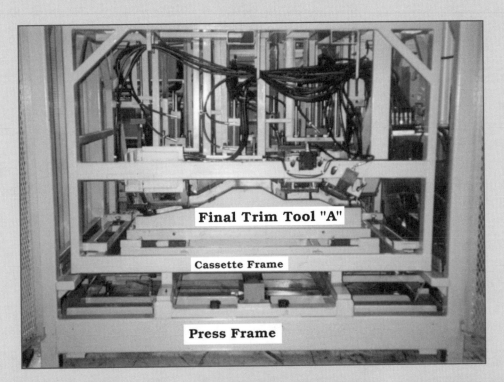

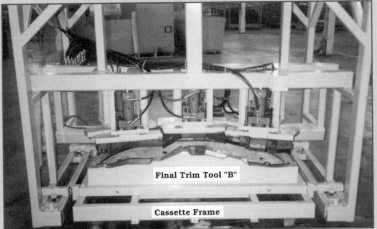

Figure 8.12

The top photo shows a press that has been designed for quick tool change using a tool cassette system. Each cassette (bottom right is tool "B" cassette) comes complete with the tool, and the air or hydraulic cylinders required to perform final trimming cuts. When a tool change is required, the cassette holding tool "A" is unclamped from the press frame, disconnected from the air and hydraulics of the press frame using the cassette quick disconnects (bottom left photo), and slid out of the frame. Tool "B" is then slid in and clamped to the press frame, and connected to air and hydraulic power.

Adjustment Waste

The goal of this section is to eliminate all tool and equipment adjustments so that the first piece out of tool "B" is a good part. Referring back to Figure 8.2, adjustments extend equipment downtime and cause scrap and/or rework. When documenting a setup remember that selecting is okay—but adjustment is waste.

Your setup team knows which elements of the setup affect the performance of the tool. Develop a constant numerical value for each of these elements and use that number for every setup.

- ◆ Eliminate all visual measurement adjustments requiring the use of scales or calipers

- ◆ Use the documented equipment or machine settings

- ◆ Use positioning pins and fixed stops

- ◆ Use block gauges and templates to select positions

- ◆ Use tooling pre-setters

- ◆ If reference points and center lines are used in the setup, make them visible

Setup Reduction Rule #6

Develop a recognition and rewards program for the setup reduction effort. Display the results of how each team is doing (see Figure 8.13). Have celebrations as milestones are reached and present the awards at your monthly plant-wide meeting.

Setup Reduction Recognition

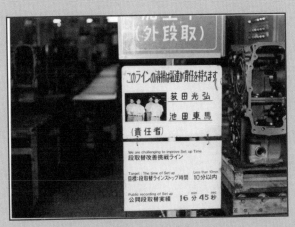

Figure 8.13
Setup Team Recognition Display Board

Note that the board gives the team's current best at 16 minutes and 45 seconds. The team's goal is stated as less than 10 minutes.

STEP #6 - CONTINUOUS IMPROVEMENT

The purpose of this step is to review the progress of the teams against their setup reduction goals.

If the goal has been met—Congratulations! The team should tell the rest of the plant how it accomplished its goal at the next plant meeting. The team should also receive recognition and the appropriate plant award. Now move on to the next setup challenge!

If the goal has not been met, move on to plan B.

Plan B involves getting some "fresh" ideas and thoughts about the setup. Everyone gets tunnel vision after they have worked on a project for awhile. We stop questioning things. We begin to think certain things are impossible. Armed with these new ideas, the team travels back through Setup Reduction Steps #2 through #5.

Begin plan B by repeating Step #2, establishing a new baseline. Revideo the setup after all the improvements have been made. The following methods are suggested for getting more ideas.

- ◆ Invite a different setup team to review the current team's setup video at one of their setup reduction meetings.

- ◆ Review the problem and solicit improvement ideas at the next plant meeting.

- ◆ Play the setup video on a repeating basis in the plant cafeteria. Put up a sign asking for help.

- ◆ Ask the equipment manufacturers to come in and give ideas.

- ◆ Find local manufacturers who have their own setup reduction initiatives and review their setup practices or have them come in and review yours (see Chapter 4 for information on how to obtain benchmarking references).

- ◆ Hire a consultant.

Setup Reduction Rule #7

After the first project teams reach their "second" baseline analysis, or meet the original setup time reduction team goal, it is time to start inviting your suppliers to attend the next training class. Remember, you cannot become a World Class Manufacturing plant without World Class Suppliers.

Summary

Setup reduction is an extremely powerful tool which improves a plant's ability to provide customer satisfaction while better utilizing its own assets.

Setup reduction initiatives are readily adopted by a plant's manufacturing team because they are easily implemented, have relatively low cost, and provide quick relief to the tedious drudgery of long setups.

How long does it take to get results? Figure 8.14 shows the actual results of a plant's setup reduction initiative. The results for each time segment are shown as a percent of all machines requiring setup (percent of 100).

Plant-wide Setup Reduction Initiative Results

Setup Time	Before	After One Year	After Four Years
Greater Than 1 Hour	30%	0	0
30 - 60 Minutes	19%	0	0
20 -30 Minutes	26%	10%	3%
10 - 20 Minutes	20%	12%	7%
5- 10 Minutes	5%	20%	12%
100 Seconds to 5 Minutes	0	17%	16%
Less Than 100 Seconds	0	41%	62%

Figure 8.14

Setup reduction results as reported by a Japanese manufacturer of automotive parts.

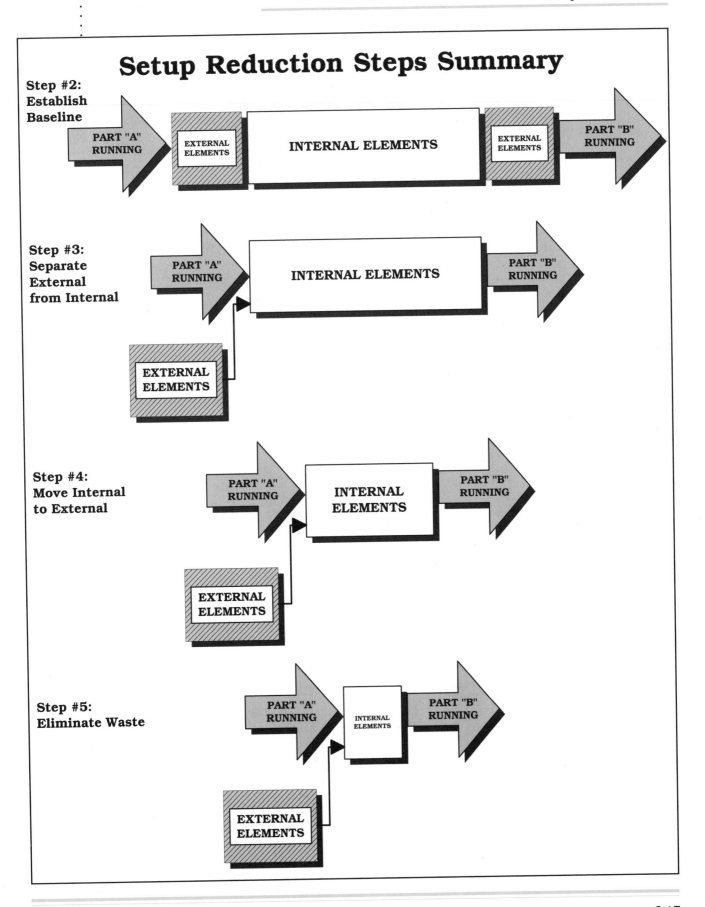

Setup Reduction Steps Summary

Step #2:
Establish
Baseline

PART "A" RUNNING | EXTERNAL ELEMENTS | INTERNAL ELEMENTS | EXTERNAL ELEMENTS | PART "B" RUNNING

Step #3:
Separate
External
from Internal

PART "A" RUNNING | INTERNAL ELEMENTS | PART "B" RUNNING

EXTERNAL ELEMENTS

Step #4:
Move Internal
to External

PART "A" RUNNING | INTERNAL ELEMENTS | PART "B" RUNNING

EXTERNAL ELEMENTS

Step #5:
Eliminate Waste

PART "A" RUNNING | INTERNAL ELEMENTS | PART "B" RUNNING

EXTERNAL ELEMENTS

SETUP REDUCTION RULES

1. Do not attempt to go to one-day customer requirement production on any machines unless your TPM initiative is in place and equipment uptime is assured.

2. 5S work place organization must be in place to receive the fifty percent or more reduction in setup times which can occur just from being organized and ready (and generally at no cost). Make sure:

    ♦ Travel distances are minimized

    ♦ Number of movements is reduced

    ♦ Tools, tool carts, jigs, fixtures, gauges, and instructions are nearby and ready.

3. No guess work—video tape all setups that you want to improve. Use the time and date function on the camera.

4. The greatest reductions in setup time occur from the elements that take the longest time. Concentrate on the longest time elements first.

5. Do not confuse motion or movement with work.

6. Develop a recognition and rewards program for the setup reduction effort. Display the results of each teams progress (see Figure 8.13). Have celebrations as milestones are reached and present the awards at your monthly plant-wide meeting.

7. After the first project teams reach their "second" baseline analysis, it is time to start inviting your suppliers to attend the next training class. Remember, you cannot become a world class manufacturing plant without world class suppliers.

Setup Reduction Worksheet

Team: **Machine/Tool:** **Date:**

No.	Setup Element	Internal	External	Waste (#)	Total Time	Net Time	Comments/Improvement Ideas

Waste Categories:

1. **Setup waste, external** - activities such as searching, finding, or transporting tools, jigs, fixtures, bolts, instructions.
2. **Setup waste, internal** - alignment activities required to remove or install tools (example - using a fork truck to remove/install tools)
3. **Replacement waste** - activities related to removing items from the "A" tool to be placed in the "B" tool (example - fasteners, etc.).
4. **Adjustment waste** - any activity which would require the machine to cycle without producing a good part (stroke/stop adjustments, etc.).

Setup Checklist

Issue Date: _____

Part Number _____	Equipment _____	Date _____
Operation # _____	Manufacturing Cell/Location _____	Reference Operating Procedures:
Setup Team _____		_____ _____

Start Setup Time _____ 1st Good piece Time _____ Setup Time _____minutes

√	#	Tools required
	1	
	2	
	3	
	4	
√	#	Gauging/Measuring Tools
	5	
	6	
	7	
	8	
√	#	Tooling/Dies/Cams/Gears/Cutting Tools
	9	
	10	
√	#	Fixtures
	11	
	12	
√	#	Instuctions/Process Sheets/Other
	13	
	14	
	15	
	15	
	16	

Chapter 9

Inventory Kanbans
Automating the Replenishment Cycle

. . . .

What is a Kanban?

Kanban is a Japanese word that means signboard or signal. Kanbans are signals developed to automate the inventory replenishment cycle for items used repetitively in a facility. Inventory kanbans communicate the need for additional material to be pulled from the supplier by the customer of that material. Kanbans are an integral part of a pull manufacturing system since material is not produced or moved until a customer (internal or external) sends a signal to do so. Kanbans tie related processes together as if they were connected by an invisible conveyor.

A typical kanban signal is an empty container designed to hold a standard quantity of material or parts. This container is sent back to the supplier from the customer when empty. Attached to the container are written instructions for refilling the container. These instructions generally include the part number, description, quantity, customer (point of use), supplier, and purchase order or work order number. If returnable containers are not used, a kanban can be as simple as a laminated card or tag which contains written instructions and is delivered back to the supplier (see Figure 9.3).

Kanbans are designed to be used for part numbers that are repetitive to your business. They can be used both internally for your own manufacturing process (operation to operation) or externally for suppliers.

Kanbans are:

♦ Communication devices from the point of use to the previous operation (customer to supplier)

♦ Purchase orders for your suppliers

♦ Work orders for your manufacturing area

♦ Visual communication tools

♦ Paperwork eliminators

Additionally, kanbans help to develop a supplier–customer relationship with the team on the shop floor, thereby pushing down the responsibility for inventory management to machine operators and assembly personnel. Kanbans reinforce the requirement for "quality at the source" and empower the team to manage its suppliers and inventory networks.

Kanbans are not appropriate for:

- Single piece or lot production

- Safety stock

- Systems which push inventory carrying requirements and the associated carrying costs back to the supplier

- Long range planning tools. Changes in part number usage, due to engineering changes or customer shifts in product usage, must be handled by more traditional methods such as Production Planners and Material Requirements Planning (MRP).

Kanban Rule #1

Do not attempt to kanban a part number without the complete involvement of all the members of the value added chain, including your external suppliers! Remember, you cannot become a World Class Enterprise without World Class Suppliers.

The Origin of Kanbans

Kanbans owe their origin to the American supermarket. After World War II, many Japanese managers and engineers came to the U.S.A. to study the manufacturing plants and systems which had so successfully supplied the American war effort. During these visits, the Japanese were exposed to the concept of the supermarket: a place where customers could buy groceries at the exact time they needed them, and only in the amount they required. Beyond that, the customer who returned to the supermarket the next day found the items restocked on the shelves.

To Taiichi Ohno, the person who ultimately developed the Toyota Production System (TPS), supermarkets eliminated waste because customers were not required to inventory any items (buy more than they needed at that time). Ohno was intrigued by this process and considered how this concept could be applied to the supplier–customer relationship in the manufacturing of products on a just–in–time basis. Ohno studied the concept and implemented a kanban system in Toyota's main machine plant in 1953. By 1962, inventory kanbans were in place company–wide at Toyota. Kanbans are used to control the flow of all products in the TPS.

It must be noted that, thirty years after complete implementation at Toyota, inventory kanbans are only in limited use in U.S. manufacturing.

How Do Kanbans Reduce Waste?

Kanbans help to eliminate or reduce waste because they:

♦ Eliminate over-production

♦ Eliminate the need for a stockroom

♦ Eliminate the need to reissue purchase orders, resulting in lower office supply costs, lower mailing costs, and lower purchasing manpower requirements

♦ Reduce the data management task for the Production Planning Department and eliminate the need for production work orders

♦ Reduce inventory (see Figure 9.0 which compares the average in-plant inventory with three different supplier delivery schedules)

♦ Reduce parts expediting

♦ Reduce parts shortages

♦ Reduce material handling (from receiving to stockroom, and from stockroom to point of use)

Kanban Rule #2

Quality at the source. Do not send defective parts to your customer. Defects must be corrected immediately! Defective parts will cause your customer's line to shut down!

Kanbans Reduce Inventory

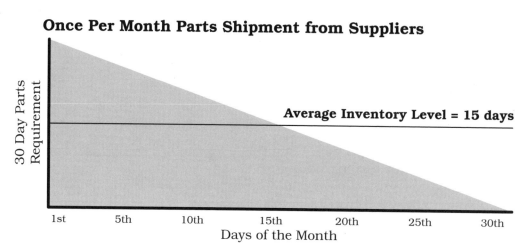

Once Per Month Parts Shipment from Suppliers

Average Inventory Level = 15 days

30 Day Parts Requirement

1st   5th   10th   15th   20th   25th   30th

Days of the Month

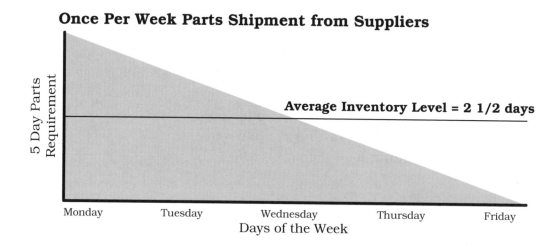

Once Per Week Parts Shipment from Suppliers

Average Inventory Level = 2 1/2 days

5 Day Parts Requirement

Monday   Tuesday   Wednesday   Thursday   Friday

Days of the Week

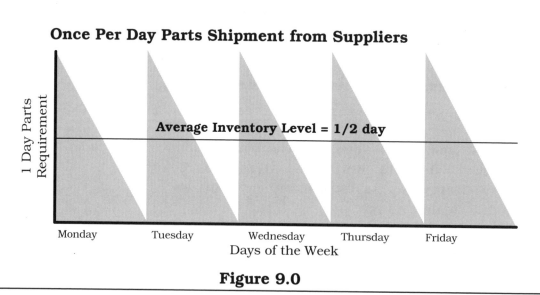

Once Per Day Parts Shipment from Suppliers

Average Inventory Level = 1/2 day

1 Day Parts Requirement

Monday   Tuesday   Wednesday   Thursday   Friday

Days of the Week

Figure 9.0

Kanban Prerequisites—Setup Reduction

If your manufacturing equipment is dedicated to run particular part numbers, reacting to a kanban is a manpower scheduling issue. Dedicated equipment is defined as that which never requires a setup change.

For equipment which runs multiple part numbers, long machine setup times limit the power of kanbans to reduce in-process inventories while maintaining production schedules. Long setup times reduce the capacity of your equipment and therefore extend kanban refill lead times. They also result in larger lot sizes per part number (see Figure 9.1).

When setup times and lead times are long, the necessary lot sizes essentially become batch production. Since customers do not order their material in batches, it becomes difficult and wasteful to attempt customer satisfaction under these conditions.

Kanban Rule #3

Kanbans require reliable equipment for support. Implement kanbans internally in areas where Total Productive Maintenance (TPM) is already in place.

Remember, any of the independent Advanced Manufacturing Techniques proposed will provide some benefit to your facility, but their real power comes from linking them to each other and in empowering your team to use them.

The Effect of Setup Times on Equipment Capacity

Setup Time	Machine Run Time	Lot Size	Number of Different Part Numbers Produced
2 HOURS	6 HOURS	512	1
1 HOUR	6 HOURS	256	2
30 MINUTES	6 HOURS	128	4
15 MINUTES	6 HOURS	64	8
7.5 MINUTES	6 HOURS	32	16
3.75 MINUTES	6 HOURS	16	32
113 SECONDS	6 HOURS	8	64
56 SECONDS	6 HOURS	4	128
28 SECONDS	6 HOURS	2	256
14 SECONDS	6 HOURS	1	512

Figure 9.1

This chart dramatically illustrates the increased flexibility of one machine as the setup time is reduced from two hours to 14 seconds per changeover. This makes last-minute schedule changes from the customer almost incidental (see Chapter 8).

Uniform or Levelized Production Schedules

Levelized production schedules have always been the goal of manufacturing companies. Companies have sought to maintain level schedules in order to keep their resources—people, equipment, and facilities—relatively constant. The term levelized production, as it is used here, includes variations up to plus or minus 20% from the average part usage.

Kanbans function efficiently when used on parts whose use or shipment is predictively repetitive as shown by part number 123 in Figure 9.2.

For part numbers with wide variations in usage, such as part number 456 in Figure 9.2, care must be exercised in applying kanbans. In this case, maximum usage exceeds the average usage by twice and minimum usage is less than 1/2 the average. This will potentially cause two problems:

> First, when demand greatly exceeds the average demand, your supplier will receive replenishment signals well before his requested lead time. If your supplier can flex his resources to respond to these signals, you will receive your parts in time; if not, your line will probably run out of parts.

> Second, when demand drops well below the average demand, replenishment will slow down or stop. At that point, you will have excess inventory.

Levelized Production Versus Erratic Demand

P/N 123

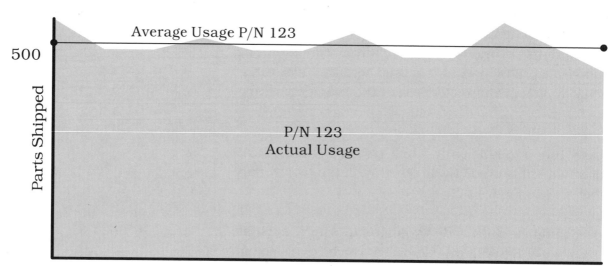

P/N 456

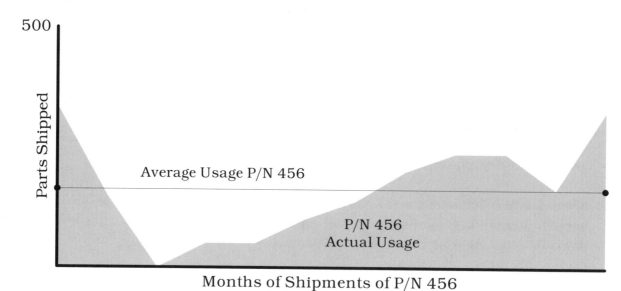

Figure 9.2

Kanban Rule #4

Focus kanbans on products and part numbers with stable month-to-month delivery requirements and short setup and lead times. Concentrate setup reduction and raw material lead time reduction efforts on the parts which have wide variations in month-to-month customer requirements.

Types of Kanbans (Pull Signals)

- **Cards attached to portable containers such as tote pans.** A business card laminator to laminate the cards works well in this application.

- **Supplier replaceable cards on cardboard boxes designed to hold a standard quantity.** Typically these cards are put on the container in a clear plastic holder (like a packing list bag) that is attached to the side of the box. When inventory is required from this box, the card is pulled from the holder. The card is either faxed to the supplier or put in the designated kanban mailbox for supplier pickup.

- **A painted spot or border on the floor around the standardized container.** The painted spot can be managed visually. No material on the spot becomes the abnormality and sends the signal.

- **Color coded striped golf balls.** These balls can be sent, via some type of conveyance such as a pneumatic tube, back to the supplier. Each color code represents a part number.

- **E-mails**

♦ **Bar code labels.**

♦ **An infinite number of variations of the above.**

SAMPLE KANBAN CARD

CUSTOMER: (This is your company for external suppliers, or the next operation for internal suppliers.)

PART NUMBER:

DESCRIPTION:

SUPPLIER:

PURCHASE ORDER OR WORK ORDER NUMBER: (Usually suppliers are given blanket orders for at least one year.)

CONTAINER QUANTITY:

NUMBER OF CONTAINERS:

Figure 9.3
Example of a Typical Kanban Card

Remember: the kanban signal represents a specific product or part number in a specific quantity. Make sure everyone understands which part number and how much of it each signal represents.

An example of a kanban card is shown in Figure 9.3.

Other information which could be included (remember that the idea is to keep it simple!):

♦ Previous process

♦ Time of delivery

♦ Where used (model number)

♦ Storage area (where the supplier is to deliver the material even if it is a location other than the customer)

Kanban Rule #5

Suppliers should deliver all material directly to their customer (point of use). For suppliers who are not certified, and therefore require incoming material inspection, the point of use should eventually be taught to perform this inspection or the supplier should be replaced with a certified supplier.

Your team can communicate directly with outside suppliers for material which is purchased finished and stored at the point of use. For example, each box containing parts can have a faxable kanban card on it. When the box or container of parts is pulled from the kanban area, the person removing the parts is responsible for pulling the card off of the box, and faxing a signal to the supplier. These faxable cards can include a preprogrammed speed dial number to eliminate the need to look up or memorize suppliers' phone numbers. Examples of actual kanban applications are shown on the following pages.

Examples of Container Signals

The picture (top left) shows a standard manufacturing rolling cart that is used as an internal kanban between the machining process (supplier) and the assembly process (customer). Parts are layered in the cart (top right) up to a mark on the side of the cart which maintains the standardized quantity. When empty, the carts are rolled back to the supplier by the customer.

The standard manufacturing totes (bottom right) use laminated luggage card holders with plastic ties as the internal supplier signal. These kanbans were used between the machining process (supplier) and the assembly process (customer).

Examples of Container Signals

Top left: Examples of corrugated and metal containers designed to hold a standard quantity. The container in the rear has metal pins which hold a standard number of cylindrical parts.

Bottom left: A reusable rack kanban designed and sized to hold raw material and to fill up (cube out) a tractor trailer. When empty, the sides fold down and the racks are stacked on top of each other for an efficient return to the supplier. The large number "15" on the card indicates the point of use for the receiving fork lift driver.

Kanban Rule #6

Use the parts only as required, and return the kanban to your supplier immediately. Deliver the empty container directly if your supplier is within your facility. If your supplier is external, an area in the plant should be designated for empty kanban container pickup by your supplier. A system must be developed so that all external suppliers pick up their containers promptly.

Examples of Faxable Signals

Three examples of external supplier faxable signal kanbans. The card (signal) is removed from its holder and faxed to the supplier by the operator when the skid/barrel/box of parts are removed from storage location. Note that the cards have the fax speed dial number of the supplier on it so the operator does not have to remember or "look up" a phone number. The operator then places the faxed signal on a spiked (nail) holder (like small restaurants do with their receipts) as the internal confirmation. An example of the faxable kanban system is shown in Figure 9.4.

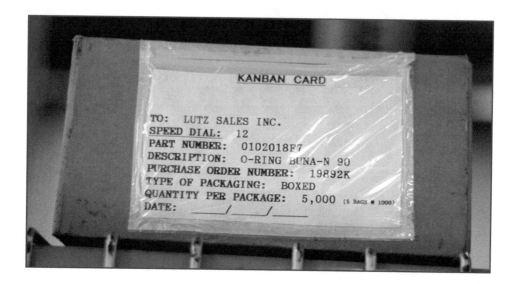

Faxable Kanban Example

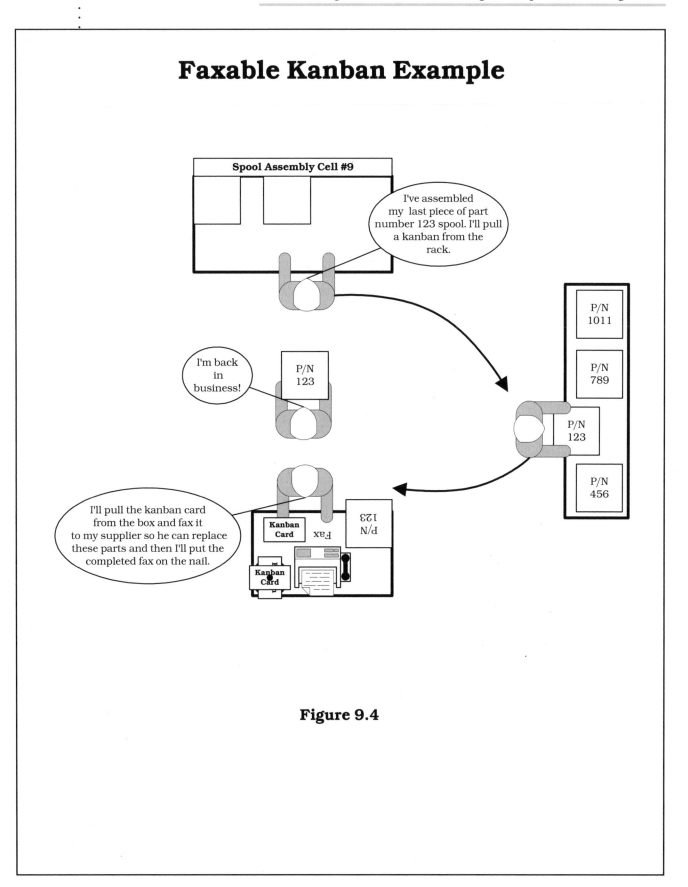

Figure 9.4

Examples of "Spot on the Floor" Signals

Top left and middle right photographs illustrate a container kanban using a "spot on the floor." Each plastic tote, when full, holds 15 circuit boards. As the internal customer (electrical box assembly) for this product empties a container stored in assembly (middle right photograph), the empty container is taken back to the supplier and placed in the "empty container" spot. When the empty container stack reaches the black line on the wall, this becomes the "signal" for the supplier to produce more circuit boards.

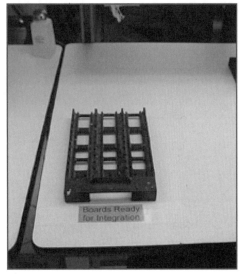

During circuit board assembly/integration operations (bottom left) an empty circuit board holder (it holds 5 boards) signals the previous operation (supplier) to produce more product. On the bottom right, the floor storage system for EC-13 parts is also a "spot on the floor kanban." When the customer for EC-13s removes a skid of these parts, the "empty spot on the floor" becomes the signal for the supplier to produce more.

More Examples of "Pull" Signals

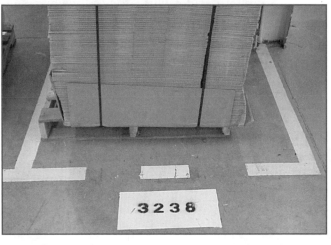

Top left: High volume chipboard packaging kanban uses column storage in a rack storage system. Skids of chipboard are removed from the rack in a top-bottom sequence. When the last skid in the column is removed, a "column signal" is faxed to the supplier. Arrows indicate which signals goes with which column. Top right: Tool crib kanban eliminates numerous trips by many people to the tool crib. Instead, tools and gages are pulled by the machine operators from the tool crib in job sequence order and delivered by the tool crib attendant. Bottom left: Defined floor storage for corrugated is the "signal" for the fork lift driver. Bottom right: Reusable container kanbans flow from the assembly area to the internal supplier and back.

Office Examples of "Pull" Signals

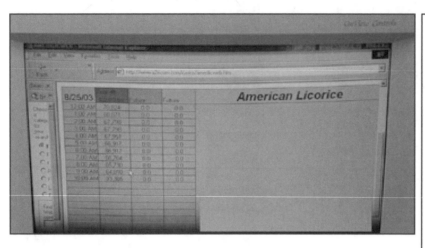

Top left: Using an internet kanban, supplier can monitor in real-time the amount of liquid (by pounds) remaining in the customer's storage tank. Supplier decides when to produce and ship product. Top right: Reordering of janitorial supplies is accomplished by custodians using faxable form. Bottom left: Ink cartridge kanbans for printers and plotters. One of each cartridge is placed in a "kanban bag." When the last cartridge of a particular color is pulled from the signal bag, the user goes to the faxable kanban holder (bottom right), selects the correct signal, and faxes it to the supplier.

***** IMPLEMENTATION NOTES *****

1. It is strongly suggested that you launch your kanban initiative with no more than 6 to 8 part numbers that represent only one area of your facility. When these part numbers are flowing smoothly and plant support for kanbans has increased, add more part numbers and more areas.

2. If your initial kanbans include outside suppliers, make sure these suppliers are "certified." Certified means that a supplier's deliveries are not subject to receiving inspection because of their outstanding quality performance on previous deliveries. Supplier part kanbans which are rejected or placed "on hold" can severely disrupt the kanban.

3. When the first internal kanbans are launched in your plant, paint all the totes, carts, and other reusable containers one new and very visible color (suggest bright green). This gives the kanban initiative great visibility to everyone in the plant during the launch period. It also gives your team an opportunity to easily spot any containers that are out of place.

4. Some team members, not familiar with kanbans, will be very nervous about launching kanbans because they fear finding kanban cards lying loose on the floor during the launch. This fear is not totally unjustified. For the first two months, on a weekly basis, the kanban champion (see launch champion page 323) should account for all containers or signals for each kanbaned part number.

Kanban Rule #7

Do not produce more parts than you have kanbans for, and produce the parts in the order the kanbans were received.

KANBAN DEVELOPMENT

STEP #1 - PICK THE PART NUMBERS

The part number to be kanbaned should be used repetitively in the facility, have shown relatively smooth month-to-month usage history, or can be forecasted to have this smooth usage.

As you gain experience with kanbans, you and your suppliers will develop methods to flex the manufacturing capacity of your facility to compensate for uneven customer demand. Flexible capacity can be achieved by using temporary or part-time employees, overtime, alternate machine routings, setup reduction, and other methods.

Ultimately, as you discover the power of kanbans, you will be able to develop kanbans specific to your operation which will manage low volume part numbers and parts with erratic usage.

Remember that the use of kanbans represents "change" in the facility and some people will doubt their effectiveness. A smooth start is essential to winning these people over early. Start the system off with relatively few part numbers, but make sure everyone who will eventually be involved in kanbans is exposed to the system.

For part numbers which involve external suppliers, do not attempt to implement a kanban without their complete understanding and support. As part of the value added chain, these suppliers must be involved in training and implementation from day one.

Finally, kanbans can also be used in the office. Do not overlook the possibility of using kanbans for office supplies, forms, janitorial supplies, and other regularly used items.

Kanban Rule #8

All internal or external suppliers must have, or should be helped to develop, setup reduction programs. The true power of kanbans can be unleashed only when setup times do not influence manufacturing capacity and, therefore, lead time.

STEP #2 - CALCULATE THE QUANTITY TO BE KANBANED FOR EACH OPERATION

KANBAN QUANTITY = (A) X (B) X (C) X (D)

"A" = WEEKLY PART USAGE.

"B" = SUPPLIER LEAD TIME IN WEEKS. The normal current lead time (5 working days per week) as given to you by your supplier.

"C" = 2 LOCATIONS. To aid in smoothly starting the kanban, we recommend that both the customer and the supplier start with full containers on day one. After start up, the WIP inventory will drop to less than one half of this level.

"D" = SMOOTHING FACTOR. This factor is used to compensate for part number demand which is not uniform in weekly or monthly usage. It is expressed in additional weeks or fractions of weeks of inventory.

Example: Part number 789 has an average weekly usage of 200 pieces. Seasonally, this demand jumps to 250 pieces/week. The smoothing factor would then calculate to be:

$$250/200 = 1.25$$

This smoothing factor would be used to increase the kanban amount during the period of increased demand. If the timing of this seasonal demand is predictable, a preferred solution to this problem is to inject additional signals into the system prior to the seasonal increase, and then remove the signals at the end of the fluctuating demand period. Such solutions must be worked out between the customer and the supplier. Use the kanban quantity formula above with the increased value of "A" to determine the new kanban quantity.

Keep the following things in mind when determining whether or not to use a smoothing factor:

♦ The variation should extend four weeks or more.

♦ The variation represents more than a 25% increase over the average.

If the demand variation does not meet this criteria, use a smoothing factor of 1.0 in the formula.

The smoothing factor represents the additional inventory (and cost) which must be kept on hand because of the inability of the supplier to flex its capacity to accommodate fluctuating demand. This inability to flex capacity is usually a result of long setup times.

STEP #3 - PICK THE TYPE OF SIGNAL AND A CONTAINER WHICH HOLDS A STANDARD QUANTITY

The container should be standardized for quantity as an aid to visual identification, ease of storage, and as an aid to the quick counting of material at the point of use. The type of signal should be picked by a joint meeting of supplier and customer.

STEP #4 - CALCULATE THE NUMBER OF CONTAINERS

$$\text{\# OF CONTAINERS} = \frac{\text{KANBAN QUANTITY}}{\text{\# OF PIECES HELD PER CONTAINER}}$$

EXAMPLE KANBAN DEVELOPMENT

STEP #1 - PICK THE PART NUMBER

For this example, we will use part number 123, a simple spool. The monthly usage is 546 parts. Multiplied by 12, we determine the annual usage is 6552 pieces. To determine the weekly usage, divide the annual usage by 52 weeks in the year.

Weekly usage = 6552 pieces/52 weeks = 126 spools per week

P/N 123

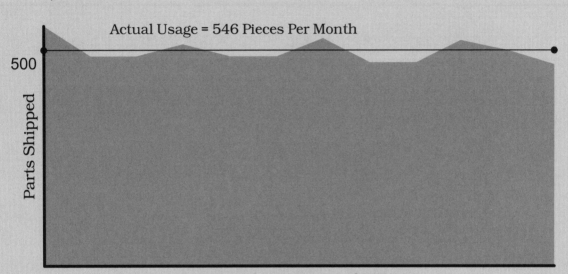

The 126 spools represent the value of "A" in the formula.

The supplier of the spool has advised that the lead time on this part is 4 weeks - this the value of "B" in the formula.

The actual shipment history is checked for the amount of weekly variation to determine if a smoothing factor is necessary. Since there is no evidence of demand variation, a smoothing of 1.0 (value "D") will be used in this kanban calculation.

STEP #2 - CALCULATE THE KANBAN QUANTITY

Use the formula to calculate the kanban quantity, substituting the actual values for the variables.

KANBAN QUANTITY = (A) X (B) X (C) X (D)

$$= \text{(weekly part usage) x (supplier lead time in weeks) x}$$
$$\text{(2 locations) x (smoothing factor)}$$

$$= \text{(126 pcs./week) x (4 weeks) x (2 locations) x (1.0)}$$

$$= 1,008 \text{ pieces}$$

The 1008 pieces will be the **maximum** number of parts moved between the customer and the supplier.

STEP #3 - PICK THE TYPE OF SIGNAL AND A STANDARDIZED CONTAINER

A laminated luggage-type tag with plastic strap will be used for the actual signal. The signal will be attached to a metal spool rack (shown below). The supplier has available fifty racks. The container has pins, which hold the spools in a vertical position, welded to the cross bars. The container holds 170 spools.

STEP #4 - CALCULATE THE NUMBER OF CONTAINERS IN THIS KANBAN

The final step is to determine the actual number of containers required to maintain the kanban quantity, in this case 1008 pieces.

$$\textbf{\# OF CONTAINERS} = \frac{\text{KANBAN QUANTITY}}{\text{\# OF PIECES HELD PER CONTAINER}}$$

$$\textbf{\# OF CONTAINERS} = \frac{1,008 \text{ pieces}}{170 \text{ pieces per container}}$$

$$\textbf{\# OF CONTAINERS} = 5.93 \text{ containers}$$

This quantity will be rounded up to six containers. Note that this will increase the kanban quantity to 1020 when all six containers are full.

Sample Kanban Container Flow for P/N 123

Day one:
Full containers at both locations.

As noted earlier, this start up technique works particularly well with a supplier starting its first kanbans. The three extra full containers, at start up, allow both the customer and supplier to "feel the flow" of kanbans. The kanban officially begins when the six full containers are reduced to three (at the customer) and the supplier must refill the three empty containers within the requested lead time. (See "B" of the example kanban development calculation.)

Also, make sure there is a clear understanding of where the supplier will pick up the empty containers.

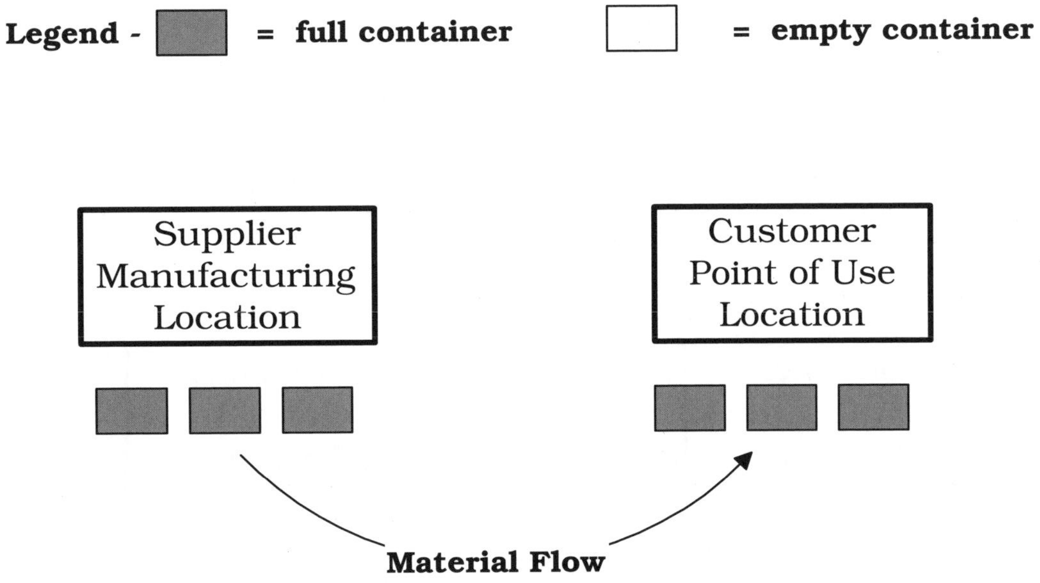
Legend -
= full container
= empty container
Supplier Manufacturing Location
Customer Point of Use Location
Material Flow

Day seven:
Customer has used all the parts in one container and returns the empty container to the supplier; the supplier sends one full container to the customer.

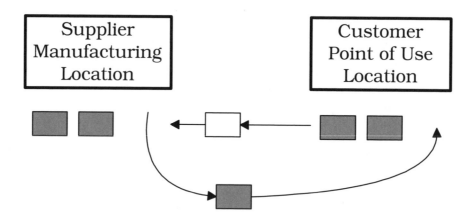

Day fourteen:
Customer returns second empty container to supplier, supplier sends one full container to customer.

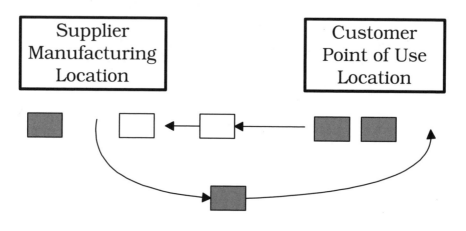

Day twenty-one :
Customer returns third empty container to supplier, supplier
sends the last full containers to customer.

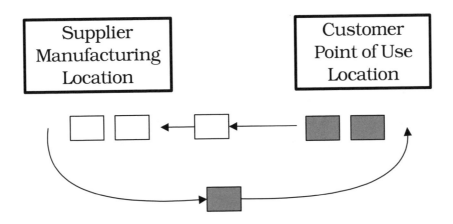

This transaction officially "kicks off" the kanban. At this time, the customer has three full containers (4 weeks/20 day supply), and the supplier has three empty with the full required lead time (4 weeks). The question arises at this point in the exercise about whether the supplier is supposed to return one container at a time or three at one time? The supplier's commitment is to return three full containers in four weeks, but we would hope that, through the setup reduction initiative, the supplier's goal would be to replace the containers one at a time.

PLEASE NOTE:

On day one of this container flow example, we started with full containers at both the supplier and the point of use locations. We found this to be helpful when working with suppliers unfamiliar with kanbans. Experienced suppliers would have three "empty" containers, while there would be three full containers at the point of use on day one of the kanban.

Summary

Kanbans will tie related processes together, for your team and your outside suppliers, as if they were connected by an invisible conveyer. Kanbans:

- ◆ Improve communication

- ◆ Improve customer satisfaction

- ◆ Reduce inventories

- ◆ Reduce waste

It should be noted that, of all the advanced manufacturing techniques discussed in this book, kanbans have the slowest initial implementation rate. It's almost as if people think they have missed something in the kanban training because it appears to be too simple. It will be frustrating in the beginning to watch members of your team be reluctant to try the method. Keep the faith—after a few success stories, your team will have those invisible conveyors everywhere!

Kanban Rule #9

Kanbans are not cast in cement — some experimentation is required. Be prepared to make adjustments initially as sales levels change, or as other improvement activities reduce the required number of containers or kanban cards.

KANBAN RULES

1. Do not attempt to kanban a part number without the complete involvement of all the members of the value added chain, including your external suppliers! Remember, you cannot become a World Class Enterprise without World Class Suppliers.

2. Quality at the source. Do not send defective parts to your customer. Defects must be corrected immediately! Defective parts will cause your customer's line to shut down!

3. Kanbans require reliable equipment for support. Implement kanbans internally in areas where Total Productive Maintenance (TPM) is already in place.

4. Focus kanbans on products and part numbers with stable month-to-month delivery requirements and short setup and lead-times. Concentrate setup reduction and raw material lead-time reduction efforts on the parts which have wide variations in month-to-month customer requirements.

5. Suppliers should deliver all material directly to their customer (point of use). For suppliers who are not certified, and therefore require incoming material inspection, the point of use should eventually be taught to perform this inspection or the supplier should be replaced with a certified supplier.

6. Use the parts only as required, and return the kanban to your supplier immediately. Deliver the empty container directly if your supplier is within the facility. If your supplier is external, an area in the plant should be designated for empty kanban container pickup by your supplier. A system must be developed so that all external suppliers pick up their containers promptly.

7. Do not produce more parts than you have kanbans for, and produce the parts in the order the kanbans were received.

8. All internal or external suppliers must have, or should be helped to develop, setup reduction programs. The true power of kanbans can be unleashed only when setup times do not influence manufacturing capacity and, therefore, the lead time.

9. Kanbans are not cast in cement—some experimentation is required. Be prepared to make adjustments initially as sales levels change, or as other improvement activities reduce the required number of containers or kanban cards.

PRACTICE KANBAN DEVELOPMENT

STEP #1 - PICK THE PART NUMBER
Part number:

Annual usage =

Weekly usage = annual usage/52 weeks =

STEP #2 - CALCULATE THE KANBAN QUANTITY
KANBAN QUANTITY = (A) X (B) X (C) X (D)

= (weekly part usage) x (supplier lead time in weeks) x
(2 locations) x (smoothing factor)

= (_____pcs./week) x (____weeks) x (2 locations) x (____)

= _____pieces

**STEP #3 - PICK THE TYPE OF SIGNAL AND A CONTAINER WHICH HOLDS A
STANDARD QUANTITY**
Container:

Signal type:

# of pieces per container:

STEP #4 - CALCULATE THE NUMBER OF CONTAINERS IN THIS KANBAN

$$\text{\# OF CONTAINERS} = \frac{\text{KANBAN QUANTITY}}{\text{\# OF PIECES HELD PER CONTAINER}}$$

$$\text{\# OF CONTAINERS} = \frac{\text{_____pieces}}{\text{pieces per container}}$$

 # OF CONTAINERS =

Chapter 10

Kaizen

Securing Your Tomorrow—Today!

. . . .

What is Kaizen?

Kaizen is a Japanese word that means to "change for the good." Doing "little things" better everyday defines kaizen—slow, gradual, but constant improvement—continuous improvement in any area that will eliminate waste and improve customer satisfaction.

Kaizen is what the Japanese did to the ideas they picked up from American manufacturers in the 1950s. The Japanese combined employee empowerment and kaizen and then had everyone in their plants doing "little things" better everyday. Kaizen is the most powerful tool in the Japanese manufacturing arsenal.

The target of kaizen is cost reduction through the elimination of waste at all levels in the manufacturing process.

The definition of kaizen has grown to mean something different in American manufacturing. Most American companies do not recognize the potential of employee empowerment. American culture, in general, struggles with techniques that are gradual and produce small improvements—even if these small improvements occur daily! Americans are innovators and that means giant steps. Home runs, not singles!

The Kaizen Event

This desire to hit home runs has led to the development of the *kaizen blitz or event.* A kaizen event concentrates a team of people, for a 3 to 10 day period, on a working production process or manufacturing cell in order to rapidly and dramatically improve the performance of that work site. Teams will consist of both trained and untrained members in WCM techniques. The improvement activities start with an analysis of the work site's performance and problems. The event then moves to a rapid implementation of any or all of the advanced manufacturing techniques described in this book to eliminate the site's problems and improve its performance. The event is usually driven by top management with the focus on making improvements on the "shop floor." It is not necessarily for the purpose of training the team members to do future kaizen events on their own.

Members of the kaizen event team are usually some of the operators from the work site and management people who interface with the site. Some events include people from other divisions of the same company, or even from other companies (noncompetitive). Event leaders are often consultants or the plant's kaizen facilitator.

Unfortunately, this home run/quick fix strategy, when used as the sole improvement strategy, has serious limitations. Becoming a world class manufacturer requires that everyone in a facility pull in the same direction. Achieving this alignment requires a consistent WCM message and WCM training that requires long term effort. Attempting to achieve this alignment with a series of hit and run events will be unsuccessful. Events must be combined with the "Japanese Kaizen" method of doing little things better everyday.

What a Kaizen Event can Accomplish

♦ Rapid improvement in the performance of a specific production process or manufacturing cell.

What a Kaizen Event will not Accomplish

♦ Long term change at the event work site. If events are used as the sole improvement strategy, backsliding will occur as soon as the event is over. Someone from the event team or the plant's kaizen facilitator must monitor the work site on a daily basis and must continue to coach and counsel the team on the improvements and why they are necessary.

♦ A significant increase in the understanding of world class manufacturing methods by the people who work daily in the event area. Again, this applies when events are used as the sole improvement strategy.

♦ Changing the culture of the people who work daily in the event area.

Kaizen Rule #1

Event-based kaizens must be used only as part of an overall continuous improvement strategy. Kaizen events by themselves will not transform you into a world class manufacturer.

Kaizen events **can** be a tremendously powerful strategy for rapid work site or manufacturing cell improvement. But events will create a new work site performance standard that is permanently effective only if events are used as part of an overall continuous improvement initiative.

Unfortunately, Americans tend to resort to kaizen events in emergencies only; for example, when the company is in financial trouble, doing kaizen events is used as a last resort.

Kaizen Rule #2

Kaizen events will make the production process or manufacturing cell more productive. Prepare a plan NOW for redeploying the members of your team who become available as a result of this initiative. Tell your team in advance what will happen.

The World Class Manufacturing Preproduction Kaizen Event

The preproduction kaizen event illustrates how "events" fit into the manufacturing strategy of world class manufacturing. The purpose of the preproduction kaizen event is to review the design of a new part, and the proposed manufacturing cell or process. Often, the major cost of the manufacturing a part is driven by the design. Preproduction analysis and simulation often reveals a need for engineering design changes, and these changes are significantly less costly since the part is not yet in production. Once the part goes into production, the cost of engineering design changes skyrockets, if the design can be changed at all. The goal of a preproduction event is to eliminate the need for engineering design changes after the production process begins.

Typically, preproduction events allow more time than a production kaizen event for orientation, training, and discussion since there is no rush to get the manufacturing cell "back into production." Preproduction kaizen events can be of shorter duration and several can be scheduled over the preproduction period. This longer period allows the continuous improvement kaizen message to be repeated, reinforced, and understood. To be successful, these events must include representatives from all departments that will interface with the cell, as well as the operators who will eventually work in the cell.

What a Preproduction Kaizen Event can Accomplish

♦ Sets the standard for how the manufacturing cell or process will begin production based on the best manufacturing practices the organization knows at that time. No "old way" of doing it, no backsliding.

♦ Creates the beginnings of a kaizen culture in the event area.

♦ Improves the design and possibly the performance of the part manufactured in the event cell.

Japanese Kaizen—Improvements on a Continuing Basis

The following seven pages are dedicated to an explanation of Japanese Kaizen—Improvements on a Continuing Basis. Remember, an event-based kaizen initiative cannot be totally successful by itself.

The remainder of the chapter will illustrate how to conduct a preproduction kaizen event.

That Short Term Thinking Shows Up Again!

This joke is told in Japanese manufacturing circles. Unfortunately, it reflects how many American manufacturers feel about kaizen ---- There were three businessmen, an American, a Japanese, and a Frenchman, who got caught up in a small third-world country's revolution. Sentenced to death by a firing squad, each man was given the opportunity for a "last request." The Frenchman asked to hear the French National Anthem. The Japanese business man asked to hear a lecture on kaizen. After hearing the Japanese man's request, the American pleaded, "shoot me first, I can't bear to hear another lecture on kaizen."

Japanese Kaizen
Improvements on a Continuing Basis

The foundation and energizer of the kaizen process is the empowerment of the work force and the development of job ownership. Job ownership inspires doing "little things" better everyday.

With job ownership in place, the kaizen effort is generated on a daily basis by the operators and supervisor of the work site. Their effort focuses on the elimination of waste at the work site or manufacturing cell based on standardized work. Work cell kaizen includes such things as revising cell layouts, improving work methods or procedures, and redistributing or balancing work within the cell.

The goal of eliminating waste is to improve the amount of operator value added time as shown in Figure 10.0. The waste targets are:

♦ **Unnecessary Motion** - Every motion of the operator that does not add value to the part. All parts, tools, and fixtures should be presented to the operators so they do not have to reach. If walking is necessary, try to combine it with a value-adding operation.

♦ **Unnecessary Material Handling -** Any movement of material or information not required to meet customer expectations. Eliminate temporary storage locations that cause material to be handled twice. All machines and equipment should be placed as close together as possible to eliminate unnecessary material movement.

♦ **Waiting Time -** Literally the operator waiting for work. Eliminate all operator waiting time. Implement setup reduction or redistribute work in the cell if necessary.

♦ **Rework/Scrap** - Repair or replacement of defective parts which do not meet customer expectations. Combine standardized work and error proofing to eliminate defects.

♦ **Unnecessary Part Processing** - Performing any operation on a part that the customer is not willing to pay for.

♦ **Excess Inventories/Over Production** - Producing at a rate greater than customer requirements. Implement setup reduction. Use kanbans to link operations and control WIP inventories. Produce only to the signals received. Adjust the number of kanbans as conditions change.

Kaizen Work Site Waste Targets

Converting an operator's time spent on waste:

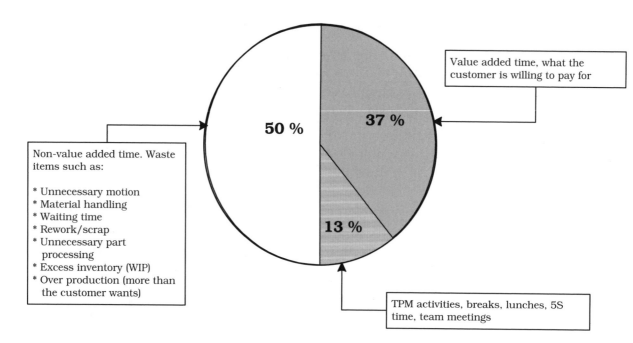

Value added time, what the customer is willing to pay for

Non-value added time. Waste items such as:

* Unnecessary motion
* Material handling
* Waiting time
* Rework/scrap
* Unnecessary part processing
* Excess inventory (WIP)
* Over production (more than the customer wants)

TPM activities, breaks, lunches, 5S time, team meetings

To value-added time:

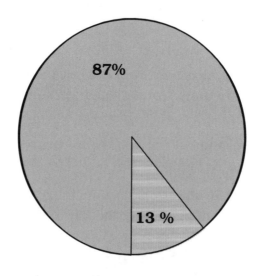

Figure 10.0

The Continuous Improvement Cycle

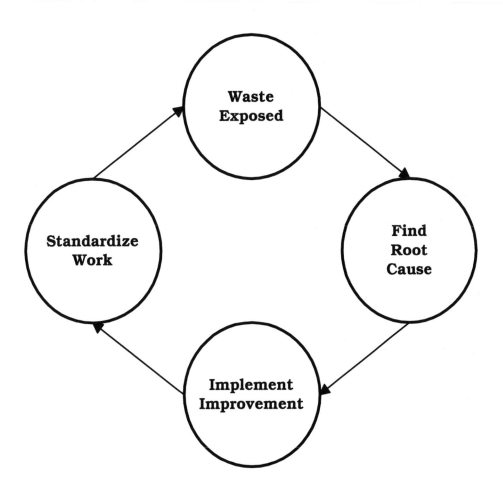

Figure 10.1

As each improvement is made, the continuous improvement cycle continues.

Suggestion Systems
A Continuous Improvement Tool

Suggestion systems can be powerful tools to unleash the ideas of the entire team by improving two-way communication between management and operators. The key question to ask before implementing a suggestion system is: at the end of the year, should the plant's improvement be measured by the ideas of a few managers or the ideas of the entire team? It is much easier for an operator to change how things are done based on his or her own suggestion than it is to implement the same change based on a manager's suggestion.

However, a suggestion system should be implemented only after the team feels empowerment and job ownership. See the blue box entitled "We Need Three More Maintenance People!"

The Japanese have been immensely successful using suggestion systems, while the average American experience has been substantially less. The numbers speak for themselves. Japanese companies average 32 suggestions per employee per year, American companies, 0.17 per year. That's a lot of wasted American brain power!

The two reasons for this success gap are empowerment and American management attitudes toward the implementation of suggestion systems. Americans view suggestion systems as something that can be stuck on or attached to their current management system. The Japanese make their suggestion systems an integral part of their management systems. The number of suggestions received and percent implemented are important measures of a supervisor's performance appraisal in Japan. It is not unusual for top Japanese managers to spend a whole day each week listening to and reviewing suggestion proposals.

The Japanese results have been dramatic! Matsushita Corporation, electronics manufacturer of the Panasonic, Technics, and National brand names, has received over 6 million suggestions in one year. Implementation rates are greater than 80%. Toyota receives 1.5 million suggestions per year and implements 95% of them.

Like empowerment and kaizen itself, suggestion systems take time and are evolutionary, not revolutionary, in their development. This development goes from fairly primitive and simple suggestions (move my machine two feet to the left) to well thought out and sophisticated suggestions (the design of a new paint booth for parts or the design of a new product). While a suggestion system will create savings immediately, the development period from simple to sophisticated suggestions generally takes at least five years.

Our guidelines on suggestion systems are these:

♦ A suggestion system is a necessary component of a continuous improvement program. It is not necessary or possible to start it on day one of a WCM implementation.

♦ Fully integrate the suggestion system into the plant's management system including the management performance appraisal system.

♦ Have a committed champion develop the program. Successful suggestion programs cannot be dictated. They are a labor of love by committed people.

♦ Recognize implemented ideas only. You not only want the operators to come up with waste elimination ideas, but you also want them to learn to manage the implementation of the ideas.

♦ Immediate implementation awards should be "tokenish" in nature. Develop annual recognition celebrations where the awards are larger for implemented ideas which meet certain criteria (most implemented ideas, largest cost savings idea, etc.).

♦ Keep the suggestion form simple—no more than one side of one page.

We Need Three More Maintenance People!

Starting a suggestion system before the team feels job ownership can be a frustrating experience for everyone. Once we created an overly sophisticated, but well thought out suggestion program at a facility. Relatively large awards, up to $250.00 per suggestion based on a five-category grading system were offered and there were three larger annual awards provided by the system. A committed champion facilitated the program and then properly communicated the program to everyone in plant-wide meetings. We were sure all the bases were covered. Well, as it turned out, we only had first and second bases covered.

We were flooded with suggestions. Unfortunately, one uncovered base was the implementation base. We were flooded with improvement ideas that everyone wanted someone else (namely, the maintenance department) to implement. These suggestors were idea generators, not implementers. Because we did not require implementation before we paid for a suggestion, we paid for many suggestions that never got implemented. Truly 70-80% of the suggestions received could have been implemented by the suggestor with the aid of the supervisor, but because we did not involve the supervisors in the design of the program, there was a general lack of supervisory "buy in" or agreement with the program. We also lacked supervisory suggestion performance measurements.

The other base that we missed was empowerment and job ownership. The payout of the suggestion system became a way for individuals to supplement incomes instead of a help to secure everyone's future in a plant that was struggling for survival.

Ultimately, the lesson learned was that we implemented the suggestion plan too early in this WCM implementation. A facility is ready for a program when people start to make improvements on their own. A suggestion system can then be used to recognize and encourage these improvements as well as to facilitate ideas which require major capital spending.

The Requirement for a Kaizen Facilitator

A kaizen facilitator is absolutely required for both kaizen events and for the ongoing continuous improvement efforts. The facilitator is a necessary source of information which keeps the kaizen efforts guided in the desired direction. This person facilitates but does **not** take responsibility for, or contribute to, the kaizen effort.

Ideally, as with any facilitator, this should be someone who is respected and trusted by everyone in the facility. Possibly this person is from the 5S Grading/Recognition Team from Chapter 4, or a Launch Champion from Chapter 7. This person should have excellent people and training skills as well as a thorough understanding of Chapters 1 through 9. The facilitator **must have kaizen event experience.** This experience can be obtained by attending another company's event. Contact the AME and Productivity references given in Chapter 4 (page 68) for the date and location of these events.

The facilitator coordinates kaizen events with plant management, visitors, the work site event team leader, and the operators from the event area. This person facilitates communication and cooperation across cross functional boundaries and is the resource for the following activities:

- Training - Provides a review of improvement information that the event team needs to make at the work site (for example, Setup Reduction or Kanbans). Updates the teams with new techniques or technology.

- Team developer - Clarifies team roles, goals, and decision processes. Builds team consensus. Helps the team overcome dispute and discipline problems from within and from outside the team. Keeps all lines of communication open.

- Coach, adviser - Helps the team stay focused and on track. Makes sure the team is measuring its own performance. Helps the team prepare for successful presentations.

- Cheerleader - Sparks synergy and encourages the team to be creative.

Also, for some length of time after the event has been completed, the facilitator follows up with the event area to make sure there are no event-related problems and that no backsliding has occurred. A highly people-skilled, knowledgeable, and organized facilitator is a prerequisite to successful kaizen events and all continuous improvement activities.

CONDUCTING A PREPRODUCTION KAIZEN EVENT

Introduction

A preproduction event was chosen for this example because it is the most powerful and useful event. It also covers almost all aspects of both events (preproduction and production). Learning to do a preproduction event is preparation for a production event.

The work site study required to perform a preproduction event is very similar to what is required to implement the manufacturing cells of Chapter 7. Knowledge of Chapter 7 is important.

Event Outline

PRE-EVENT

> STEP #1 - Determine the preproduction event area and define the event goals.

> STEP #2 - Choose/recruit kaizen event team members.

> STEP #3 - Choose event team leader.

> STEP #4 - Plan the event, create the team package.

EVENT

> STEP #5 - Introduce event team and plant contacts. Review applicable plant and safety rules

> STEP #6 - Present event goals and review event team package.

> STEP #7 - Team review of the event area.

> STEP #8 - Develop production process summary chart. Team members are assigned to or volunteer for a process or workstation.

> STEP #9 - Simulate production, take time observations for all processes. Videotape all processes.

STEP #10 - Develop the following charts:

- Production Capacity By Process
- Standard Work Sequence Sheet
- Standard Work Sheet
- Process Map

STEP #11 - Calculate the takt time and create a chart of cycle time versus takt time.

STEP #12 - Identify problem areas in the process that prevent reaching the event goals. Brainstorm solutions.

STEP #13 - Perform improvements.

STEP #14 - Repeat improvement process Steps #9 through 13 until event goals are reached or exceeded.

STEP #15 - Summarize event results. Make results-versus-goals presentation to plant management. Give recommendations for further improvements.

Kaizen Rule #3

Kaizen events require an investment by management in terms of people and material resources. If the event is performed in a production area, it will result in lost productivity. Management must understand and agree with this investment before the event can begin.

CONDUCTING A PREPRODUCTION KAIZEN EVENT

PRE-EVENT
STEP #1 - DETERMINE THE PREPRODUCTION EVENT AREA AND DEFINE THE EVENT GOALS

A preproduction event area is usually selected based on the perceived risk or reward that a new part or product carries from the marketing or customer quoting process. Risk may stem from an aggressive "buy the business" pricing strategy on a part where that part is knowingly sold below cost to gain a foothold in the business or at the customer. Risk can occur when a product is purchased from another company or transferred from another division of the same company. Risk may stem also from scrap/rework losses, delivery, or quality issues when new part designs are manufactured with unproven production processes. Reward may stem from the potentially improved profitability from a very high volume, average profit margin part, if the cost can be reduced.

For production events: The primary consideration for choosing an event area is usually profitability or the lack of it.

The area selection criteria should consider the experience the facility has with conducting events. If this is the plant's first event, choose a high-volume single manufacturing cell or single product area with a proposed manning of three to six operators. As the facility gains experience doing events, larger and more complex (large multiple product line areas) can be chosen.

The goals for an event are generally an outgrowth of the reason the event area was chosen. These goals should be developed by top management and should be consistent with the goals and vision communicated during the launch of the WCM implementation. All goals must be quantifiable and attainable. To be attainable, a goal must be based on a workable plan. Remember, "a goal without a plan is a dream."

The goals should be written on the Kaizen Event Summary Sheet which is shown on the following page. This sheet is included in the package given to the team at the start of the event.

STEP #2 - CHOOSE/RECRUIT KAIZEN EVENT TEAM MEMBERS
With top management's help and advice, the kaizen facilitator has the responsibility for putting the event team together. Volunteers work best in events because they tend to come to the events with an open mind. While the number of volunteers may be limited when the events first start, their numbers will grow as the word of success spreads.

Kaizen Event Summary Sheet

Plant		Team Leader		Operation #		Date	
Cell		Team #		Process		Takt Time	

Performance Measurement	Before Event	Event Goal (% improvement)	Actual Results	% Improvement
Cell Crew Size				
Productivity (pcs/person)				
Cycle Time				
WIP Inventory				
Raw Inventory				
Quality (reject rate)				
Setup Time (minutes)				
Part Travel Distance				
Floor Space				
5S Rating				

Some members of the event team should always be from outside the event area (other companies, other divisions, if possible) to be studied. These members provide "fresh eyes" and a different perspective for viewing the manufacturing process. The general rule is that half of the members of the team should be from outside the event area.

Kaizen Rule #4

Some members of the event team should always be from outside the event area (other companies, other divisions, if possible) to be studied. These members provide "fresh eyes" and a different perspective for viewing the manufacturing process.

The event team size should be approximately 25–50% larger than the number of operators in the manufacturing cell or area, with a maximum of ten on the team. For larger manufacturing areas, and after experiencing several single team kaizen events, use multiple teams.

The team **must include** operators from all proposed production shifts and a representative from the maintenance department. Operators must learn the processing of the new part and communicate it to the rest of the operators on all shifts. Additionally, operators must learn this aspect of the kaizen process so that manufacturing cell teams can apply this kaizen improvement process on a daily basis.

In production events, operators are the experts in the current process and operation of the entire manufacturing cell or production area.

A maintenance representative is required to help the team succeed. Maintenance people have excellent knowledge of the plant and are experienced in making and repairing things. They give the team someone who knows what can be accomplished in the plant and who can help convert the team's ideas into mock-ups or prototypes.

Kaizen Rule #5

Kaizen events in production areas should include representatives from all production shifts in that area.

STEP #3 - CHOOSE EVENT TEAM LEADER

Team leaders determine the success of the event. Team leaders accept responsibility for achieving the event's goals and, like facilitators, use coaching and leadership skills to lead, encourage, and coax the team to attain these goals. Additionally, the team leader should:

♦ Be a recognized leader in the plant with excellent people skills

♦ Be from outside the event area—fresh eyes, no preconceived notions, and no day-to-day involvement in the event area.

♦ Have a "gut wrenching" desire to make the event successful.

Often, for large teams, co-leaders or assistant leaders are also chosen. These people can coach and train future team leaders. Co-leaders are usually from the event area.

Note to the Team Leader

1. Team leaders are the center of the kaizen event. Your job is to keep the team involved, communicating, and focused on the event's goals. Avoid getting bogged down in the detail work—your job is to lead. Discuss any questions you have about the team leader position with the event facilitator.

2. Since you and your team will spend most of the time on the shop floor, set up a working/meeting table and chairs in or close to the event site. Include a flip chart, markers, pencils, paper, etc. The conference room used for the initial kickoff meeting will be used thereafter only for the daily management update meetings (or maybe lunch).

3. Review the team package and event site before the first day of the event so that you have a clear understanding of the team objective. Meet with the plant event support contacts.

STEP #4 - PLANNING THE EVENT, CREATING THE TEAM PACKAGE

The facilitator is responsible for all event planning and for creating the team package.

Determine Event Start Date and Duration. Typically, events last from three to ten days on the shop floor, but their length of time depends on two things. First, is the team trained in the event techniques necessary to accomplish the stated goals? Trained means knowledge of the applicable chapters in this book. Does this team need to be trained in these techniques or will the facilitator only be required to update or refresh their knowledge. Second, what is the scope of the event? A preproduction event to layout, develop, move equipment, and make operational a four-machine manufacturing cell is probably a three-day event for a trained team. It is probably a five-to seven-day event for an untrained team. Obviously, much of this comes with experience. In the worst case, a second event can be scheduled to move forward from where the first event ended.

For production events: A starting date consideration may include building a "product bank" to bridge the customer requirements while the event area is shut down due to the kaizen process. This bank will be used to keep the customer supplied with product while the manufacturing cell is out of production for the event.

Facilities Planning:

- ♦ Notify the entire plant that the event will occur. Schedule required support departments (maintenance, riggers, outside contractors, etc.).

- ♦ Reserve a kaizen team conference or meeting room through the event's end date. This room will be used for the initial kickoff meeting and for the daily management updates (the event team will also set up a working meeting table in or close to the work site). Coordinate soft drinks, coffee, and lunches. Check supply availability of: name tags (if required), paper, pencils, calculators, safety glasses, tape measures, stop watches, flip charts, ink makers, floor marking tape, walking wheels, ultra slow-motion video camera, monitor, and overhead transparency film.

- ♦ 5S the event area before the start date.

Kaizen Rule #6

The basic nature of kaizen is to make improvements with what is available. It generally doesn't cost money to do kaizen. If you must spend money, perform simulation using cardboard or wood (or other low-cost available material).

Creating the Team Package. The team package is the written set of documents the team will use as background and reference information to perform the event. At a minimum, the facilitator will include:

♦ A clear definition of the problem and a set of quantifiable goals (Kaizen Event Summary Sheet, see event goals from Step #1)

♦ Product or part specifications/drawings

♦ The customer's requirements in pieces per shift or day

♦ The technical requirements of making the part at each operation or at each operation number

♦ How many hours per day or per week the event site will be available for production (when the site goes into production)

♦ How to handle abnormal cell conditions (scrap/rework/downtime etc.)

♦ An event budget and how the team will purchase any required supplies

♦ Event support personnel contact list

♦ The results of any prior kaizen events at the work site

♦ A complete set of blank process documentation sheets (Production Process Summary, Time Observation Sheet, Process Map, Production Capacity By Process, Standard Work Combination Sheet, Standard Work Sheet, Takt Time vs. Cycle Time, Kaizen Event Summary Sheet, Kaizen Event Projects Sheet, 5S Rating sheets). Blank sheets which can be copied are available in Chapters 4, 7, and this chapter.

For production events: Include the current area layout, Part Routing With Cycle Time sheets, completed process documentation sheets, and any other baseline event area production performance measurements.

EVENT

STEP #5 - INTRODUCTIONS OF EVENT TEAM AND PLANT CONTACTS—REVIEW APPLICABLE PLANT AND SAFETY RULES

The facilitator will set up an event kickoff meeting. This meeting should include at least the plant's top management and the event support personnel from the plant. Any applicable plant rules such as requirements for safety glasses, ear protection, or work rules should be discussed.

STEP #6 - PRESENTATION OF EVENT GOALS AND EVENT TEAM PACKAGE REVIEW

While everyone is still in attendance, the facilitator reviews the event goals and the event team package. The goal here is to make sure top management and the team clearly understand the event objectives.

STEP #7 - TEAM REVIEW OF THE EVENT AREA

The team leader will introduce the team to the work site and the part or product to be kaizened.

For production events: Video tape the original or starting event area process.

STEP #8 - DEVELOPMENT OF PRODUCTION PROCESS SUMMARY CHART—TEAM MEMBERS ARE ASSIGNED/VOLUNTEER FOR A PROCESS OR WORKSTATION

A Production Process Summary Chart example is shown in Figure 10.2. For a preproduction event, this chart is used to summarize the methods, machines, and people required to produce the part. This chart serves as a double check that all necessary gauges, fixtures, and tools needed to produce the part have been designed and are accounted for. In some cases, this may be the first time everything required to produce the part has been listed on one page.

When the team constructs a Production Process Summary Chart, include a column for each separate operation required to produce the part. In the Figure 10.2 example there are five different operations required to produce the part. Data to fill in all spaces on the

Production Process Summary Chart

Method	Operation 1	Operation 2	Operation 3	Operation 4	Operation 5
Gauges					
Fixtures					
Tools					
Machines					
Time — People					
Time — Machine					

Figure 10.2

Note to the Team Leader

Team leaders are responsible for daily updates to plant management on the status of the event. The purpose of this meeting is to report the results of the team's daily activities, receive confirmation by the management group that the team's direction and objectives are correct, and to request management's answer to any team questions.

In this twenty-minute meeting, the team leader will use the Kaizen Event Summary Sheet to detail the team results to date. The Kaizen Event Projects Sheet (shown on the following page) will then be used to review what the team is presently working on. Ten (of the twenty) minutes should be made available for questions and answers.

Team leaders (and co-leaders) are the only team members required to attend the daily update meetings. The remainder of the team continues their improvement activities. The team leader then updates the team with the meeting results soon after the meeting is over.

Kaizen Event Projects Sheet

Page ____ of ____

Plant		Team Leader		Operation #		Date	
Cell		Team #		Process		Takt Time	

#	Event Goal Roadblock	Proposed Root Cause Solution	Who	When	Results

chart may not be available until the production simulation of Step #9 is accomplished. This chart should be constructed on a large sheet of paper (flip chart paper or larger) and hung permanently in the work site.

At this point, team members volunteer or are assigned by the team leader to each of the different operations.

STEP #9 - SIMULATE PRODUCTION— TAKE TIME OBSERVATIONS FOR ALL PROCESSES—VIDEO TAPE ALL PROCESSES

This step involves the team performing a simulation of producing a part. If the actual production machines are available, a manufacturing cell should be designed (Chapter 7) and the machines moved into those positions. Remember that the equipment will probably be moved several times during the event (and possibly several more times as other improvements are made during the life of the part) so all utilities (air, electrical, and water) should be hooked up with quick disconnects. Equipment and machines on wheels would be ideal.

If not all machines, fixtures, and tools are available, "to scale" mock-ups will have to be made. Use cardboard, wood, or any other material that is cheap, easily fabricated, and readily available. The idea is to simulate, **as closely as possible**, the actual production environment. Team members assigned to an operation should create their own job instructions/requirements based on the Production Process Summary Chart, the part drawings/specification, and technical requirements for making the part which were included in the team package.

The production simulation will be performed by the team. Team members will operate the machine (operation number) they are assigned. The remaining members are responsible for keeping the operators supplied with material, video taping, and taking time observation measurements (see next section).

For production events: Time observations should be taken based on the cell's already established standard work.

TIME OBSERVATIONS

Accurate time studies require that an operation be broken down into elements or blocks of time. Analyzing these small elements makes it easier it to discover areas of waste in the operation. For example: if an entire operation number takes sixty seconds, break this operation down to a minimum of 7-10 elements of 6-9 seconds (2-3 seconds if possible) each. In this example, the sixty-second molding of a part in a forming press can be broken down as follows:

1. Pick up and load raw material into press.

2. Add decorative cover material.

3. Trim.

4. Push double palm buttons to cycle forming press.

5. Remove part from press and inspect.

6. Perform final trimming operation and inspect.

7. Place part in shipping container.

Each block should have a clear visual sign or audible signal for the starting and stopping point of the element such as the picking up of a part or the pushing of the palm buttons. These signs aid in collecting accurate clock times over repeated observations.

Use a stop watch with a "split/lap" feature. This feature allows for continuous timing of the entire operation while recording the actual times of each block using the split/lap feature. Several complete cycles of the operation can usually be completed without stopping the watch.

Other things to consider!

♦ Make sure the operator knows who you are and what the purpose of the study is. Ask the operator to perform the tasks using the same method each time.

Time Observation Sheet

Page ___ of ___

☐ Before Kaizen ☐ After Kaizen

| Plant | | Part Number | | Operation # | | Date | |
| Area | | Process | | Observer(s) | | Time | |

#	Operation/Task	Observation #											Best	Notes (Waste etc.)
1														
Total Time for 1 Cycle														

Other Notes _____

Figure 10.4

♦ Before starting the time study, observe enough complete cycles of the operation so that you clearly understand what is occurring. If you have any questions, ask the operator.

♦ Record times for at least ten continuous cycles. Use the best <u>repeatable</u> time because it is considered to have the least amount of waste.

♦ Note any observed opportunities to reduce waste on the Time Observation Sheet (Figure 10.4).

Kaizen Rule #7

The keys to eliminating motion waste are:

♦ Operators never have to turn around
♦ Operators never have to search for anything
♦ Operators never have to walk. If walking between machines is necessary to meet customer requirements (takt time), it is combined with a value added operation

STEP #10 - DEVELOP A PRODUCTION CAPACITY BY PROCESS SHEET (FROM CHAPTER 7), "STANDARD OPERATIONS" FOR THE CELL, AND A PROCESS MAP

Standard operations is the documentation of how people and machines produce a part in a work cell while minimizing all forms of waste. Standard operations establish patterns for the work performed in producing the part. Additionally, standard operations are used for:

♦ Determining the number of work cell operators and their work sequence

♦ Instructing cell operator

♦ Training new cell operator

The three elements of standard operations are:

♦ Takt time

♦ Cell work distribution and sequence (Standard Work Sequence Sheet, Figure 10.6)

♦ Standard cell Work-In-Process (WIP) (Standard Work Sheet, Figure 10.7)

Takt Time

Takt is a German word that means "time beat" or rhythm. In standard operations, it represents the amount of time given by the customer to produce the parts which have been sold to them. In other words, takt time is the "beat" at which we must produce parts to meet the customer's requirements. Takt time is important because producing at too slow a beat may shut down our customer's assembly line, while producing at too fast a beat produces excess inventory which is waste.

Takt time is calculated as follows:

$$\text{Takt Time} = \frac{\textbf{Total Weekly Operating Time}}{\textbf{Total Weekly Customer Requirements}}$$

Remember that operating time does not include TPM activities, breaks, lunches, 5S, or meeting time.

For manufacturing cells which only produce one part number, or for cells with three minutes or less setup time between part numbers, use the daily operating time and daily customer requirements.

Ultimately the takt time analysis is used to determine cell manning to match the "beat" of the customer. As customer requirements change, takt time is recalculated allowing us to adjust the cell manning up or down to stay in rhythm with the customer (refer to Chapter 7 for a detailed explanation of takt time).

PRODUCTION CAPACITY BY PROCESS SHEET
STANDARD WORK SEQUENCE SHEET
STANDARD WORK SHEET
Blank forms of these charts are shown in Figures 10.5 through 10.7. Explanations of how to fill in these charts are available in Chapter 7.

Production Capacity By Process

Part Number:				Max. Output Per Shift (pieces):			Dept. or Cell #:	
Part Name:				Available Operator Time Per shift (minutes):				
Operation Description	Machine Number	Base Time				Processing Capability Per Shift (pieces)	Remarks	
		Manual Time (seconds)	Machine Time (seconds)	Time to Complete (seconds)	Setup Time (hours)			

Operation #	Operation Description	Machine Number	Manual Time (seconds)	Machine Time (seconds)	Time to Complete (seconds)	Setup Time (hours)	Processing Capability Per Shift (pieces)	Remarks		
1										
2										
3										
4										
Total										

Figure 10.5

Standard Work Sequence Sheet

	Part Number	Output Per Shift (pieces)	Date Prepared or Revised :	Cell #
	Part Name	Takt Time (seconds)	Operator #	

| Step # | Process Description | Time (seconds) | | | Operation Time (seconds) |
		Man Time	Auto Time	Walk Time	Manual ——— Machine – – – – Walking 〰〰
					20 40 60 80 100 120 140
Total					

Figure 10.6

Standard Work Sheet	Part Number		Process		Date Prepared or Revised :
	Part Name		Cell #		

Takt Time:	Cycle Time:
Standard WIP:	Operator:

Safety Precaution	✚
Quality Check	◇
Standard WIP	⬤

Figure 10.7

PROCESS MAP

The purpose of a Process Map (sometimes called a spaghetti chart) is to track operators' movements while they are performing their operations. The operators' movements are analyzed for motion or movement waste. Every operator movement should be in support of value adding. An example of a Process Map is shown in Figure 10.8.

The map is constructed by viewing the video tape. The video tape can then be used to analyze arm and body motions while the operator is standing in one position. This is best accomplished using a camera with slow motion speeds down to 0.01 seconds.

STEP #11 - CREATE CHART OF CYCLE TIME (CT) VERSUS TAKT TIME (TT) AND CALCULATE OPTIMUM CELL MANNING

The purpose of completing a CT vs. TT chart is:

♦ to view how the work site with multiple operators performs against the customer's requirement

♦ to display the workload balance in the cell

♦ to serve as a visual tool for improvement opportunities in the cell

A filled-out sample CT vs. TT chart is shown in Figure 10.9. A blank form is included at the end of this chapter.

The sample chart presents examples of several different problems. Operator "A's" cycle time currently exceeds the TT. This problem can be solved by eliminating or reducing this operator's walk time. Operator "B's" machine cycle time exceeds TT. This machine's cycle time must be sped up or some of the operations it performs on the part must be accomplished by another piece of equipment. Observations on the chart indicate that, if all walking time were eliminated, the required manning for this cell would be three people, not five.

CALCULATION OF THE OPTIMUM NUMBER OF CELL OPERATORS

This calculation tells the event team what the optimum cell manning would be, assuming no walk time. This can possibly be a target to aim for if the goal of the event team is cell productivity/part cost. The optimum number of cell operators is calculated by dividing the total amount of manual work required to produce one piece (from Figure 10.5, Production Capability By Process) by the takt time.

Setup Reduction Process Map

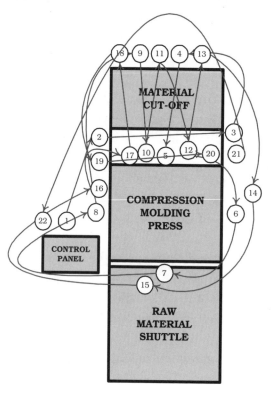

①- **Single Setup Person**

Figure 10.8

Each number represents the sequence of operations that must be accomplished to complete the setup of this molding press.

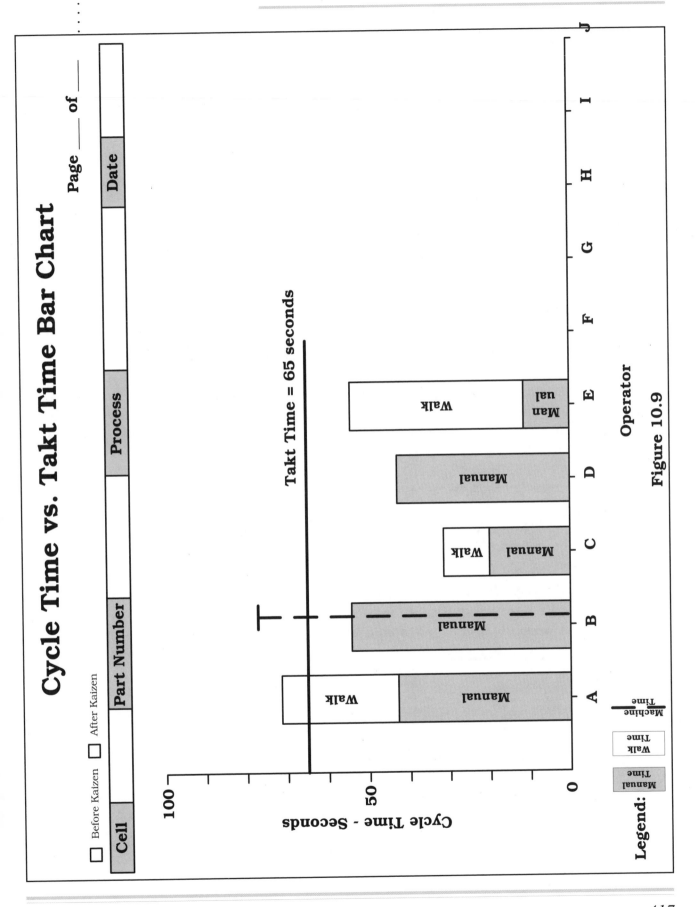

Figure 10.9

$$\text{Cell Operators} = \frac{\text{Total Manual Time}}{\text{Takt Time}}$$

Since we cannot have fractional parts of operators in a cell, any answer that includes a fraction must be rounded to the next whole number.

Machine and wait time are not included in this calculation. Machine time is not included because operators can complete other work while the machine cycles. All wait time must be eliminated or replaced with value added time. Attempt to include value adding operations to all walk time. Any walk time that does not include value added time must be accounted for. At this point we have not reassigned machines and work sequences to each operator (this is the next improvement step) so we do not know what machine walking route to measure. The normal assumption is to allow from two and five seconds for walking time for a "U" shaped work cell. What does all this mean? When work is reassigned to each operator, the manual work time required must be less than the takt time to account for walking time. (If, in the above calculation, the answer would have been 3.0 operators, "round up" to 4 operators because the answer does not include allowance for walk time.) Ideally, the sum of the operators' manual time and walk time should be equal to the takt time. With at least one operator's time equal to the takt time, the cell with be in exact rhythm with the customer's requirements.

Kaizen Rule #8

To reduce operator walking or manual times, concentrate on these improvement areas:

- ♦ **Transportation of material and parts within the cell**
- ♦ **Loading and unloading of machines**
- ♦ **The presentation of parts to the operator**

STEP #12 - IDENTIFY PROBLEM AREAS THAT PREVENT REACHING THE EVENT GOALS AND THEN BRAINSTORM SOLUTIONS

Depending on the background of the group, the team may want to review the section on "Brainstorming" and "Making Group Decisions" in Chapter 5.

Make a comparison of the event goals and the current performance of the cell as measured in the previous steps. The key is for the team to quickly "home in" on what areas of improvement are necessary to achieve or exceed the event goals.

After reviewing the "kaizen guidelines" shown at the end of this chapter, the team brainstorms solutions to these problems which attack the root cause. The team then establishes an implementation plan.

Kaizen Rule #9

Try to make all improvements within the event area. Avoid the tendency to blame suppliers (internal or external) for the event area's problems.

STEP #13 - PERFORM IMPROVEMENTS FROM STEP #12

STEP #14 - REPEAT IMPROVEMENT PROCESS STEPS #9 THROUGH 13 UNTIL EVENT GOALS ARE REACHED OR EXCEEDED

STEP #15 - SUMMARIZE EVENT RESULTS—MAKE A RESULTS-VERSUS-GOALS PRESENTATION TO PLANT MANAGEMENT—GIVE RECOMMENDATIONS FOR FURTHER IMPROVEMENTS.

On the final event day, there is a team presentation to the management group. This thirty-minute presentation should follow this outline:

♦ Restatement of the original management goals for the event (from Kaizen Event Summary Sheet)

♦ A "before" work site or cell layout

♦ A comparison of the cell "before" and "after" using any or all sheets and charts used in this chapter, Chapter 7 (Production Process Summary, Time Observation Sheet, Process Map, Production Capacity By Process, Standard Work Combination Sheet, Standard Work Sheet, Cycle Time vs Takt Time, Kaizen Event Summary Sheet, Kaizen Event Projects Sheet), and Chapter 4 (5S Rating sheets)

♦ Any "before and "after" videos that might be appropriate

♦ A completely filled-out Kaizen Event Summary Sheet showing all improvements

♦ All successful events never fully implement all of their improvement ideas. Therefore, it is extremely important to record all of these un-implemented ideas on a Kaizen Event Projects Sheet for review here

<u>For production event:</u> The event is not officially over until the cell is fully production ready, all "standard work" has been updated and posted, and all operators have been trained in the new sequences or methods.

KAIZEN RULES

1. Event-based kaizens must be used only as part of an overall continuous improvement strategy. Kaizen events by themselves will not transform you into a world class manufacturer.

2. Kaizen events will make the production process or manufacturing cell more productive. Prepare a plan NOW for redeploying the members of your team who become available as a result of this initiative. Tell your team in advance what will happen.

3. Kaizen events require an investment by management in terms of people and material resources. If the event is performed in a production area, it will result in lost productivity. Management must understand and agree with this investment before the event can begin.

4. Some members of the event team should always be from outside the event area (other companies, other divisions, if possible) to be studied. These members provide "fresh eyes" and a different perspective for viewing the manufacturing process.

5. Kaizen events in production areas should include representatives from all production shifts in that area.

6. The basic nature of kaizen is to make improvements with what is available. It generally doesn't cost money to do kaizen. If you must spend money, perform simulation using cardboard or wood (or other low-cost available material).

7. The keys to eliminating motion waste are:

    ♦ Operators never have to turn around
    ♦ Operators never have to search for anything
    ♦ Operators never have to walk. If walking between machines is necessary to meet customer requirements (takt time), it is combined with a value added operation

8. To reduce operator walking or manual times, concentrate on these improvement areas:

- ♦ Transportation of material and parts within the cell
- ♦ Loading and unloading of machines
- ♦ The presentation of parts to the operator

9. Try to make all improvements within the event area. Avoid the tendency to blame suppliers (internal or external) for the event area's problems.

KAIZEN GUIDELINES

♦ Don't accept excuses. Just say no to "we've always done it that way" and the status quo. Keep an open mind to change.

♦ Think of how it can be done, not why it won't work. Don't make excuses—just make improvements happen.

♦ Ask "why" five time until you get to the root cause of the problem.

♦ The team solution is the best solution.

♦ Avoid the event shutdown that comes from over-analysis. Develop a propensity for action. Understand the process, then "just do it," and see if it works.

♦ Don't seek perfection the first time. Do something now—a 50% improvement is better than no improvement.

♦ "Fast and crude" is better than "slow and elegant" or "maybe never".

♦ Correct/reverse mistakes immediately.

♦ In the worst case, the original process can be restored.

♦ Keep a positive attitude and have fun. The possibilities for improvements are unlimited!

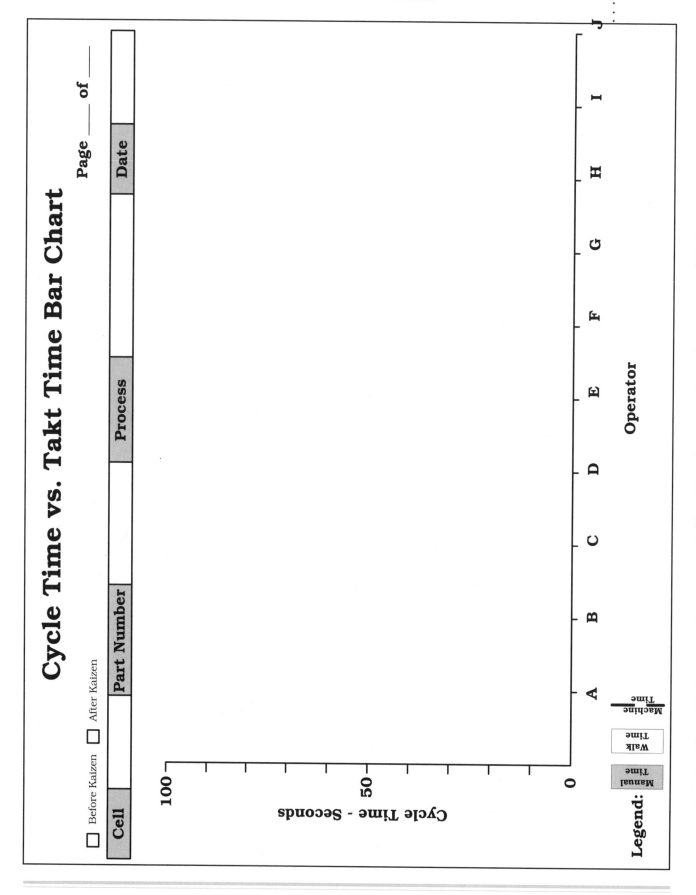

Cycle Time vs. Takt Time Bar Chart

Bibliography

Chapter 1
Dana Corporation, ed. Excellence In Manufacturing - Facilitator Training Notes. Toledo, OH.: Dana Corporation.

Keller, M. 1989. Rude Awakenening: the rise, fall, and struggle for recovery of General Motors. New York: Morrow.

Ohno, T. and S. Mito. 1988. Just-In-Time: For Today and Tomorrow. Cambridge, MA: Productivity Press, Inc.

Peters, T. J. and R. H. Waterman. 1982. In Search of Excellence. New York: Harper and Rowe.

World Almanac Books, ed. 1996. The World Almanac: And Book Of Facts 1997. Mahwah, New Jersey: World Almanac Books.

Chapter 2
Dana Corporation, ed. Excellence In Manufacturing - Facilitator Training Notes. Toledo, OH.: Dana Corporation.

Huge, E. C. and A. D. Anderson. 1988. The Spirit of Manufacturing Excellence: An Executives Guide to the New Mind Set. United States: Richard D. Irwin Inc.

Chapter 4
Dana Corporation, ed. Why Do We want To Be World Class Clean? Minneapolis, MN.: Dana Corporation.

Hirano, H. 1995. 5 Pillars of the Visual Workplace: The Sourcebook for 5S Implementation. Portland, Oregon: Productivity Press, Inc.

The Productivity Press Development Team. 1996. 5S for Operators: 5 Pillars Of The Visual Workplace. Portland, Oregon: Productivity Press, Inc.

TBM Consulting Group, ed. 1994. 5-S Program. TBM Consulting Group Inc.

United Technologies Automotive, ed. 1996. 5S Implementation Plan. Detroit, MI.: United Technologies Automotive.

United Technologies Corporation, ed. Flexible Manufacturing: Instructor's Notes. Hartford, CT.: United Technologies Corporation.

Chapter 5

Greif, M. 1991. The Visual Factory: Building Participation Through Shared Information. Portland, Oregon: Productivity Press, Inc.

NKS/Factory Magazine, ed. 1988. Poka-Yoke: Improving Product Quality By Preventing Defects. Cambridge MA: Productivity Press, Inc.

Scholtes, P. R. 1988. The Team Handbook. Madison, WI. Joiner Associates Inc.

Shingo, S. 1986. Zero Quality Control: Source Inspection and the Poka-yoke System. Portland, Oregon: Productivity Press, Inc.

Chapter 6

Campbell, J. D. 1995. Uptime: Strategies for Excellence in Maintenance Management. Portland, Oregon: Productivity Press, Inc.

Chudakov, S. 1994. Improving PM of Hydraulic Systems. Plant Engineering. November, 60-62.

Ginder, A. P. and C. J. Robinson. 1995. Implementing TPM: The North American Experience. Portland, Oregon: Productivity Press, Inc.

Japan Institute of Plant Maintenance, ed. 1996. TPM for Every Operator. Portland, Oregon: Productivity Press, Inc.

MPE Consulting Group Inc., ed. 1995. Introduction to TQM/Continuous Improvement Workbook. St. Louis, MO.: MPE Consulting Group Inc.

Productivity Press, Inc., ed. 1994. TPM Strategies for the 90's. Norwalk, CT.: Productivity Press, Inc.

Productivity Press, Inc., ed. 1995. Perspectives On TPM. Norwalk, CT.: Productivity Press, Inc.

Productivity Press, Inc., ed. 1996. North American TPM Success Stories. Norwalk, CT.: Productivity Press, Inc.

Shirose, K., ed. 1995. TPM Team Guide. Portland, Oregon: Productivity Press, Inc.

Shirose, K. 1992. TPM for Workshop Leaders. Portland, Oregon: Productivity Press, Inc.

Shirose, K., ed. 1992. TPM for Operators. Portland, Oregon: Productivity Press, Inc.

Shulak, B. ed., 1996. TPM Newsletter. Tips For A Smoother TPM Implementation. AITPM. October: 4.

Shulak, B. ed., 1996. TPM Newsletter. Equipment Restoration. AITPM. November: 8-9.

Shulak, B. ed., 1996. TPM Newsletter. Early Equipment Management Tips. AITPM. May: 8.

Steinbacher, H. R. and N. L. Steinbacher. 1993. TPM for America: What It Is and Why You Need It. Portland, Oregon: Productivity Press, Inc.

Suzaki, K. 1987. The New Manufacturing Challenge: Techniques For Continuous Improvement. New York: Simon & Schuster Inc.

Tel-A-Train, Inc. 1996. TPM, Total Productive Maintenance: Facilitators Guide. Chattanooga, TN.

Willmott, P. 1994. TPM: The Western Way. Oxford: Butterworth-Heinemann Ltd.

Wireman, T. 1991. Total Productive Maintenance: An American Approach. New York: Industrial Press Inc.

Wireman, T. 1992. Inspection and Training for TPM. New York: Industrial Press Inc.

World Mining Equipment, ed. 1995. "Just-in-Time Maintenance: Myth or Must?" World Mining Equipment: March, 42-43.

Chapter 7

General Electric Corporation, ed. 1995. Lean Production System. GE Aircraft Engines Production Division.

Sekine, K. 1992. One Piece Flow: Cell Design for Transforming the Production Process. Portland, Oregon: Productivity Press, Inc.

United Technologies Corporation, ed. Flexible Manufacturing: Instructor's Notes. Hartford, CT.: United Technologies Corporation.

United Technologies Sikorsky Aircraft, ed. 1995. Agile Manufacturing. Hartford, CT.: United Technologies Sikorsky Aircraft.

United Technologies Automotive, ed. 1996. Waste Elimination Through Standaed Work. Detroit, MI.: United Technologies Automotive.

Chapter 8

Bibby, G. 1993. Quick Die Change Comparison. Metal Forming. April: 38-42.

Dana Corporation, ed. Excellence In Manufacturing - Facilitator Training Notes. Toledo, OH.: Dana Corporation.

Hall, R. 1992. Setup Reduction: The Building Blocks for Time-Based Improvements. American National Can.

Harley-Davidson Motor Company, ed. Material As Needed. Milwaukee, WI.: Harley-Davidson Motor Company.

Kostika, Itzik. 1994. Setup Reduction: does it yield lower cost? Tooling & Production. December: 7.

Sekine, K. and K. Arai. 1992. Kaizen For Quick Changeover: Going Beyond SMED. Portland, Oregon: Productivity Press, Inc.

Shingo, S. 1985. A Revolution in Manufacturing: The SMED System. Portland, Oregon: Productivity Press, Inc.

The Productivity Press Development Team. 1996. Quick Changeover for Operators: The SMED System. Portland, Oregon: Productivity Press, Inc.

United Technologies Corporation, ed. Flexible Manufacturing: Instructor's Notes. Hartford, CT.: United Technologies Corporation.

Chapter 9

Japan Management Association, ed. 1989. Kanban: Just-In-Time At Toyota. Portland, Oregon: Productivity Press, Inc.

Louis, R. S. 1992. How To Implement Kanban For American Industry. Portland, Oregon: Productivity Press, Inc.

Ohno, T. 1988. Toyota Production System: Beyond Large Scale Production. Portland, Oregon: Productivity Press, Inc.

Chapter 10

General Electric Corporation, ed. 1995. Lean Production System. GE Aircraft Engines Production Division.

Imai, M. 1986. Kaizen: The Key to Japan's Competitive Success. New York: McGraw-Hill Publishing Company.

Suzaki, K. 1987. The New Manufacturing Challenge: Techniques For Continuous Improvement. New York: Simon & Schuster Inc.

United Technologies Corporation, ed. Flexible Manufacturing: Instructor's Notes. Hartford, CT.: United Technologies Corporation.

Shingijutsu Co., Ltd., ed. How to implement Kaizen in manufacturing. Japan: Shingijutsu Co., Ltd.

TBM Consulting Group, ed. Shopfloor Kaizen Breakthrough. TBM Consulting Group Inc.

United Technologies Automotive, ed. 1996. Continuous Improvement Kaizen. Detroit, MI.: United Technologies Automotive.

General

Ohno, T. 1988. Toyota Production System: Beyond Large Scale Production. Portland, Oregon: Productivity Press, Inc.

Poynter, Dan. 1996. The Self-Publishing Manual: How to Write, Print and Sell Your Own Book. Santa Barbara, CA.: Para Publishing.

Index

with 5S, 71, 322

Waste Identification
in cell design, 281
in process flowcharting, 154
using a process map, 415
using a video camera, 326
using time observation studies, 408

Waste Targets
in kaizen, 389
in manufacturing cells, 269, 271
in setup reduction, 320
in TPM, equipment losses and conditions, 227
in TPM implementation, 215
inventory carrying costs, 15

WIP Inventory
for a standard work sheet, 301

Work Instructions, 81

Workforce Reduction
as a result of setup reduction, 319
from manufacturing cells, 267

World Class
safety, 188

World Class Enterprise, 19, 20, 59, 66